THE MYXOMYCETES OF BRITAIN AND IRELAND

An Identification Handbook

BRUCE ING

The Richmond Publishing Co. Ltd. would like to thank
Professor David Hawksworth CBE for his comments on
the text and layout and Jane Bulleid for copy-editing.

ISBN 085546 251 5 (Hardback only)

The Richmond Publishing Co. Ltd.
P.O. Box 963, Slough SL2 3RS England

Telephone +44 (0) 1753 643104
Fax +44 (0) 1753 646553
email rpc@richmond.co.uk

Printed in Great Britain

Front cover photographs:

Top row left to right:

Willkommlangea reticulata: © Jack Houghton (deceased)
Comatricha tenerrima: © Paul Brustkern
Enerthenema papillatum: © Paul Brustkern

Bottom row left to right:

Lycogala terrestre: © Bruce Ing
Ceratiomyxa fruticulosa: © Gordon Rutter
Leocarpus fragilis: © Bruce Ing

CONTENTS

AUTHOR'S PREFACE

This book has been gestating for about forty years and is based on a lifetime of field observation, herbarium study and culture of living material. It is designed to be as user-friendly as possible, with a minimum of technical jargon and a maximum of helpful hints. Of great importance is the reliance placed on field characters and, especially, habitat details. Until recently the ecology of myxomycetes has been poorly studied – we now know that many species have quite precise ecological requirements, and this is valuable data in the process of identification.

This book would never have been written if I had not received much help and encouragement over the course of my studies on myxomycetes. It is impossible to name everyone who has contributed to this development but I should like to record my gratitude to John Ramsbottom, Grace Waterhouse, G.W. Martin, C.J. Alexopoulos, Bernard Ward, Douglas Graddon, Geoffrey Ainsworth, Lilian Hawker and Michael Carlile for help and encouragement in my 'formative' years. Anyone who has studied myxomycetes in the second half of this century will appreciate the contribution made by Elly Nannenga-Bremekamp; her friendship, collaboration and continued enthusiasm through long years of illness were an inspiration. Many field mycologists have figured prominently in the collection and study of myxomycetes in Britain and Ireland in the last forty years and I should like to record my special thanks to Malcolm and Marjorie Clark, David Mitchell, Peter Holland, Stanley Carter and Roland McHugh for the contributions they have made. That many of the above named are no longer with us is a measure of the length of my indebtedness to them.

My family have been incredibly tolerant, with holidays always including visits to 'interesting' sites and routes chosen to take in unrecorded areas. They have encouraged and supported me throughout, particularly my wife, Eleanor, to whom I referred in 1968 as a 'long-suffering slime-mould widow' – since then she has suffered thirty more years and is still smiling! I am deeply grateful to Eleanor, Hazel and Gareth for putting up with a fanatic in the family.

iv

INTRODUCTION

Myxomycetes are defined as eukaryotic microorganisms with a plasmodium as the assimilative stage and a sexually produced resting spore as the propagule. This does not really tell us very much about them or their relationships. For generations they have been shuffled back and forth between the animal and plant kingdoms, being regarded either as amoeboid protozoans, the *Mycetozoa*, or as a group of fungi, the *Myxomycetes*. In these more enlightened, and better equipped, times we are able to show that they possess mitochondria with tubular cristae and this makes them clearly members of the kingdom *Protozoa*, not fungi, and indeed, not animals! This fact does not stop them being treated as 'honorary fungi' as they occupy the same habitats, disperse their spores and are studied by methods which are characteristic of the fungi in the broadest sense. In this book two species of classes not now included in the *Myxomycetes* are covered: one has traditionally been associated with them and the other is frequently found in bark cultures. Both are members of the phylum *Myxomycota*; the differences are indicated in the key to families.

Phylogeny

It is now generally accepted that the various groups of slime moulds have evolved from soil amoebo-flagellate protozoans. The simplest, and probably the most primitive, are the *protostelids*, which have a small plasmodium, a tubular stalk, little evidence of sexuality and either flagellate or non-flagellate vegetative cells. The alternative cell types have led to the later groups. The non-flagellate, non-sexual lines have developed cellular stalks and evolved into the *dictyostelids*, the cellular slime moulds. These are abundant in forest soils, even on high mountains, and may also be found on herbivore dung.

One flagellate, sexual line developed into *Ceratiomyxa*, which has a massive plasmodium and a fruit body which consists of finger-like extensions of the hypothallus bearing minute, eight-spored sporangia, which are superficially similar to the spores of some hyphomycete fungi, but quite unlike those of true myxomycetes.

The other line evolved into *Myxomycetes*. The simplest structures are found in *Echinostelium*, which has a tubular stalk and not much else, and is very like a large protostelid. From this simple stalked form the more elaborate *Clastoderma* and *Barbeyella* may have led to the *Stemonitales*, with a concurrent origin of subhypothallic development. The echinostelioid *Protophysarum* has probably given rise to the *Physarales*. It seems that the stalked sporangium is primitive and therefore such simple forms as *Licea operculata*, with a stalk reminiscent of *Clastoderma*, may be ancestral to the sessile species of the genus. Those sessile *Licea* species with peridial plates are very similar to *Listerella*, which has a rudimentary capillitium and may have led to the *Trichiales*. Other *Licea* species, such as *variabilis*, are morphologically similar to some species of *Perichaena*, and there are other tentative links between *Liceales* and *Trichiales*.

In general stalked sporangia may be regarded as primitive and aethalia as advanced, a pattern which appears in most orders of myxomycetes. Fig. A provides a diagrammatic scheme for the evolution of the slime moulds. The

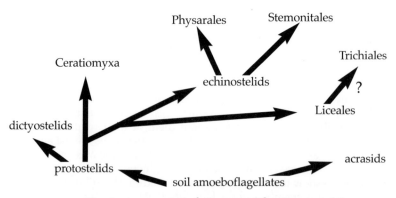

Fig. A. A suggested phylogeny of the slime moulds.

acrasids are not closely related to the other groups and do not appear to have originated from organisms with tubular stalks. They also have pseudopodia of the myxamoebae; of a different type to those of the other slime moulds, they may also have flagellated or non-flagellated cells and are not consistently sexual or non-sexual. They therefore constitute a parallel group to the protostelid-derived slime moulds.

Life cycle

In order to appreciate the significance of the structures used to identify myxomycetes it is useful to follow through a typical life cycle and meet these structures as they appear.

The **spores** are usually spherical (*globose*) and may be smooth, with or without a thinner area of wall which corresponds to the *germination pore*, or be covered in a variety of ornamentation (Fig. B). This ranges from broad, short *warts* to pointed or blunt *spines* or *spinules* of various lengths and widths to short folds or *ridges* on the wall. Any of these may be arranged uniformly across the spore or confined to regions or grouped in small clusters. *Reticulated* spores have a network of spines or bands and it is important to focus on an optical section of the spore to determine whether it is banded or spiny reticulate. In one or two species the bands are perforated at the level of the spore wall but this can usually only be seen under the scanning electron microscope. No reliance will be put on such features in the keys as it is assumed that most field mycologists will not have access to this equipment! The size of spores and the precise nature of the ornamentation is of major importance in separating species. In several genera spores may be clustered, in groups of various sizes. In these species the inner, contact face of the spore is often smooth, with the often reticular ornamentation on the outside; the spores may be pear-shaped when in clusters. Spores remain viable for decades if kept dry and cool.

On reaching a suitably moist and warm substrate the spore germinates, frequently splitting at the germination pore or zone to release a single-celled **myxoflagellate**. This has two flagella, one long and motile, the other short, rigid and usually non-motile. On moist surfaces and in the interstices of wood and soil these myxoflagellates divide repeatedly to form a large clonal population. Feeding is by ingestion and the main diet consists of bacteria. Fluctuation in

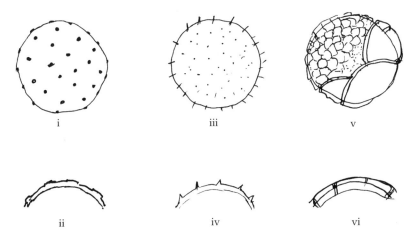

Fig. B. Spore marking: (i) warted; (ii) optical section of warted spore; (iii) spiny; (iv) optical section of spiny spore; (v) types of reticulation; (vi) border of reticulated spore in optical section.

moisture content and temperature may induce the myxoflagellates to absorb their flagella and develop pseudopodia at one end, the other end being sticky. These are now *myxamoebae* and they also form clones which flow around and then ingest bacteria. If the temperature becomes too low or too high or the water dries up, the *myxomonads* (myxoflagellates and myxamoebae) may round up their protoplasm and secrete a thick and resistant wall to become *microcysts*. On the return of optimal conditions these cysts germinate to release myxamoebae. Myxomonads are among the most abundant and significant microorganisms in soil, being important in carbon, nitrogen and phosphorus cycles.

The reproduction of myxomycetes is essentially sexual and three strategies exist. The most important is *heterothallism*, where myxamoebae fuse in pairs of different mating types, thereby ensuring cross-fertilisation with the products of different spore sources. This outbreeding is valuable as it maintains and increases variation within the species. It is dependent on the presence of two compatible, but different, genetic strains in close proximity and is thus found in many of the commonest, and most variable, species. *Homothallism* allows myxamoebae of the same mating type, and therefore originally from the same spore, to fuse. The last option, *agamism*, has no sexual fusion and individual myxamoebae proceed to the next stage of what is, in essence, a haploid life cycle.

The next stage is the rapid division of the nucleus, either the diploid zygote nucleus or the haploid agamic nucleus, but not the protoplasm, to produce a multinucleate *plasmodium*. This is the final feeding stage in the life cycle and, depending on size, it will ingest bacteria, protozoans, yeasts, algal cells and, in a few species, even fungal mycelia. Within the plasmodium all the nuclei are accurately synchronised and are always in the same stages of division. Plasmodia may be very minute, as in *Echinostelium* and *Licea*, or qualify for the largest single cells known. Two examples will suffice. A hollow elm log nine metres long and half a metre wide, at Woodwalton Fen in 1963, was filled with a development of *Trichia scabra*, whose hypothallus (see below) entirely covered the inside of the trunk and was itself completely covered with closely clustered sporangia; this could only have developed from one plasmodium. The second example is one which occurs frequently at Loggerheads, near Mold in north Wales. Here stumps may look as if covered with bucketfuls of cold porridge and this may cover an area of a square metre and be up to one centimetre thick. This is the plasmodium of the largest myxomycete known, *Brefeldia maxima,* and in the example quoted may have been a cell weighing 20 kg!

There are four types of plasmodium. The simplest is the ***protoplasmodium,*** which is characteristic of the species inhabiting the bark of living trees, such as *Echinostelium* and *Licea* species. This is a globular blob of protoplasm with a dense, often pigmented inner region and a narrow, clear outer layer. It does not move about and gives rise to a single sporangium on maturation. The most familiar type is the large, highly mobile, often brightly coloured ***phaneroplasmodium.***

This is characteristic of the *Physarales,* is robust and consists of a network of veins, having a dense inner region and a clear outer layer. The cytoplasm can be seen under x20 magnification streaming along the veins, slowing, reversing, speeding up, and so on. This streaming, or *cyclosis,* is absent from the protoplasmodium, which is often regarded as a juvenile form of the phaneroplasmodium, adapted to a rapid response to the wetting of the bark by showers. Phaneroplasmodia are tolerant of drier conditions than the other types and may also take several months to mature.

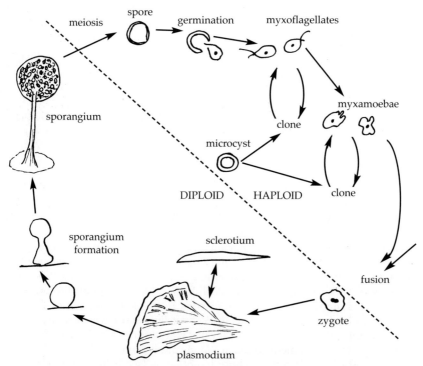

Fig. C. Life cycle of a typical myxomycete.

The *aphanoplasmodium,* characteristic of the *Stemonitales,* is delicate and usually transparent. It is also effectively aquatic and only survives if covered with a thin film of water. This makes it much more difficult to cultivate. There is no distinction between the inner and outer layers of the cytoplasm and the plasmodia move more slowly than phaneroplasmodia.

The last type is the *trichiaceous,* or *aphano-phaneroplasmodium,* which is intermediate in character. It is typical of the *Trichiales* and remains concealed in the substrate and produces fruiting structures at the surface without emerging. Whatever the plasmodial type the onset of dry, hot or cold conditions triggers one of three responses – the plasmodium dies, moves on to maturation or encapsulates itself in a horny covering and becomes a resting *macrocyst* or *sclerotium.* On the return of optimal conditions this is reconstituted as a plasmodium, smaller than before, which usually matures without further delay. When the food material is exhausted, or as one option when the microclimate becomes unfavourable, the plasmodium enters the last phase of the life cycle, *sporulation.* It emerges from the feeding substrate onto a suitable surface for spore dispersal, such as the upper layers of leaf litter or the surface of rotten wood. The life cycle is shown diagrammatically in Fig. C.

The production of spores and related tissues within a **sporocarp** now begins. Depending on the type of fruit body to be produced the plasmodial material then forms blobs of various sizes and, where appropriate, stalk formation begins. There are two contrasting types of development, *epihypothallic,* in which the spore capsule develops first, at the surface of the plasmodium and is then lifted up on the still developing stalk, and *subhypothallic,* in which the stalk develops first from below the surface and the pre-sporangial blob of

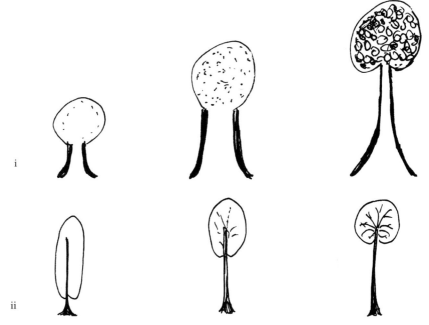

Fig. D. Sporangial development: (i) subhypothallic; (ii) epihypothallic.

plasmodium moves up to the tip and is characteristic of the *Stemonitales* [Fig. D]. The plasmodium is almost completely transformed into sporocarp and spores but in many species a thin film of horny material remains on the surface of the substrate, connecting the bases of the sporocarps. This is the **hypothallus** and may have useful diagnostic features.

The sporocarp may be a *stalked* or stalkless (*sessile*), more or less rounded ***sporangium,*** which may be scattered, gregarious, clustered or heaped [Fig. E]. It may be slightly longer than broad, as a short ***plasmodiocarp,*** or long and sinuous, following the lines of the plasmodial veins and sometimes forming a branching network one sporangial diameter wide and several centimetres long. Plasmodiocarps are usually associated with a phaneroplasmodium and are therefore commonest in the *Physarales*. In several genera the whole plasmodium develops into a single, large sporocarp in which individual sporangia are difficult to discern. This is an ***aethalium*** and may be covered with a tough, common outer crust, or ***cortex.*** Aethalia are found in *Physarales* (*Fuligo, Mucilago*), *Stemonitales* (*Amaurochaete, Brefeldia*) and *Liceales* (*Enteridium, Lycogala*) but are absent from *Echinosteliales* and *Trichiales*. An intermediate structure also occurs which is midway between clustered sporangia and an aethalium. Here the individual sporangia can be identified but they share common internal structures and may also have a cortex. This is a *pseudoaethalium* and is found in *Physarales* (*Physarum gyrosum*), *Stemonitales* (*Symphytocarpus*), *Liceales* (*Lindbladia, Dictydiaethalium, Tubifera*) and *Trichiales* (*Minakatella*).

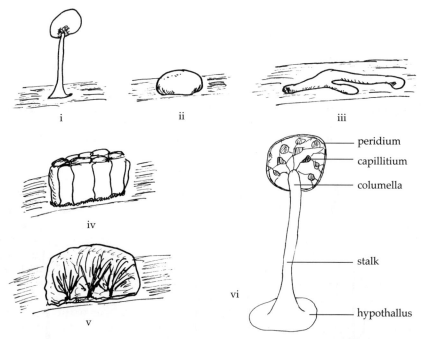

Fig. E. Types of sporocarp: (i) stalked sporangium; (ii) sessile sporangium; (iii) plasmodiocarp; (iv) pseudoaethalium; (v) aethalium; (vi) structure of typical sporangium.

Where present the **stalk** has a number of useful features. It is basically a hollow tube connecting the hypothallus to the sporangium and may remain hollow or be filled with debris or spore-like cells. Calcium salts may be secreted both inside and on the outer surface. Rather than being hollow the stalk may be fibrous. To view the stalk structure it is important to use a high level of transmitted light. The presence of calcium carbonate may be demonstrated with dilute acid, such as vinegar.

The centre of the sporangium, either at the base in sessile species or at the tip of the stalk, is often provided with a **columella**. This is frequently just an extension of the stalk into the sporangium, as in *Echinosteliales* and *Stemonitales*, or a globular, calcareous mass occupying much of the sporangial volume in many *Physarales*. The detailed nature of the columella is of diagnostic value. In some species the structure is not attached to the stalk and develops independently of it, and is then known as a **pseudocolumella**. It is usually necessary to make a longitudinal section of the sporangium to see the exact nature of this structure. A columella is absent from the *Trichiales*.

The wall of the sporocarp is the **peridium** and may consist of three distinct layers, although they are not always easy to see. The innermost layer is usually thin, membranous and may appear iridescent because of minute ridges on the surface which act as diffraction gratings. The middle layer, when it occurs, may contain crystalline material. The outer layer may be membranous or leathery and is frequently covered with calcium salts, whether as a characteristic feature in the *Physarales*, or as an occasional deposit of calcium oxalate on some *Perichaena* species. Calcium carbonate may appear as granules, either scattered or combined into a smooth crust (*Physaraceae, Diderma*), as *stellate* crystals, giving a powdered appearance or forming an egg-shell crust, (*Didymium, Mucilago*) or as small, flat, plates (*Lepidoderma*). In *Cribraria* the peridium remains as a network of branching threads connected by small, dense **nodes** containing **dictydine granules**, which may be calcareous. The basket-like structure of this sporangium is clearly acting as a pepper pot spore dispersal mechanism. Under transmitted light the peridium layers may appear smooth, warted or containing a variety of coloured inclusions, some of which are of diagnostic value. The base of the sporangium and the lower part of the peridium may persist as a cup and are then thicker and continuous with the columella and stalk. In other species the peridium is short-lived and disappears before the spores are ripe.

Within the sporocarp, attached to the inner peridium, columella, sporangial base or tip of stalk is the **capillitium** (absent from *Licea* and some species of *Echinostelium*). The main function is to separate and assist the dispersal of the spores, which surround it. The capillitium consists of tubes, plates or threads, calcareous or not, hollow or solid, ornamented or plain. In *Trichiaceae* the capillitium may be loofah-like or form a network of spirally bound threads or consist of short, spirally bound *elaters*. In *Physaraceae* the capillitium contains calcium salts, either in branching, hollow calcareous tubes (*Badhamia*), or as calcareous vesicles (*nodes*) connected by thin, hollow, branching threads (*Physarum*). Many kinds of capillitial structure are able to respond to changes in atmospheric humidity by sudden and often violent movement. In this respect the elaters of *Trichia* mirror those of liverworts, kicking the spores out of the sporangium into dry air. In other cases the size of the meshes of the capillitium may increase and allow spores to escape, or close up to keep them in. In aethalia and pseudoaethalia, true capillitium may be replaced by a pseudocapillitium derived from the frayed walls of the component sporangia. In *Lycogala* these form well-marked, ornamented tubes, but in *Enteridium* they are perforated plates or frayed threads.

During the formation of the sporocarp the plasmodial nuclei undergo reduction division (*meiosis*) and produce haploid spore mother cells. These secrete a resistant wall and become the spores. Dispersal is aided by the capillitium and mostly utilises wind, but insects and other invertebrates are important in many species. Some of the larger aethalia may also be scattered by falling raindrops or even form rudimentary splash cups. Myxomycete spores have been trapped on sticky slides exposed by aircraft high over the oceans as well as in routine spore trapping over terrestrial sites at low level. They are rapidly and efficiently dispersed and simply require appropriate conditions for germination and survival to colonise new areas.

Occurrence and distribution

The occurrence of myxomycetes in the wild is governed by a combination of appropriate microclimatic factors, a suitable infrastructure within the habitat and the availability of food organisms. The major geographic zones, such as tropical forest, desert or high mountains, have a few distinctive species which are restricted and characteristic, but the great majority of myxomycetes are cosmopolitan. These may be expected to occur anywhere in the world which offers plant remains and a regime of adequate rainfall and temperature. There are few endemic species in any part of the world, as is to be expected with such an ancient group with efficient dispersal agents as wind and insects, and these are usually just rare or confined to habitats which have been little investigated by students of myxomycetes.

This account of the myxomycetes found in Britain and Ireland includes details of a few species characteristic of much warmer climates, which have been found on a few occasions. This is an indication of the efficiency of long-distance dispersal. These casuals occur either as accidental introductions with plant material, into heated greenhouses and mostly in botanical gardens where they rarely persist for more than a few years, or outdoors. The latter group occur in semi-natural habitats in our temperate zone but are normally resident in the tropics or subtropics. Their spores were able to survive and the life-cycle was completed because of unusually high temperatures pertaining in the British Isles at the time. That they were found and recorded suggests that these events are less rare than previously supposed, as the chances of the coincidence of suitable growing conditions and the collection, identification and recording of material are likely to be very small. The advent of climatic change may allow more of these southern species to colonise our islands in the future.

The likelihood of long-term ecological change triggered by global warming may also result in the loss of some northern assemblages, such as the snowline species and those characteristic of the Caledonian pine forests. The fluctuations of snowfall in the Scottish Highlands during the last decade presents a threat not only to the skiing industry but also to nivicolous plant, fungal (including lichen), and myxomycete communities. This may be balanced by the arrival of species more usually found in the Mediterranean region.

ECOLOGY AND DISTRIBUTION

Myxomycetes are found in a very wide range of ecosystems and their relationship with different vegetation types is discussed on a world scale by Ing (1994). In the British Isles, as may be expected, a smaller range of habitats exists. Nevertheless the range of substrates for myxomycetes to exploit is large and varied.

WOODLAND

The majority of species occur in woodland where the major microhabitats are: the bark of living trees, dead standing trunks, fallen trunks and branches, leaf litter, soil, terrestrial mosses and herbivore dung.

Corticolous species

The bark of living trees has been studied as a habitat since the early part of the 19th century when an Aberdeenshire clergyman, the Rev. William Cran, a man possessed of extraordinary eyesight, collected sporangia of minute myxomycetes in the field. Later, following the work of Gilbert and Martin (1933), the culture of bark samples in moist chambers (see pp.18–19) has become a routine method for discovering and collecting these species. *Obligate corticoles* characteristically live on the bark of living trees and are rarely found elsewhere. They have a protoplasmodium and are adapted to complete their life-cycle in a few days after a shower of rain has moistened the bark. They are usually too small to see in the field. Many are restricted to bark covered with mosses, liverworts or lichens; for example, *Paradiacheopsis fimbriata* and *Pocheina rosea* are regularly found on the green algal crust on trees, some *Licea* species are confined to liverworts, *Macbrideola cornea* is mostly found on the leaves of mosses, and *Diacheopsis insessa* is confined to lichens. Others are mostly found on acid bark or bark affected by deposition from acid rain, such as *P. fimbriata* and *P. rosea*. The older, more plate-like, the bark the greater chance of a rich corticolous myxomycota. Roughness, nutrient levels and water holding potential are key factors in this richness. Conversely young, smooth bark has few, if any species. However, virtually every piece of bark sampled from any tree will yield at least one species in culture, indicating just how abundant and widespread these corticoles are. Little is known about the bacteria inhabiting tree bark, or indeed other microorganisms that might be used as food by the myxomycetes. As may be expected, the damper, cleaner areas of western Britain and Ireland are richer in species than the dry, often more polluted east. Nevertheless, the centres of cities, notably in London, are extremely rich in species. It may be that the variety of planted trees, including many exotics, such as London Plane, *Platanus* x *hispanica*, coupled with large amounts of droppings from roosting birds which neutralises acid deposition and encourages bacterial activity, are contributory.

Some bark myxomycetes are found on recently fallen branches and large twigs, or on fallen trunks, especially when they are covered in mosses. These *facultative corticoles* may have been present on the bark while it was still attached to the tree and shed with the branch, either in a resting stage or as sporocarps. A further, smaller group, *casual corticoles*, consists of species whose usual habitat is fallen wood or leaf litter. Bark is able to trap spores of many organisms and the conditions of the moist chamber allow these species, with longer development times, to produce plasmodia and, in many cases, sporocarps.

Lignicolous species

Dead standing trunks are important sites for many organisms from birds and insects to fungi. A few myxomycetes are characteristic of this microhabitat, such as *Enteridium lycoperdon* which is very common on dead alder trunks and *Symphytocarpus flaccidus* which is typical of skeletal pines in both native forest and plantations. The abundant *Fuligo septica* and *Lycogala terrestre* are also frequently found on these vertical surfaces, having emerged from the wood via beetle escape holes.

A large number of species are habitually found on fallen wood in various stages of decay. Recently felled conifer logs yield *Amaurochaete atra* whereas really rotten, soggy wood is the site for *Stemonitopsis typhina* and *Trichia varia*. Some species are more likely to be on mosses or lichens than on the bare wood. Coniferous wood is apparently preferred by most species of the genus *Cribraria* and *Tubifera ferruginosa* is also characteristic. However, as with some fungi, birch is a suitable substitute for conifers, and in the case of *Tubifera*, alder is often utilised. So little is known about the chemistry or microbiology of wood that no detailed explanation is available for these observations. However, they are useful guidelines when searching for myxomycetes.

Foliicolous species

Leaf litter is the second most important substrate for forest myxomycetes. Most of these have feeding stages in the soil and the plasmodia migrate onto leaf litter or even up the stems of living plants to sporulate. The type of leaf litter, and soil, may determine which species are present. Very characteristic of conifer needle litter are *Leocarpus fragilis* and *Didymium melanospermum*, whereas *Lamproderma scintillans* and *Didymium nigripes* are typical of holly leaf-litter. This latter is an excellent, if uncomfortable, habitat to investigate. Beech and oak woodland litter are rich, the slow breakdown of the leaves providing a range of suitable substrates. In the London area deep *Castanea* (sweet chestnut) litter is the habitat for *Didymium laxifilum*, a characteristic Mediterranean species whose southern European substrate is the litter of *Quercus ilex* (holm oak). The leaf litter of bramble clumps and the lower parts of dead arching stems are rich sites for myxomycetes, including *Diachea leucopodia*, *Physarum bitectum* and *Licea clarkii*. In autumn the previous years stems of rosebay, *Chamaerion angustifolium*, may also be productive, notably for *Physarum galbeum*, which also occurs on brambles, especially if mixed with rosebay, and for species of *Didymium* and *Craterium*. The soil around this plant is rich in free phosphates and there is now abundant evidence to link the presence of large populations of myxomonads and the release of phosphate from their bacterial food. The litter of ferns, especially *Dryopteris* and *Pteridium*, holds moisture well and several species are typically found here, for example *Comatricha pulchella* and *Craterium dictyosporum*. Other types of litter may be productive, including ivy and nettle.

Muscicolous species

On the fronds of terrestrial mosses in damp, western woods may be found the apricot plasmodia and developing aethalia of *Fuligo muscorum,* the yellow, then green plasmodia and sporangia of *Physarum virescens* and the pink plasmodia and black sporangia of the rare *P. confertum.* These three species are more or less confined to mosses but many of the litter species will sporulate just as well on bryophytes. In Atlantic woodlands where the high rainfall and hard rocks are associated with deep, vertical sided ravines a highly specialised assemblage of species has been found. This ravine association (Ing, 1983) is found on wet, moss-covered rocks, often close to the spray of waterfalls. It consists of *Craterium muscorum, Diderma lucidum, D. ochraceum, D. sauteri, Fuligo muscorum, Lamproderma columbinum* and *Lepidoderma tigrinum.* Often present is the cyanobacterium *Nostoc muscorum* and there is some evidence to suggest that transfer of carbon and nitrogen based nutrients may be made from the alga to the myxomycete plasmodium.

Fungicolous species

Some myxomycetes found in leaf litter may, by chance, develop their sporocarps on the stems or caps of terrestrial basidiomycetes, but a few species are obligate fungivores. Of these *Badhamia utricularis* is the best studied. Its bright yellow plasmodium is frequently found on the basidiocarps of *Trametes versicolor, Stereum hirsutum* and *Phlebia radiata* and careful observation will show that the fungus is being actively devoured. This myxomycete will utilise a wide range of agarics, including cultivated mushrooms, but rejects *Coprinus* species! *Badhamia nitens* is frequently found on bracket fungi on living trees and a number of other species occasionally sporulate on lignicolous fungi.

MOORLAND AND GRASSLAND

Lowland and upland heath

In deep litter of *Calluna* (heather) and other heathland plants a few myxomycetes may be found, including *Diderma simplex, Didymium melanospermum* and *Lepidoderma chailletii*; at one site on the Isle of Man, *Licea operculata* was found on *Calluna* stems close to the sea. Where gorse bushes are found it is worth looking at the litter beneath them for *D. melanospermum* and *Leocarpus fragilis.* Upland heath has no characteristic species and grades into alpine habitats (see below.)

Lowland grassland

Grazed grassland, playing fields and lawns, especially where the soil is calcareous, have three common myxomycetes, viz. *Badhamia foliicola, Mucilago crustacea* and *Physarum cinereum.* The last two are often so abundant as to disfigure lawns or even pastures and cause alarm to grassland managers. They are, of course, harmless.

Ungrazed grasslands and tall-herb communities, with hogweed, *Heracleum sphondylium* and other herbaceous perennials, are worth searching for *Comatricha tenerrima* and *Physarum bivalve* on old stems near the ground.

Alpine grassland and heath
Where snow lies late in the spring, and particularly where a snow-patch has lain for at least three months on a mountain side, characteristic vegetation develops, including a number of myxomycetes which are rare or absent in other habitats. The snow cover maintains an above-zero temperature during the winter, allowing the myxomycetes to develop on the previous year's litter and current year's shoots. When the snow melts in April and May the sporocarps are to be found close to the edge of the melting snow, especially on *Nardus stricta, Vaccinium myrtillus, Empetrum nigrum* and clubmosses. The commonest species is *Diderma niveum* and this is accompanied by *D. alpinum, D. lyallii, Lepidoderma aggregatum, L. carestianum, Didymium dubium, D. nivicola, Physarum albescens, P. vernum, Lamproderma atrosporum, L. carestiae, L. cribrarioides, L. sauteri,* and *Dianema nivale.* A common alpine species, in the rest of Europe, *Trichia alpina* has only been recorded once, from a frozen ditch in Surrey, and should be searched for on woody herbaceous stems. In the Alps it is characteristic of old stems of *Cirsium spinossisimum.* Tall-herb vegetation on ledges on Scottish mountains should be suitable, if there is adequate snow cover. A fuller account of this fascinating group is given by Ing (1998).

WETLANDS

Carr woodlands
Alder and willow carrs associated with high water tables are ideal places to search for myxomycetes. The leaf litter in late autumn is rich in the common species of *Physaraceae* and *Didymiaceae* and small branches lying on wet soil or even in shallow water, are the main habitat for *Arcyodes incarnata* and both species of *Oligonema.*

Marshes and fens
In these communities, dominated by tall herbs and grasses, in autumn the litter is very rich in leaf and stem myxomycetes, such as *Diderma hemisphaericum, D. globosum, Physarum pusillum* and *Comatricha tenerrima,* as well as more familiar species. Reedswamps in particular are highly productive, especially in the broadlands of East Anglia.

Ponds and streams
It may seem unlikely that myxomycetes may occur in water but they are typically members of the soil water microbiota and feed in the mud and detritus at the bottom of ponds and streams. Sporocarps of *Didymium difforme, Collaria* species and *Lamproderma scintillans* have been collected on the emergent stems of aquatic plants several centimetres from the edge of ponds and streams. *D. difforme* is well known to inhabit water cultures of bulbs and is common on the soaked roots of rose bushes in transit. Some years ago *Physarum lividum* was collected on the shoots of watercress at the edge of a stream in Derbyshire. Shallow water vegetation cast up on the bank of a lake and a gravel pit (in Devon and Worcestershire, respectively) has provided the only British records of *Didymium applanatum,* which seems to qualify, at least, as an amphibious species.

Sphagnum bogs

Where extensive areas of *Sphagnum* have formed raised or valley bogs, or even in *Sphagnum*-dominated areas of poor fen, the characteristic egg-yolk yellow plasmodia of *Badhamia lilacina* may be found. From below the water surface they migrate onto vegetation, such as the drier parts of the moss, heather or grass stems, and form lilac-grey clumps of small, calcareous sporangia. A much rarer species in this habitat is *Symphytocarpus trechisporus*, with its reddish brown aethalia. On small patches of *Sphagnum* in pine forests *Lamproderma columbinum* and *Lepidoderma tigrinum* have also been regularly found.

COASTAL HABITATS

Shingle beaches

On the crests of shingle beaches, mats of vegetation with *Beta, Atriplex, Silene* and *Crambe* are worth searching. Underneath the decaying parts of these plants a number of myxomycetes have been found. Where large tracts of lichen heath occur, as at Dungeness, the *Cladonia portentosa* clumps have yielded the very rare *Listerella paradoxa* and *Diacheopsis mitchlelii* as well as *Licea* species.

Sand dunes

Listerella has also been found on *Cladonia* at Tentsmuir Point near St Andrews, Scotland and other parts of sand-dune systems also have characteristic myxomycetes. In particular mossy dune grasslands support *Diderma spumarioides* and *Mucilago* and the litter of *Ammophila* has *Physarum pusillum*, amongst others.

Saltmarshes and cliffs are less productive but beach driftwood often has common lignicolous species, notably on the Scottish islands.

AGRICULTURAL AND URBAN HABITATS

Arable land

Cultivated soil is well populated with myxomonads and plasmodia, especially of species of *Didymium* and *Physarum* which produce sporocarps on pieces of vegetable matter or even soil particles at the surface. Remains of crops, such as potato haulms, bean pods and general vegetable waste at the sides of fields are characterised by *Physarum compressum*, which also occurs in garden compost heaps.

In the early part of this century piles of straw were a familiar feature at the edges of cereal fields. These were abundantly covered with *Fuligo cinerea, Physarum pusillum, P. didermoides, P. straminipes, Didymium vaccinum, D. trachysporum* and many others. Mechanical methods of harvesting have eliminated these straw heaps and most of the myxomycetes on them. The tightly packed straw bale, if left for a year or so, will develop some of these species, but not with the same diversity or abundance. However, the very rare *Comatricha mirabilis*, was found for a number of years in the 1970s on a pile of bales at the corner of a field in Sussex. Dung heaps and stable waste also used to carry *F. cinerea*; but this species is now thought to be extinct in the British Isles. Old thatched roofs occasionally have straw species, such as *D. vaccinum*, but this is not an easy habitat to investigate!

Urban parks and gardens

Perhaps unexpectedly, city parks and gardens provide good microhabitats for myxomycetes. The wide variety of tree species, juxtaposition of grassland, herbaceous material, fallen branches and leaf litter ensure that suitable substrates are available for many woodland and grassland species. The London Plane, *Platanus* x *hispanica*, with its characteristically flaking bark, is especially rich. Areas of uncultivated, derelict or waste land become colonised with tall herbs, such as rosebay, and even the poor soils of these sites are inhabited by *Didymium* species, *Craterium minutum* and *Physarum bivalve*, among others, which fruit on the old stems. Old spent tan heaps, piles of oak bark once used in the leather industry but now themselves rare, were typically covered with 'Flowers of Tan' *Fuligo septica*, *Oligonema schweinitzii*, and once in Cornwall, *Cornuvia serpula*. Hothouses, especially orchid houses in botanical gardens, shelter a number of species more usually found in the tropics or warm temperate regions. These may have been imported with the plants or compost and are, at best, temporary residents. The list of these species includes *Cribraria dictydioides*, *Fuligo gyrosa*, *Hemitrichia leiocarpa*, *H. serpula* and *Physarum echinosporum*; none have been found out of doors in Britain.

ASSOCIATIONS WITH OTHER ORGANISMS

Insects

The sporocarps of myxomycetes, especially the large aethalia of *Enteridium*, *Tubifera* or *Fuligo* and clumps of *Stemonitis fusca*, are frequently the home of beetles, notably *Anisotoma humeralis* and several other species of the families *Anisotomidae*, *Leiodidae* and *Agathidiidae*. These beetles breed exclusively in myxomycete fructifications and the adult females have mandibles with cavities which always seem to contain myxomycete spores. The inference is that the females sow spores to provide suitable food and environment for later generations of the insect. Some aethalia also have pupal cases of mycetophilid midges and plasmodia are often eaten by the larvae of these fungus midges. Corticolous myxomycetes are eaten by a wide range of invertebrates, especially acarine mites, psocids, collembolans and dipterous larvae. The spores of the myxomycetes are regularly found in the faecal pellets of these arthropods and this may be part of their dispersal mechanism. Some litter species are also dispersed via the gut of woodlice. Insect relationships were reviewed by Ing (1994).

Fungi

Myxomycetes frequently have structural chitin in their sporocarps and are parasitised by a number of filamentous fungi, mostly the anamorphs of Hypocreaceae. The most familiar are the synnematous conidiomata of *Polycephalomyces tomentosus* which is very common on species of *Trichia*, *Verticillium rexianum* on *Metatrichia floriformis*, and *Sesquicillium microsporum* on *Stemonitidaceae*. These myxomyceticolous fungi are not narrowly host specific and a few species, such as *Verticillium catenulatum*, are also found on insects. A valuable account of these fungi is given by Rogerson & Stephenson (1993).

Seasonality

The majority of myxomycete species are found in the autumn fungus collecting season and October is the best month in much of the British Isles. However, the corticolous species may be isolated all year round, although the number which develop is frequently lower during the spring. Lignicoles are found from late spring through to winter, with *Enteridium, Lycogala, Ceratiomyxa, Fuligo* and *Stemonitis* appearing early and *Arcyria* and *Trichia* coming later in the sequence. Some species are very regular in their appearance. On rotting beech logs in the Alyn Valley near Mold, north Wales, *Physarum psittacinum* and *Lycogala conicum*, two indicators of ancient woodland, have appeared during the first week of July for six years running. In September 1978 elm bark sampled from a wood in Snowdonia developed *Cribraria violacea*; in September 1988 the same tree was again sampled and *C. violacea* duly appeared. Foliicolous species in woodlands and wetlands, are best in late autumn and winter and the ravine association and others on terrestrial mosses peak in October. Coastal species are best in late autumn and winter. The snow-patch species are only to be found from late April to mid-June in the Scottish Highlands, and from late March in the English Lake District, depending on the snow lie.

DISTRIBUTION

A significant number of myxomycete species are cosmopolitan and this supports the idea that the group is ancient. However, some species are associated with particular climatic or ecological conditions and are therefore limited by the distribution of those conditions. As myxomycetes largely consume bacteria they are also limited by the availability of this food supply, on which little biogeographical data is available. In spite of this there are certain groups with a well-marked pattern of occurrence. A small, but distinctive group is confined to the tropics and this is unlikely to be part of the British scene, except as casuals in hothouses. At the other extreme, there are numerous species associated with snow on mountains and at the poles, and some of these do occur in Scotland and north-west England.

In the west of Britain and in Ireland there is an Atlantic element including a considerable number of corticoles and the ravine assemblage; their distribution corresponds with the areas of higher rainfall. A few species seem to be found especially in ancient woodland, such as *Lycogala conicum, Metatrichia vesparium* and *Physarum psittacinum*, and these are therefore, mainly found in lowland forests and old parks. Many British and Irish species have a southerly trend in their distribution and represent genera which probably have their headquarters in the tropics and subtropics. Examples are: *Diachea leucopodia*, which barely reaches Scotland, is rare in west Wales and unknown in Ireland, although it is quite common in southern England; *Physarum galbeum*, which just reaches the Midlands of England; *Perichaena depressa*, which is rare in Scotland, although recorded from Orkney; *Didymium anellus*, which is absent from Scotland and Ireland, has a single record in north-east Wales, and is rare in the north of England, and *D. serpula*, which just reaches mid-west Scotland with a few records on the east coast of

Ireland. Provisional maps to 99 species were given by Ing (1982). The distribution of species in the British Isles has also been recorded on the basis of occurrence in Watsonian vice-counties and has been regularly updated.

COLLECTION, CULTURE, EXAMINATION AND PRESERVATION

COLLECTION

The collection of myxomycetes involves the finding, gathering and transportation of sporocarp material, plasmodia or potential substrates such as bark, wood, leaf litter and dung. All these will require different methods and apparatus. The section on ecology gives an idea of the habitats worth searching and the most likely substrates.

Myxomycetes on logs, branches and other large woody remains are best removed with a sharp knife, taking as much substrate as necessary to ensure a rigid base for the specimen. This material can either be fixed with large-headed pins (map pins are the best) into a cork-lined box, placed in the small compartments of a plastic, lidded, box – the sort used for screws or fishing flies is ideal – or glued directly into the base of a small cardboard box (but only if the specimen can be processed that day). Special care must be taken with immature material that has not yet developed mature spores or even colouration. This must be kept in moist conditions for several hours, ideally overnight. Specimens on leaf and other herbaceous litter may be treated in the same way – it is important to reduce the amount of vibration during transport back to base, so as to allow as regular maturation as possible. Other useful field equipment includes scissors, a small saw, secateurs, and a small rake; most of these tools are available on larger versions of Swiss army-type knives!

> **Conservation note**: Whenever possible replace turned-over logs and branches in their original position after examination so as not to alter the microclimate for other organisms. Do not collect more material than you need for study or herbarium. If you have good gatherings of nice material, consider making duplicates for exchange.

Material being collected for later culture requires special treatment. Bark from living trees should be carefully removed so as not to cut into the phloem or cambium under the bark. Not only does this damage the tree but the sample will contain too much sugar and may be rapidly colonised by filamentous moulds. The bark sample is placed in a clean envelope (never use a polythene bag for this) and details of tree species, location and date are written on the envelope. (The author uses the reply envelopes sent with junk mail – they are uncirculated, free and abundant!) It is useful to collect some bark with epiphytic mosses, liverworts and lichens as these provide additional substrates for myxomycetes. Large shrubby lichens, such as *Usnea* and *Ramalina*, should not, however, be collected, partly on lichen conservation grounds but also because they rarely produce myxomycetes and often encourage unwanted contaminants in the culture. Bark from large branches and from the base of the tree is also worth collecting for culture. The best results are obtained when bark is collected during a dry spell of weather; after prolonged rain most myxomycetes will have completed their life-cycle and been washed away, and the bark is also liable to become mouldy very quickly.

Leaf litter with plasmodia is best placed into plastic pots – yoghurt or margarine pots are suitable. Leaf litter for later culture may be placed either in plastic collecting boxes or in polythene bags and must be kept damp in transit. Dung of herbivores, such as rabbit or deer, may also be collected in plastic pots or bags.

Whatever is collected should be accompanied by notes, either in a field notebook or on a pocket tape recorder. It is very helpful to have as precise habitat details as possible when identifying specimens. It is a good idea to number the collecting boxes and the individual compartments in them. If the pins/cork method is used numbered labels can be pinned with the specimen. Nice specimens without data are much less useful than poor specimens with full data!

Collecting boxes can be carried in trugs or baskets or in a haversack and should be kept as near horizontal as possible. Avoid sudden shocks when transporting plasmodia or immature sporocarps.

CULTURE

A most important method used in investigating myxomycetes is the moist chamber culture of bark from living trees. The samples should be placed in culture as soon as possible after collection, certainly within three months, or fewer myxomycetes will develop. If the bark is wet when collected it should either be placed in culture the same day or lightly dried, without heat, until is can be cultured.

The basic requirements are 9 cm plastic petri dishes, 9 cm filter paper circles (cheapest quality) and a supply of water; sterile, distilled or de-ionised water are all suitable if available, but bottled, still mineral water, melted ice cubes or cooled, boiled tap water will all suffice. The bark samples, keeping different trees/localities separate, are placed on filter paper in the bottom of the petri dish and covered with water. After soaking for 24 hours the excess water is decanted or pipetted off (wash out the pipette between dishes so as not to transfer spores or other propagules). The culture should be kept moist enough to inhibit filamentous fungi but not so wet that plasmodia disintegrate or bacteria become too abundant. In general if moulds grow the culture is too dry, and if it smells badly it is too wet! It is not necessary to incubate the cultures, room temperature is quite sufficient. Examine the cultures under the stereomicroscope every day for the first week, then thrice, twice and, finally, once weekly. Sporocarps or plasmodia appear within a few hours of the original moistening of the bark so it is important to set up cultures when time will be available to examine them. Some species will only be present for a few days and are easily missed. The myxomycetes may be eaten by invertebrates so, from time to time, it may be necessary to physically remove, with fine forceps, snails, insect adults and larvae, collembolans, and mites. Cultures should be maintained for at least three months – longer if plasmodia are present but not yet producing sporocarps. This method is remarkably successful and it is rare for any bark sample not to produce at least one species of myxomycete.

Plasmodia of non-bark species collected in the field may be cultured on the field substrate in plastic boxes or petri dishes until they mature. This usually happens within a day or so; indeed, if they do not mature quickly they have probably been damaged in transit and are best discarded. Plasmodia may also be cultured on standard nutrient agar, sprinkled with porridge oats. Bacteria from the surface of the field-collected material will multiply in this culture and keep the plasmodium fed. If sporocarps are required the supply of bacteria should be discouraged, by adding no further oats, and a dry surface for sporulation should be provided – filter paper pieces on the surface will enable the plasmodium to mature. The pure culture of myxomycetes is not dealt with further as it is outside the scope of a book on identification. The reader is invited to consult Carlisle (1971).

Dung samples can be cultured in moist chambers, the size depending on the size of the dung and treated much like bark cultures. Pieces of dead wood, fallen bark, mosses, etc., may also be left in moist chambers, often with excellent results.

EXAMINATION

Initial examination of all specimens is best done with a x10 hand lens. A good quality aplanatic and apochromatic lens will repay with information the extra money spent. The use of a x20 hand lens is not necessary if a simple stereomicroscope, giving x20 to x40 magnification, is available. The general shape of the sporocarp, colour, details of variation in terms of presence or absence of stalk, peridium reflections, colour of spores in mass can all be determined without use of the compound microscope, even in the field in many cases. It is important to have good lighting and the use of a high intensity, low wattage halide lamp attached to the stereomicroscope, or cold illumination from a fibre optic lamp is ideal. It is necessary to use a good stereomicroscope for the examination of bark cultures and it assists enormously in the examination of all myxomycete material. If funds are limited it is probably better to opt for a standard compound microscope and a good quality stereo rather than the other way round.

After initial examination, which in many cases will allow identification to species, it is important to check details under the compound microscope. A magnification of x600 is sufficient for the majority of species but it cannot be stressed too often that spore ornamentation is best seen at x1000 under oil immersion; the measurement of spores is also best carried out at this level. A calibrated eyepiece graticule is essential.

For all routine examinations and the preparation of permanent microscope slides, material should be mounted in a medium such as Hoyer's gum chloral. This can be washed off with water if the slide is not required or the mount may be ringed with colourless (or coloured) nail varnish (two coats are recommended). Very fine watchmakers' forceps are ideal for removing sporocarps or pieces of capillitium and spore mass onto the slide. Fine pointed needles and flattened Borradaille needles are also valuable in removing material from bark cultures. Well prepared slides make examination so much easier. Gentle pressure on the cover slip will disperse spores from the sporocarp and allow details of the capillitium, peridium and stalk to be seen, as well as making spore measurement easier. If air bubbles persist, gentle heating of the slide will usually clear them. It is important to measure a number of spores, at least ten, and note the range as well as the modal values. A wide range of size indicates poor maturation or a mixed sample. As with all work with myxomycetes, detailed labelling of permanent slides is essential. There is no need to use any stains when examining myxomycetes – in fact, this might conceal the true colour of spores in transmitted light which is frequently of significance at specific level. The use of Cotton blue for mounting the minute species of *Echinostelium* helps to locate them on the slide but has no other use, and may be a hindrance.

The information obtained from this examination includes presence and structure of peridial or capillitial calcium salts; size, colour and markings of spores; structure of capillitium, including shape, size and colour of calcareous nodes; colour and ornamentation of peridium in transmitted light, and stalk structure – whether hollow or fibrous, stuffed or empty, colour in transmitted light, and presence or absence of calcium salts. As much of this data as possible should be recorded in a notebook or accession book, together with all collection details.

RECIPE FOR HOYER'S GUM CHLORAL

Soak 30 g of gum arabic for 24 hours in 50 ml of distilled water, then add 200 g of chloral hydrate. [**Note**: this is a scheduled poison and must be treated with great respect according to the safety instructions provided by suppliers]. Seal the mixture in a dark glass jar and leave for at least a month, until the chloral has dissolved, then add 20 ml of glycerine. The mixture may be filtered through glass wool and kept in a dark stock bottle. For regular use a small, dark dropper bottle is convenient and should be washed out thoroughly with water before being refilled. The spores will swell in this medium if they have been wetted with a drop of alcohol on the slide before the mountant is added. It is important to keep to the same routine - with or without alcohol - so that spore measurements are comparable. The difference is likely to be about 1 μm diameter and should not lead to misidentifications, but the results may be at the upper limit of spore sizes. In this book all measurements have been made in Hoyer's but without the use of alcohol.

PRESERVATION

Myxomycete specimens are easy to preserve indefinitely if carefully dried. Field collections and cultured material may be air-dried without heat or gently heated over a radiator, in an airing-cupboard or in a special fungus/fruit drier. The sporocarps dry quickly, often in a few minutes, but the substrate, especially damp wood, must also be completely dry before storage. After drying, steps should be taken to protect the material from insect and mite attack, the biggest danger coming from the Museum beetle, *Anthrenus verbasci*. If possible place the specimens in a freezer for at least a week to kill arthropod pests. The earlier use of moth-balls, based on naphtha, or paradichlorbenzene, is not to be advocated because of health risks. In addition the latter substance is teratogenic and also inhibits spore germination, thus rendering the material useless for future culture work.

When dry the substrate holding the specimens should be glued to a white cardboard slip which fits inside a herbarium box, allowing easy and safe removal of the specimen for later examination. The ideal boxes are match-boxes. If it is possible to obtain boxes from the manufacturers before they have been printed or provided with a striking strip, so much the better. If not it will be necessary to collect boxes, or at worst, buy them and throw away the matches! The outside of the box should bear a label with the name of the species, locality, date, collector, identifier, substrate data and an accession number. This number should also be written on the mounting slip or slides made from the specimen. The mounting slips can be cut from plain postcards or from recycled greetings cards. Large specimens can be either divided or preserved in larger boxes, such as kitchen-size matchboxes or small cardboard boxes available in gift shops. The use of self-assembly white, card boxes is also becoming popular and these may also be used for field collection. Drying the specimens in these boxes takes longer and it may often be preferable to remount them. The glue used should be colourless and quick drying – there are many suitable solvent-free products on the market.

The boxes can be stored in trays, drawers, or stacked on shelves, but it is important to arrange them in an easy access way. Storing in alphabetical order of species is very useful and arranging them in order of accession number also has its merits, particularly if the collection is growing quickly. I use the former method and find that metal, 15-drawer document cabinets provide safe and neat storage but any other kind of drawer/cabinet system will suffice. The use of silica gel in the drawers is a valuable way of keeping the collection dry. Microscope slides should be kept flat in appropriate storage trays, preferably close to the box storage for easy cross reference. The whole collection should be housed in a dry, warm environment, not in a damp, unheated outbuilding.

Whichever method of storage is used it is very important to keep accession records, either in a notebook or as a computer file, in which all relevant information about each specimen is recorded. If using a computerised record system this can also be used for generating suitable labels for the herbarium boxes.

HOW TO USE THE KEYS

The identification of myxomycetes can only be achieved with mature sporocarps so material must be allowed to ripen in moist conditions or spores and capillitium will not be fully developed. The colour of the plasmodium is a useful guide but is not necessarily diagnostic. Having collected and prepared the material it is important to note the colour of spores in mass before making microscope preparations. The keys use a mixture of microscopic, macroscopic and field characters so try to amass as much information as possible about the specimen before using the keys. All keys are strictly dichotomous and the characters used at each stage should contrast well. Please read all the details of each couplet – some characters may not be available in your specimen but there may be sufficient information to use alternative characters in the couplet.

There are a few species described as new in this book. In order to satisfy the International Rules of Botanical Nomenclature these are described in Latin, in a standard form. The normal English description follows. Type material will, in due course, be deposited in the Kew Herbarium.

The species entries follow a set pattern, as follows:
Number. **Currently accepted name** and author citation.
Place and date of publication. Type locality.
Synonyms in current literature and in those listed for illustrations.
Description: sufficient details to separate the species from similar or related taxa, using the structures described in the Introduction. [Reference to a text figure].
Illustrations: reference to drawings and photographs in the following works:

DM 1   – *Die Myxomyceten* Band 1 (Neubert, Nowotny & Baumann, 1993)
DM 2   – *Die Myxomyceten* Band 2 (Neubert, Nowotny, Baumann & Marx, 1995)
E   – *The Myxomycetes of Japan* (Emoto, 1977)
FMI 2 – *Flora Mycologia Iberica* Vol. 2 (Lado & Pando, 1997)
L3   – *Monograph of the Mycetozoa* Edn. 3 (Lister, 1925)
MA   – *The Myxomycetes* (Martin & Alexopoulos, 1969)
NB   – *A Guide to Temperate Myxomycetes* (Nannenga-Bremekamp, 1991)

Habitat: where the species is usually found, with mention of exceptional places.
Distribution: a general comment on the distribution pattern in Britain and Ireland with the number of Watsonian vice-counties from which the species has been reliably recorded (data accurate to January 1999) in the form – [number of vice-counties in England, Wales and Scotland combined, number in Ireland (H), whether recorded, or not, from the Channel Islands (C)]. Extra-British distribution.

Notes: differences between similar or related species, any special features which should be looked for, special ecological clues, or any other information which will be helpful in identification.

KEYS TO ORDERS AND FAMILIES

1 Spores apparently borne externally, on outside of fruit body, not enclosed 2
– Spores produced internally, enclosed (**Myxomycetes**) 3

2 (1) Sporophores finger-like processes with spores borne on individual stalks
Ceratiomyxomycetes – Ceratiomyxales – Ceratiomyxaceae (p. 25)
– Sporophores and stalks composed of layers of cells, spores clustered in a
sorus at the tip of the stalk
Acrasiomycetes – Acrasidales – Acrasidaceae (p. 27)

3 (1) Spores in mass pale or coloured, rarely black and then never purple-
brown by transmitted light; calcium salts usually absent, if present only
deposited as a layer on the surface of the peridium 4
– Spores in mass dark, deeply coloured in transmitted light; when calcium
salts are present they are structural, secreted in characteristic fashion,
often internally 14

4 (3) True capillitium absent, pseudocapillitium when present, of tubules or
perforated plates, often with frayed ends (**Liceales**) 5
– True capillitium present, when lacking a columella usually present 9

5 (4) Peridium a basket-like net of fine threads with dark thickenings
Cribrariaceae (p. 65)
– Peridium not perforated 6

6 (5) Sporocarp an aethalium or pseudoaethalium 7
– Sporocarp sporangiate or plasmodiocarpous 8

7 (6) Aethalium flat, pseudocapillitium of coarse threads extending down from
the flat tops of constituent sporangia; spore mass yellow
Dictydiaethaliaceae (p. 82)
– Aethalium or pseudoaethalium usually rounded, pseudocapillitium of
tubes, perforated plates or irregularly branched threads; spore mass
pinkish or brown, never yellow **Lycogalaceae** (p. 83)

8 (6) No trace of capillitium or pseudocapillitium **Liceaceae** (p. 39)
– Beaded threads of pseudocapillitium attached to inner wall of peridium,
which is also marked with lines of dehiscence; on *Cladonia*
Listerellaceae (p. 64)

9 (4) Stalked, minute, pale coloured; spore mass white, pink, yellow or pale
brown; stalk tubular, filled with debris; capillitium, when present, a
simple branching net of threads; columella often well developed;
peridium delicate, soon disappearing; more or less confined to the bark of
living trees (**Echinosteliales**) 10

–   Stalked or sessile, of moderate size; spore mass yellow or reddish; columella absent; capillitium usually abundant, of sculptured threads; peridium firm, persistent (**Trichiales**)   11

10 (9)   Spore mass pale brown; capillitium adhering to fragments of peridium; columella well developed   **Clastodermataceae** (p. 29)
–   Spore mass pale; capillitium sparse, not attached to peridium; columella rarely a major feature but may be replaced by a spore-like body at the tip of the stalk   **Echinosteliaceae** (p. 31)

11 (9)   Capillitium of tubular, ornamented threads, either free (*elaters*) or a branching network, attached to the base of the sporangium   12
–   Capillitium of solid threads, attached to walls as well as base of sporangium, not forming a network; spore mass pink or brown   13

12 (11) Capillitium ornamented with 2–3 spiral bands   **Trichiaceae** (p. 124)
–   Capillitium with spines or cogs but not spirals   **Arcyriaceae** (p. 103)

13 (11) Sporocarp a small aethalium; spore mass dark brown
                                                                        Minakatellaceae (p.102)
–   Sporocarp sporangiate; spore mass pink or pinkish brown
                                                                        Dianemataceae (p. 96)

14 (3)   Calcium salts absent from sporocarp; stalk structure not continuous with peridium   **Stemonitales – Stemonitidaceae** (p. 153)
–   Calcium salts widely present in sporocarp; stalk continuous with peridium (**Physarales**)   15

15 (14) Oil or wax droplets present in the stalk and columella
                                                                        Elaeomyxaceae (p. 293)
–   Oil or wax absent   16

16 (15) Calcium salts present in the stalk, peridium, columella and capillitium, but never crystalline   **Physaraceae** (p. 219)
–   Calcium salts present except in the capillitium but, if capillitium has such inclusions, the peridial covering is crystalline   **Didymiaceae** (p. 294)

CERATIOMYXOMYCETES

CERATIOMYXALES G.W. Martin
Mycotaxon **6**: 213. 1977.

Sporocarps single or gregarious, effused or poroid, white or pale pink, blue or yellow, watery when immature, bearing finger-like processes which form erect, or at least ascending, simple or sparsely branched columns on a spreading basal hypothallus. **Peridium** and **capillitium** absent. **Spores** borne externally at the tip of fine, thread-like stalks, smooth, colourless. A single family.

Notes: the order is sometimes included with the primitive *Protosteliomycetes* but our species differs in its phaneroplasmodium, sexual reproduction and massive (in comparison) sporocarps.

CERATIOMYXACEAE J. Schröt.
in Engler & Prantl, *Nat. Pflanzenfam.* 1(i): 15. 1989.

With the characters of the order. A single genus.

CERATIOMYXA J. Schröt.
in Engler & Prantl, *Nat. Pflanzenfam.* 1(i): 16. 1989.

With the characters of the order. Seven species, mostly tropical, of which the following, type species, is widespread.

Ceratiomyxa fruticulosa (F. Muell.) T. Macbr.
North American Slime-Moulds: 18. 1899. Europe.
var. **fruticulosa**

Sporocarps effused, up to 10 cm long, white, rarely pale yellow, pink or blue; finger-like processes up to 4 mm high, sparsely branched, more or less erect. **Spores** ellipsoid, 10–14 x 6–8 µm, or subglobose, 8–9 µm, smooth, colourless. **Phaneroplasmodium** transparent watery white or pale yellow. [Fig. 1]

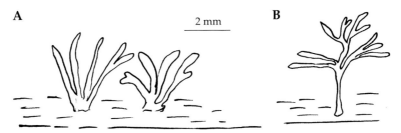

Fig. 1. *Ceratiomyxa fruticulosa*: A: var. *fruticulosa*; B: var. *arbuscula*.

Illustrations: DM 1: 41,42; E: pl. 2; FMI 2: 23; L3: pl. 1; MA: fig. 1; NB: 32.
Habitat: on fallen trunks, branches and stumps, especially of conifers.
Distribution: abundant in the British Isles, from early summer onwards [111, H39, C]. Cosmopolitan and abundant, especially in the tropics.

var. **arbuscula** (Berk. & Broome) Nann.-Bremek.
Guide to temperate myxomycetes: 32. 1991. Borneo.
Syn. *Ceratiomyxa fruticulosa* var. *flexuosa* Lister

Differs from the type in having thicker, trunk-like processes with a tree-like cluster of branches. [Fig. 1] So far known from Brecon and Kirkudbright; abundant in the tropics where it is the dominant form.

Notes: in Central and southern Europe *C. porioides* is not uncommon. It resembles poroid basidiomycetes such as *Physisporinus sanguinolentus* or *Trechispora mollusca* and is found on stumps of *Fagus* or conifers. Treated by many authors as a variety of *C. fruticulosa* it is constant in its poroid features and biogeography and is here regarded as distinct. It should be looked for in warm, southern areas with a Mediterranean-like vegetation, such as the New Forest.

ACRASIOMYCETES

ACRASIDALES K.B. Raper
in Ainsworth, Sparrow and Sussman, *The Fungi* **IVB**: 18. 1973.

Sporocarp comprising a sorus, or spore mass, on a stalk consisting of cells in a chain. **Peridium** and **capillitium** absent. Four families of which only one is considered here.

ACRASIDACEAE van Tieghem
Bull. Soc. bot. Fr. **27**: 319. 1880.

With the characters of the order. Two genera, one common on bark (*Pocheina*, below) and *Acrasis*, with the spores in a chain like the stalk, of which *A. rosea* is rare on bark, plant litter and rabbit dung.

POCHEINA A.R. Loebl. & Tappan
J. Paleontol. **35**: 256. 1961.

Sporocarp with a stalk of cells and an ovoid, terminal sorus of spores. Two species of which the following, type species, is very common in bark cultures and, therefore, frequently met with when sampling for corticolous myxomycetes.

Pocheina rosea (Cienk.) A.R. Loebl. & Tappan
J. Paleontol. **35**: 245. 1961. Poland.
Syn. *Guttulina rosea* Cienk.

Sporocarp to 300 μm high, stalked, with one or two rows of rounded, rectangular cells arranged like bricks to build the stalk, pale bright pink or, rarely, white. Terminal sorus subglobose to ovoid, 40–110 μm diam. **Spores** coloured as rest of sporocarp, globose, faintly punctate, with thickened areas of spore-to-spore contact, 7–12 μm diam. [Fig. 2]
Habitat: on bark of living trees, especially conifers and other acid-barked trees or other trees in areas affected by atmospheric pollution; therefore characteristic of the bark of urban trees.

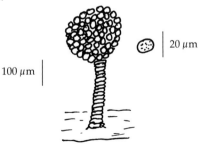

100 μm

20 μm

Fig. 2. *Pocheina rosea*

Distribution: common in the British Isles [99, H10, C]. Widespread in temperate Europe and probably common in North America; reported from New Zealand and Chile.

Notes: this species is included because of its frequency in bark cultures where its chunky shape and bright pink colour, notwithstanding its cellular stalk, immediately separate it from species of *Echinostelium*.

MYXOMYCETES

ECHINOSTELIALES G.W. Martin
Mycologia **52**: 127. 1961.

Sporocarp small, stalked, up to 1.5 mm high. **Stalk** hollow, longer than the diameter of the sporangium, usually stuffed with granular material. **Columella** a short extension of the stalk or globose and spore-like, or absent. **Capillitium** a simple, branching network or absent. **Spore** mass white, cream, pale pink, pale yellow, grey or brown. **Plasmodium** a protoplasmodium. Two families.

CLASTODERMATACEAE Alexop. & T.E. Brooks
Mycologia **63**: 926. 1971.

Peridium persistent, often breaking up into plates which are attached to the ends of the branches of the capillitium. **Spore** mass brown. Two genera: *Clastoderma* (below) and *Barbeyella* Meyl., with a single, montane species, *minutissima* Mey., on liverworts on conifer logs, which may yet be found in Scotland.

CLASTODERMA A. Blytt
Bot. Zeit. **38**: 343. 1880.

Sporocarps usually in groups. Stalk with enclosed granular matter below, tubular and horny above, often with a well-marked swelling or collar at the junction of the two sections. Peridial fragments small angular plates which are clearly attached to the capillitium. Capillitial threads branching and sometimes forming a surface net with open meshes. Four species, two of which are included below; type is *C. debaryanum* Blytt.

KEY TO SPECIES

1   Capillitium branching once, forming an open meshed net; total height less than 0.5 mm; spores 12–14 μm   *pachypus*

–   Capillitium branching dichotomously from the tip of the columella, anastomosing but not forming a well-marked net; total height 1–1.5 mm; spores less than 12 μm   *debaryanum*

Clastoderma debaryanum A. Blytt
Bot. Zeit. **38**: 343. 1880. Norway.

Sporocarps often in small groups but not tufted, long-stalked, to 1.5 mm tall. **Stalk** hollow, tapering from a broad, stuffed base with a distinct swelling below the sporangium, above which the stalk is horny and usually darker than the pale brown of the lower part. **Sporangium** dark brown, 0.1–0.2 mm diam, sometimes slightly shiny from the reflections from the smooth red-brown peridial fragments. **Columella** branching in the lower part of the sporangium to give rise to the major branches of the capillitium. **Capillitium** branching dichotomously two or three times before reaching the peridial fragments. **Spores** in mass dark brown, pale rose-red in transmitted light, covered in fine warts, 8–12 μm diam. **Protoplasmodium** translucent white. [Fig. 3]

Illustrations: DM 1: 48; E: pl. 64; FMI 2: 29; L3: pl. 135; MA: fig. 184; NB: 38.
Habitat: bark of living trees, especially oaks. In the tropics this species also occurs widely on such debris as coconut husks.
Distribution: rare, in the milder regions of England and Ireland, so far recorded from Somerset, Wiltshire, Sussex, Hertfordshire, Yorkshire, Westmorland, Co. Leix and Co. Mayo [6, H2]. Scattered in Europe but abundant in the tropics of the Americas, Asia and Australasia.

Notes: in moist chamber culture of bark this species at first resembles an *Echinostelium* but soon appears to be more robust and is easily identified at low magnification when the brown spores ripen.

Clastoderma pachypus Nann.-Bremek.
Proc. K. Ned. Akad. Wet. C **71**: 44. 1968. France.

Sporocarp stalked, the stalk only twice as long as the diameter of the sporangium. Stalk hollow, tapering from a broad base, stuffed with granular matter and narrowing sharply below the sporangium but without a distinct swelling. There is a collar-like remnant of the peridium. Sporocarps not usually in groups. **Sporangium** dark brown, peridium glistening when first ripe but soon disappearing leaving a few small fragments attached to the net of the capillitium. **Columella** very short and immediately branching once into the net-like capillitium. **Spores** in mass dark brown, pale reddish-brown by transmitted light, very finely warted, 12–14 μm diam. **Protoplasmodium** pale brown. [Fig. 4]

Illustrations: DM 1: 50 (as *microcarpum*); FMI 2: 29.
Habitat: bark of living trees, especially oaks with epiphytic mosses.

Fig. 3. *Clastoderma debaryanum*

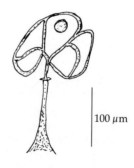

Fig. 4. *Clastoderma pachypus*

100 μm

100 μm

Distribution: distinctly Atlantic in the British Isles, along the south coast of England and up the western seaboard to the north-west Highlands of Scotland; along the east coast of Ireland [15, H2]. The species has a wide, if scattered, distribution in Europe, India, and the Caribbean.

Notes: the species was originally confused with the much rarer, and characteristically Mediterranean *Echinostelium cribrarioides*, which also has a netted capillitium, but that has a yellow spore mass and spores with distinct articular surfaces. An interesting account of its Irish distribution is given by McHugh (1986).

ECHINOSTELIACEAE Rostaf. ex Cooke
Contr. Mycol. Br.: **53**. 1877.

Peridium evanescent, often leaving a collar-like relic at the base of the sporangium. **Spore** mass white, cream, pale yellow, pink, pale grey or beige. **Columella** present or absent, sometimes globular and resembling a large spore. Spores often with articular surfaces – thickened plates where they touch each other. A single genus.

ECHINOSTELIUM de Bary
in Rostefinskiy *Vers. Synt. Mycet.*: 7. 1873.

Fourteen species, largely world-wide, including the smallest known myxomycetes. All are characteristic of the bark of living trees and can usually only be found using moist chamber culture. Their small size, delicacy of construction and the facility with which the spore mass detaches from the sporocarp make them extremely difficult to mount for microscopic study. Great patience and a steady hand, coupled to fine forceps, needles or scalpel tips are necessary to remove them from the substrate. Fortunately they frequently occur in large fruitings so some material may survive for identification. A valuable monograph is given by Whitney (1980). The type species is *E. minutum* de Bary.

KEY TO SPECIES

1	Capillitium present	2
–	Capillitium absent	4

2 (1) Capillitium of short unbranched filaments arising directly from the apex of the stalk, difficult to see with the light microscope; rare   *elachiston*
–   Capillitium of well-developed branches arising from a distinct columella, easily seen with the light microscope   3

3 (2) Columella stout, cylindrical; peridium persistent; sporangia pale yellow, less than 150 μm high; rare   *arboreum*
–   Columella conical or slightly elongate, never cylindrical; peridium fugacious; sporangia white or pale pink, 300–500 μm high; common
       minutum

| 4 (1) | Columella absent, rare | *elachiston* |
| – | Columella present | 5 |

| 5 (4) | Columella globose, spore-like | 6 |
| – | Columella peg-like, elliptical, lenticular or hemispherical | 8 |

| 6 (5) | Spores with prominent, thickenings at points of spore-to-spore contact | 7 |
| – | Spores without distinct thickenings | *apitectum* |

| 7 (6) | Sporocarp minute, less than 70 μm high; spore-to-spore articulations thick, with sharply defined margins | *coelocephalum* |
| – | Sporocarps larger, 70–130 μm high; spore-to-spore articulations thinner, with tapered margins; common | *colliculosum* |

| 8 (5) | Spore walls with thickened areas; columella hemispherical, hyaline to yellowish-brown; spore mass white; frequent | *corynophorum* |
| – | Spore walls without thickened areas; spore mass pink | 9 |

| 9 (8) | True columella minute, peg-like, enclosed in a globose, spore-like cover; frequent | *apitectum* |
| – | Columella elliptical/fusiform or lenticular/hemispherical | 10 |

| 10 (9) | Columella elliptical to fusiform | *fragile* |
| – | Columella lenticular to hemispherical | *brooksii* |

Echinostelium apitectum K.D. Whitney
Mycologia **72**: 954. 1980. California.
Syn. *Echinostelium vanderpoelii* Nann.-Bremek, D.W. Mitchell, T.N. Lakh. & R.K. Chopra

Sporocarp 100–350 μm high, white or pale pink. **Sporangium** globose, 30–65 μm diam. **Stalk** transparent, white or pale yellow. **Peridium** remaining as a collar or cup-like base, up to 10 μm diam. **Columella** a short peg-like structure enclosed in a globose cover, often absent. **Capillitium** absent. **Spore** mass pale pink or pale tan; under transmitted light spores are hyaline, pale pink or pale grey, 6–10 μm diam, wall of uniform thickness.
Protoplasmodium hyaline. [Fig. 5]

Illustrations: FMI 2: 34.
Habitat: on bark of living trees.
Distribution: rare in the British Isles, except in south-east England [13, H1]. Widely recorded in Europe, Asia, Australia, Africa and North America but nowhere common.

Notes: the concept of this species has recently been expanded by Lado and Pando (1997) who combine it with *E. vanderpoelii*, which was originally described from Wales and Scotland. The gradations in spore size and in the variation of spore colour and development of the columella do not allow the maintenance of two species.

Echinostelium arboreum H.W. Keller & T.E. Brooks
Mycologia **68**: 1207. 1977. Mexico.

Sporocarps scattered, 100–150 μm high, bright yellow. **Sporangium** globose, 40–50 μm diam. Stalk tapering, bright yellow, stuffed with granular matter. **Peridium** remaining as a small collar at the base of the sporangium. **Columella** cylindrical, reaching to at least two thirds of the sporangial height, pale yellow, branching into a tree-like capillitium, which varies in the degree of branching. **Capillitium** does not form a net at the surface. Spore mass yellow, spores hyaline or pale yellow by transmitted light, 6–9 μm diam, wall of uniform thickness. **Protoplasmodium** yellow. [Fig. 6]

Illustrations: FMI 2: 42.
Habitat: bark of living sycamore.
Distribution: known from a single collection from Peebles-shire in 1997. [1]. Apart from the North and Central American records it is known in Europe from Mallorca, Montenegro and Switzerland.

Notes: the bright yellow colour, the relatively large sporangia and the well-developed arborescent capillitium make this a readily recognised species.

Echinostelium brooksii K.D. Whitney
Mycologia **72**: 957. 1980. California.

Sporocarps in groups, often of several hundred, 100–200 μm high, pink. **Sporangia** 35–60 μm diam. **Stalk** transparent but, at least in the lower half, stuffed with granular matter. **Peridium** persisting as a small collar. **Columella** stalked, lenticular to hemispherical, dark brown. **Capillitium** absent. **Spore** mass pink, spores pale pink by transmitted light, 10–14 μm diam, wall without obvious thickenings. **Protoplasmodium** pale pink. [Fig. 7]

Illustrations: DM 1: 52; FMI 2: 37; NB: 37.
Habitat: on bark of living trees, especially solitary trees.

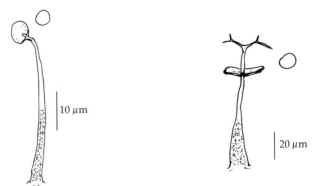

Fig. 5. *Echinostelium apitectum*   Fig. 6. *Echinostelium arboreum*

Distribution: common in the British Isles [54, H8, C]. Common throughout Europe and North America and recently found in South America and Africa; widespread in Asia.

Notes: found on trees with more acid bark than the superficially similar *E. fragile*. Can be told from the similar *E. corynophorum* by the spore wall structure and the pink, rather than white, sporocarps. This species is one of the first myxomycetes to appear in moist chamber cultures of bark, often after 24 hours following moistening.

Fig. 7. *Echinostelium brooksii*

Echinostelium coelocephalum T.E. Brooks & H.W. Keller
Mycologia **68**: 1212. 1977. Arkansas.

Sporocarps scattered or in small groups, 45–80 μm high, white. **Sporangium** 30–40 μm diam. **Stalk** translucent, pale yellow in transmitted light. **Peridium** persisting as a small collar. **Columella** absent, instead a spore-like body sits at the top of the stalk. **Capillitium** absent. **Spore** mass very pale yellow, spores colourless by transmitted light, 9–12 μm diam, with thickened circular articulation surfaces, these having sharply defined margins. **Protoplasmodium** colourless. [Fig. 8]

Illustrations: FMI 2: 34.
Habitat: bark of living trees.
Distribution: only known in the British Isles from Co. Donegal [H1]. Elsewhere known from North America, Belize, France, Spain and Turkey.

Notes: this minute species resembles small samples of *E. colliculosum* but may be readily separated from that species by the spore articulations.

Echinostelium colliculosum K.D. Whitney & H.W. Keller
Mycologia **72**: 641. 1980. Nevada.

Sporocarps usually scattered, 70–150 μm high, white. **Sporangium** 30–50 μm diam. **Peridium** persisting as a closely appressed collar. **Columella** absent, replaced by globose spore-like body. **Capillitium** absent. **Spore** mass white or very pale pink, spores colourless in transmitted light, 9–13 μm diam, with articulations which have tapered margins so that they are much less obvious than in *E. coelocephalum*. **Protoplasmodium** colourless. [Fig. 9]

Illustrations: FMI 2: 34.
Habitat: bark of living trees.
Distribution: common and widespread in the British Isles [72, H6, C]. Found throughout Europe and the Americas and known from Africa, Australia and Asia.

Notes: this species was originally confused with *E. elachiston*, indeed most of the Greek collections on which that species was based were transferred here by Whitney (1980). This species usually appears later in cultures than *E. brooksii* or *E. fragile*, but before *E. minutum*.

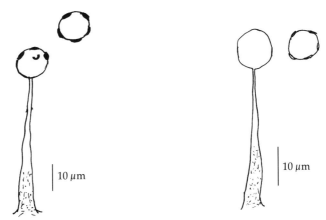

Fig. 8. *Echinostelium coelocephalum*   Fig. 9. *Echinostelium colliculosum*

Echinostelium corynophorum K.D. Whitney
Mycologia **72**: 963. 1980. California.

Sporocarps scattered, rarely in groups, 90–150 μm high, white. **Sporangium** 40–60 μm in diam. **Stalk** colourless, lower part filled with granular matter. **Peridium** persisting as a small basal cup. **Columella** short-stalked, hemispherical or lenticular, light brown, but appearing lighter than in *E. brooksii* by direct, not transmitted, light. **Capillitium** absent. **Spore** mass white, spores colourless in transmitted light, 9–15 μm diam, articular areas thin, with tapering margins. **Protoplasmodium** colourless. [Fig. 10]

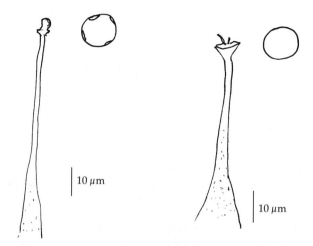

Fig. 10. *Echinostelium corynophorum*   Fig. 11. *Echinostelium elachiston*

Illustrations: DM 1: 52; FMI 2: 37.
Habitat: on bark of living trees.
Distribution: uncommon in Great Britain, rare in Ireland [22, H1, C]. Widely distributed in Europe, Asia Minor, Australia and North America, but never common.

Notes: the obvious distinguishing character from *E. brooksii* is the white, rather than pink, spore mass under the stereomicroscope. However, the most reliable is the presence of articular surfaces on the spores, which are absent in *E. brooksii*.

Echinostelium elachiston Alexop.
Mycologia **50**: 52. 1958. Greece.

Sporocarps scattered, 90–110 μm high, bright yellow. **Sporangium** 30–40 μm diam. **Stalk** very broad at the base but quickly tapering, bright yellow. **Peridium** persisting as a basal collar. **Columella** and spore-like body absent. **Capillitium** consisting at most of a few short, solid threads, usually absent. **Spore** mass yellow, spores pale yellow by transmitted light, 6–8 μm diam, smooth, with uniform surface. **Protoplasmodium** bright yellow. [Fig. 11]

Illustrations: FMI 2: 37.
Habitat: bark of living trees.
Distribution: rare in Britain, recorded from Devon, Dumfries and the Channel Islands [3, C]. Scattered, but rare, across Europe, Asia and North America.

Notes: originally confused with the much commoner *E. colliculosum*, this species is superficially similar to *E. arboreum* but lacks the well-developed capillitium of that species and appears less squat and robust on the bark.

Echinostelium fragile Nann.-Bremek.
Acta Bot.Neerl. **10**: 65. 1961. Netherlands.

Sporocarps scattered, 100–150 µm high, pink. **Sporangium** 30–50 µm diam. **Stalk** translucent, pale yellowish-pink. **Peridium** persisting as a basal collar. **Columella** cylindrical to fusiform, up to 10 µm long, dark olive-brown. **Capillitium** absent. **Spore** mass pink, spores 11–14 µm diam, without articular surfaces. **Protoplasmodium** watery pink. [Fig. 12]

Illustrations: DM 1: 52; FMI 2: 37; MA: fig. 59; NB: 37.
Habitat: bark of living trees, especially isolated trees.
Distribution: common and widespread in the British Isles [65, H15, C]. Nearly cosmopolitan but not yet reported from Africa.

Notes: easily separated from the similar, and equally common, *E. brooksii*, by the columella. This can be seen in older sporocarps even with the x40 stereomicroscope.

Echinostelium minutum de Bary
in Rostafinski, *Sluzowce Monogr.*: 215. 1874. Germany.

Sporocarps scattered or in large groups, 250–550 µm high, white or pale pink. **Sporangium** 40–70 µm diam, often nodding. **Stalk** longer than in all other species, to 500 µm high, colourless or pale yellow by transmitted light. **Peridium**

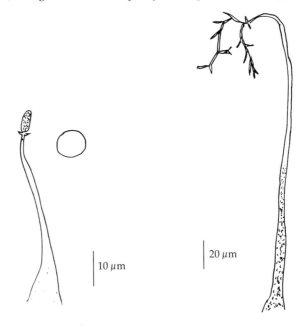

Fig. 12. *Echinostelium fragile*   Fig. 13. *Echinostelium minutum*

persisting as a small basal collar. **Columella** conical or short-cylindrical, merging into the primary branches of the capillitium. **Capillitium** varies from a few unbranched, solid threads, to a well-developed, dichotomously branched system, but without a peripheral net. **Spore** mass white, or rarely pale pink, spores colourless by transmitted light, 6–8 µm diam, with faint suggestions of articular surfaces. **Protoplasmodium** colourless. [Fig. 13]

Illustrations: DM 2: 53; FMI 2: 42; MA: fig. 60; NB: 35.
Habitat: bark of living trees, occasionally on wood and herbaceous litter.
Distribution: very common in the British Isles [108, H36, C]. Cosmopolitan.

Notes: the largest and commonest species of the genus, it tends to appear later in bark cultures than most of the other species. It is the only species regularly visible to the naked eye.

EXCLUDED SPECIES

Echinostelium roseum Ing was described from Kindrogan, Scotland from cultures of sycamore bark. Subsequent study showed that the sporocarps were actually an undescribed myxobacterium and the spores belonged to an *Echinostelium*, probably *E. colliculosum*, which occurred on the same tree (see Ing, 1984).

LICEALES E. Jahn
in Engler & Prantl, *Nat. Pflanzenfam.* **2** (ii): 319. 1928.

Sporocarps forming sporangia, sessile or stalked, plasmodiocarps, pseudoaethalia and true aethalia. **Columella** and true capillitium absent (except in *Listerella*) but a pseudocapillitium, made from walls of constituent sporangial units of aethalia, may be present. **Sporangial wall** may be perforated to allow spores to escape (Cribrariaceae). Spore masses vary from white to black, through pinks, browns and yellow shades. **Calcium salts** absent from fruit bodies. **Plasmodium** either a protoplasmodium in corticolous species or a phaneroplasmodium. Five families, all represented here.

LICEACEAE Chevall.
Fl. Gén. Env. Paris **1**: 343. 1826.

Sporocarps sporangiate or plasmodiocarpous, no columella, capillitium or pseudocapillitium. **Spore** masses lacking pale pink shades. Two genera, the following and the non-European *Kelleromyxa* Eliasson.

LICEA Schrader
Nov. Gen. Pl.: **16**. 1797.

Sporocarps usually sporangiate, in a few species plasmodiocarpous, usually sessile but in a few species with a well-developed stalk. **Peridium** wall double, the inner membranous, the outer leathery or horny, often breaking up into pre-formed plates, or gelatinous; the base of the outer wall often persists as a cup. **Columella, capillitium** and **pseudocapillitium** absent. **Spores** usually free, sometimes smooth, sometimes ornamented, either of uniform thickness or with a thinner, paler area. More than 50 species, worldwide; the type is *L. pusilla* Schrad.

Notes: the majority of species are corticolous and very small and usually met with in moist chamber cultures of bark. It is essential that they be allowed as much time as possible, often several weeks, to mature properly, i.e. spores should be of uniform size and shape, before reliable identification may be achieved. In the key some species appear more than once – this is because they have more than one habitat or vary in possession of a stalk.

KEY TO SPECIES

1	On bark of living trees	2
–	On other substrates	28
2 (1)	Sporocarp clearly stalked	3
–	Sporocarp with no trace of stalk	9
3 (2)	Stalk clearly more than half total height	4
–	Stalk less than half total height	5

4 (3)   Stalk slender, abruptly widening into a goblet-shaped, thin-walled,
        smooth, sporangium, with or without a well-defined lid   *operculata*
–   Stalk stout, gradually widening to a thick-walled, roughened, tumbler-
        shaped sporangium, without a lid   *eleanorae*

5 (3)   Dehiscence by a well-defined lid, looking like a shiny kettle-drum,
        short-stalked, widest at mouth   *crateriformis*
–   Dehiscence not by a lid   6

6 (5)   Dehiscence by an equatorial fissure, leaving the lower half of the
        sporangium as a cup   *scyphoides*
–   Dehiscence not equatorial   7

7 (6)   Dehiscence by small peridial plates   *pedicellata*
–   Dehiscence not by plates   8

8 (7)   Dehiscence by fragmentation of peridium, spores with pale area,
        8.5–10.5 μm diam   *perexigua*
–   Dehiscence by apical, vertical split, spores without pale area,
        11.5–12.5 μm diam   *erddigensis*

9 (2)   Peridium with well-marked plates with prominent lines of dehiscence   10
–   Dehiscence otherwise   16

10 (9) Spores smooth   11
–   Spores ornamented   12

11 (10) Peridial plates with marginal pegs, sporangium flattened, pale   *castanea*
–   Peridial plates without marginal pegs, sporangium dark, not noticeably
        flattened   *belmontiana*

12 (10) Sporangium 0.1–0.2 mm diam   *pygmaea*
–   Sporangium larger   13

13 (12) Spores 15–18 μm diam   14
–   Spores 11–14 μm diam   15

14 (13) Spores coarsely warted, warts deciduous, pale reddish by
        transmitted light   *chelonoides*
–   Spores minutely warted, warts persistent, pale olivaceous by
        transmitted light   *pusilla*

15 (13) Peridial plates 6–14 per sporangium, spore mass dark brown, spores
        with paler area under transmitted light   *testudinacea*
–   Peridial plates fewer than six per sporangium, spore mass reddish-brown,
        spores without pale area   *minima*

16 (9) Dehiscence by well-defined lid   17
–   Dehiscence otherwise   18

17 (16) Lid metallic, with outgrowths on inner surface, sporangium resembles a
       tiny, neat, shining coin   *kleistobolus*
–   Lid not metallic, appearing as a dark ring in immature sporangia, without
       in-growths, sporangium resembles a plump, dark pork pie   *parasitica*

18 (16) Dehiscence by a prominent longitudinal slit, sporangium resembles a
       miniature date stone   *biforis*
–   Dehiscence irregular   19

19 (18) Spores clustered   *synsporos*
–   Spores free   20

20 (19) Minute sporangia surrounded by a black basal ring   *marginata*
–   No black basal ring present   21

21 (20) Spores in mass dark   22
–   Spores in mass pale   23

22 (21) Spores smooth, paler on one side, outer wall of peridium gelatinous
                                             denudescens
–   Spores warted, uniformly coloured, peridium iridescent   *iridis*

23 (21) Spore mass reddish-orange   *inconspicua*
–   Spore mass ochraceous, yellow or paler   24

24 (23) Associated with leafy liverworts   25
–   Not on liverworts   26

25 (24) On *Frullania*, spores 11–12 μm diam   *gloeoderma*
–   On *Radula* and *Metzgeria*, spores 14–15 μm diam   *bryophila*

26 (24) Sporangia minute, pale, shining, spores smooth   27
–   Sporangia larger, not shining, spores roughened   *tenera*

27 (26) Sporangium gelatinous, spores 15–17 μm; rare   *microscopica*
–   Sporangium not gelatinous, spores 8–10 μm   *perexigua*

28 (1) On dead wood   29
–   On other substrates   31

29 (28) Plasmodiocarps dehiscing irregularly, on decorticated conifer branches
                                             variabilis
–   Sporangia dehiscing by peridial plates   30

30 (29) Spore mass black, spores 15–18 μm diam   *pusilla*
–   Spore mass reddish brown, spores 11–14 μm diam   *minima*

31 (28)	On bramble or woody herbaceous stems	32
–	On other substrates	33
32 (31)	Dehiscing by a lid, resembling an open oyster	*clarkii*
–	Dehiscing by a slit, resembling a date stone	*biforis*
33 (31)	On living *Calluna* stems	*operculata*
–	On other substrates	34
34 (33)	On decaying bracket fungi	*minima*
–	On other substrates	35
35 (34)	On leaf litter	36
–	On other substrates	37
36 (35)	Spores smooth, pale yellow by transmitted light	*deplanata*
–	Spores warted, pale brown by transmitted light	*testudinacea*
37 (35)	On herbivore dung	38
–	On living *Cladonia pudetia*	*minima*
38 (37)	Sporangia with peridial plates	*testudinacea*
–	Sporangia without peridial plates	*tenera*

Licea belmontiana Nann.-Bremek.
Proc. K. Ned. Akad. Wet. C **69**: 337. 1966. Netherlands.

Sporocarps gregarious, sessile, almost spherical, 0.05–0.15 mm diam, dark brown, glossy, with dark lines of dehiscence between the peridial plates. **Peridium** smooth, dividing into lobes which have smooth margins. **Spores** in mass dark brown, rosy-brown in transmitted light, smooth, 13 μm diam, wall thick with a paler area on one side. **Protoplasmodium** colourless. [Fig. 14]

Illustrations: NB: 43.
Habitat: only known from the bark of living trees.
Distribution: well distributed and not uncommon in Great Britain but not yet reported from Ireland [36]. Not uncommon in many parts of western and Central Europe and also known from India.

Notes: the smooth margins of the peridial plates and the darker, rather than lighter, lines of dehiscence are the key features of this minute species.

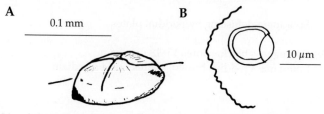

Fig. 14. *Licea belmontiana*: A: sporangium; B: peridial lobe and spore.

Licea biforis Morgan
J. Cinc. Soc. Nat. Hist. **15**: 131. 1893. Ohio.
Syn. *Licea sinuosa* Nann.-Bremek.

Sporocarps scattered or gregarious, fusiform, with an obvious longitudinal split, pale yellow to dark ochraceous with age, 0.2–1.5 mm long and 0.1–0.3 mm wide. On dehiscence the lobes separate along the split and roll back exposing the yellow or paler spore mass and the sporangium often arches with the release of tension. **Spores** globose to slightly ovate, minutely roughened, 9–12 μm diam. **Protoplasmodium** honey-coloured, often immersed in a cyanobacterial slime. [Fig. 15]

Illustrations: DM 1: 148; E: pl. 5; FMI 2: 113; L3: pl. 149; MA: fig. 4; NB: 47.
Habitat: primarily the bark of living trees and rarely (as a casual?) in leaf litter in moist chambers. However, in 1998 it developed on dead stems of *Eupatorium* and *Rubus* kept in moist chamber, producing abundant, somewhat smaller than usual, sporangia.
Distribution: mostly southern in Britain, with only three Scottish records, but becoming quite common in Central London parks [28, H9, C]. Common in the warmer parts of Europe, found throughout North America and Asia and reported from Australia, New Zealand, Africa, Belize and Chile.

Notes: the characteristic date-stone shape of this species is sufficient to identify it. Occasionally some sporangia appear to be branched and look more like damaged starfish. These occur, however, with the typical form and are not worth distinguishing as *L. sinuosa*. The colour of the spore mass varies from a brownish yellow to almost white but all other characters are unchanged.

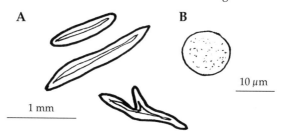

A   B

1 mm   10 μm

Fig. 15. *Licea biforis*: A: sporangia; B: spore.

Licea bryophila Nann.-Bremek.
Proc. K. Ned. Akad. Wet. C **79**: 382. 1976. France.

Sporocarps scattered, globose, sessile on a constricted base, 0.1–0.2 mm diam, varying in colour from pale brown to black, often with a silvery sheen. **Peridium** with a thick outer layer, slimy with granular matter, the inner layer thin and densely warted. Dehiscence involves fragmentation of the wall but without pre-formed lines so that no true lid or plates are present. **Spore** mass greyish ochraceous brown, spores pale ochraceous in transmitted light, minutely spinulose, with a paler area to one side, 14–15 μm diam. **Protoplasmodium** pale pink. [Fig. 16]

Illustrations: original publication only.
Habitat: on fronds of the liverworts *Metzgeria* and *Radula* on the bark of living trees.
Distribution: scattered in western Britain and distinctly Atlantic [11, H1]. In Europe known with certainty from France and Switzerland.

Notes: the habitat, small size and distinctively warted inner peridium separate this species. It takes more than a week to mature from the first small blob of pink plasmodium on the liverwort, which darkens to a brownish colour as the outer peridium dries. When this breaks away the shiny inner membrane shows through. The species is often associated with cyanobacteria and reports of a blue-green sheen on it are probably due to this.

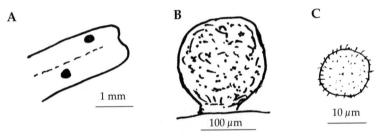

Fig. 16. *Licea bryophila*: A: sporangia on *Metzgeria*; B: sporangium; C: spore.

Licea castanea G. Lister
J. Bot., Lond. **49**: 61. 1911. Lesmoir, Aberdeenshire.

Sporocarps flattened sporangia to short plasmodiocarps, sessile, pale yellow-brown to chestnut, with prominent yellow lines of dehiscence, 0.1–0.4 mm diam or 0.1–0.9 mm long. **Peridium** leathery with paler lines separating the peridial plates. The plate margins are not raised in mature sporangia, leaving a smooth outline. The margins have a single row of papillae behind the edge, leaving a clear strip. **Spore** mass mid-brown, spores pale ochraceous brown in transmitted light, smooth, 9–10 μm diam; the wall thick with a prominent thinner zone. **Protoplasmodium** honey-coloured. [Fig. 17]

Illustrations: DM 1: 149; E: pl. 4; FMI 2: 114; L3: pl. 219; MA: fig. 5; NB: 41.
Habitat: the bark of living trees, and very rarely on fallen bark.
Distribution: scattered throughout the British Isles but much less common than most other species with platelets [19, H2]. Similarly scattered in Europe, North America, New Zealand and Asia.

Notes: the smooth spores and plate margins with papillae are sufficient to separate this species.

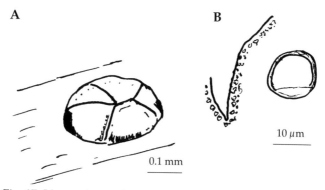

Fig. 17. *Licea castanea*: A: sporangium; B: peridial lobe and spore.

Licea chelonoides Nann.-Bremek.
Acta Bot. Neerl. **14**: 136. 1965. Netherlands.

Sporocarps scattered or in small groups of sessile, pulvinate sporangia, angular with raised ridges, 0.5–0.8 mm diam, to 0.5 mm tall, dull, dark reddish-brown to black. **Peridium** thick, of two or three layers, the outer being dark and dull and the inner shining; divided into peridial plates whose margins have several rows of tubercles. **Spores** in mass dark brown, rose or pale reddish-brown by transmitted light, 15–18 µm diam, warted with some fine warts and a variable number of larger warts which are deciduous and may be found alongside the spores in a mount. **Protoplasmodium** brown, becoming yellow, reddish and finally black. [Fig. 18]

Illustrations: NB: 45.
Habitat: on bark of living trees, rarely on dead wood (type only!)
Distribution: rare, scattered in England and Wales [5]. Known from the Netherlands, Germany, Switzerland and Sierra Leone.

Notes: the large reddish-brown sporangia and reddish spores with the characteristic deciduous warts, serve to distinguish this species which is rarely reported anywhere although said to be common in the Netherlands.

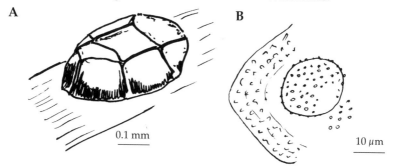

Fig. 18. *Licea chelonoides*: A: sporangium; B: peridial lobe and spore.

Licea clarkii Ing
Trans. Br. mycol. Soc. **78**: 439. 1982. Forshaw Heath, Warwickshire.

Sporocarps scattered, sessile, orange-brown, depressed, 0.2 mm diam or elongate-elliptic, 0.3–0.35 x 0.2 mm, total height 0.15 mm. **Peridium** thin, light orange-brown, often densely covered with a scurf of yellow granular material. Dehiscence circumscissile, the upper half of the sporangium lifting from one side to give the appearance of an open oyster, the lower half remaining as a cup-like base. **Spore** mass dark brown to black, greyish-yellow by transmitted light, 12–16 μm diam, minutely warted to almost smooth, the warts when present giving the impression of a faint reticulum. **Plasmodium** unknown. [Fig. 19]

Illustrations: original description.
Habitat: on dead arching stems of brambles (*Rubus*) and dead standing stems of rosebay (*Chamaerion*) up to a metre above ground level.
Distribution: scattered in the southern half of Britain with one record from Co. Wicklow [12, H1]. Not yet recorded outside the British Isles.

Notes: the habitat and the characteristic oyster-shell shape of the dehisced sporangia are sufficient to identify this species which is undoubtedly commoner than the records suggest – it is abundant in the West Midlands.

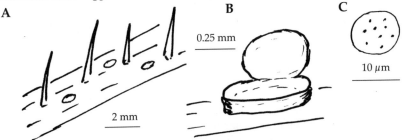

Fig. 19. *Licea clarkii*: A: sporangia on *Rubus*; B: sporangium; C: spore.

Licea crateriformis Ing **nov. spec.**

Sporangia brevistipitata, in formam crateris. Stipes rugosus, e hypothallo discoideo. Peridium obscure fuscum, laeve, 0.8 mm alto, 0.7–0.75 mm in diam., cum operculum distinctum, aureo-aereum, nitidum. Sporae in cumulo pallido-ochraceae, per luce transmissa incoloratae, laeves, globosae, 7–9.5 μm in diam. Plasmodium ignotum.
Habitat in thallo vivo *Radulae complanatae* in rame vivo *Coryli avellanae*.
HOLOTYPUS: Kings Cross Point, Isle of Arran, Scotland, 2 September 1998, legit B. Ing, (**Hb. B. Ing** No. 98068).

Sporocarps short-stalked, shaped like a *Craterium*, 0.8 mm high, 0.7–0.75 mm in diam. **Stalk** furrowed, arising from a discoid hypothallus. **Peridium** dark brown to chestnut with a well-developed, flat lid which is shining golden-bronze, the lid colour forming a distinct ring around the top of the sporangial cup. Dehiscence is by the separation of the lid, which falls away as a single unit. **Spore** mass pale ochraceous, spores colourless by transmitted light, smooth, 7–9.5 µm diam, the wall of moderate thickness, without thinner regions. **Plasmodium** not seen. [Fig. 20]

Habitat: on liverworts (*Radula complanata*) on living branches, in the type on hazel.

Distribution: so far known only from the type collection made during the British Mycological Society's foray to Arran in September 1998 [1].

Notes: this beautiful species is very distinctive. The sporangia resemble miniature tympani (kettle drums) with shining golden lids. The Japanese *L. craterioides* is quite different in appearance and structure.

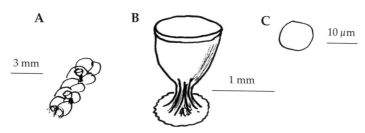

Fig. 20. *Licea crateriformis*: A: sporangia on *Radula*; B: sporangium; C: spore.

Licea denudescens H.W. Keller & T.E. Brooks
Mycologia **69**: 668. 1977. Florida.

Sporocarps scattered or gregarious, sessile with a constricted base, black when mature, pulvinate or almost globose, 0.2–0.4 mm diam. **Peridium** two-layered, thin, the outer layer gelatinous when wet, slowly eroding away to reveal the inner, membranous layer which is shiny. Dehiscence by irregular splitting. **Spore** mass glossy brown, spores light olive-brown in transmitted light, smooth, with a pale area occupying nearly half the spore, 8.5–11 µm diam. **Protoplasmodium** pale brown. [Fig. 21]

Illustrations: FMI 2: 116.
Habitat: bark of living trees.
Distribution: widespread in the British Isles, especially the damper regions to the west [38, H10]. Well distributed in Europe and North America, reported from Belize.

Notes: the rather nondescript sporangia with a deciduous outer peridium and half light/half dark spores are characteristic. This species is slow to mature and requires several weeks of moist chamber culture to enable it to mature the spores.

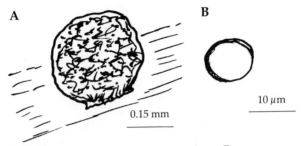

Fig. 21. *Licea denudescens*: A: sporangium; B: spore.

Licea deplanata Kowalski
Madroño **21**: 455. 1972. California.

Sporocarps scattered, sessile, greyish or purplish-brown to black, pulvinate, 0.1–0.5 mm diam. **Peridium** single, divided into 3–6 platelets, smooth, the margins of the platelets bearing several rows of papillae, right to the edge. **Spore** mass yellowish-brown, spores yellowish-white by transmitted light, smooth, 11–13 μm diam, with a paler or thinner area. **Protoplasmodium** light brown. [Fig. 22]

Illustrations: FMI 2: 117.
Habitat: leaf litter, especially of sclerophyllous trees such as *Buxus*, *Eucalyptus* and *Hedera*.
Distribution: known from Surrey, Worcestershire and Mull [3]. Elsewhere recorded from California and Spain.

Notes: the pegs right up to the edge of the platelet margin, the pale spores and the habitat are sufficient to separate this species from others having peridial platelets.

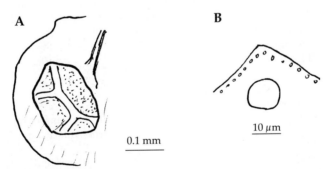

Fig. 22. *Licea deplanata*: A: sporangium; B: peridial lobe and spore.

Licea erddigensis Ing **nov. spec.**

Sporangia stipitata, globosa, 0.25-0.35 mm in diam., ad 0.55 mm alto, aurantiaca hinc aerea. Hypothallus nullus. Stipes crassus, cylindricus, niger, sulcatus, cum pigmento in granis confinis ad sulcis, reliquum ochraceum in luce transmissa. Peridium singulare, membranosum, rugosum, lucente, in luce transmissa fumoso-ochraceum, laeve, scindens irregulariter et apicaliter. Columella nulla. Capillitium nullum.

Sporae in cumulo rubro-fuscae, pallide rubro-fuscae in luce transmissa, iuvenes incoloratae, 11.5–12.5 μm in diam., laeves. Protoplasmodium aurantiacum.
HOLOTYPUS: in cortice vivo *Aceris pseudoplatanis* in camera humida, Erddig Park, Wrexham, Gallia septentrionalis, March 1999, legit B. Ing, (**Hb. B. Ing** No. 99006).
Other material studied: Erddig Park, February 1999, No. 99005.

Sporocarps stalked sporangia, globose, 0.25–0.35 mm diam to 0.55 mm tall, orange when young, becoming bronze. **Hypothallus** absent. **Stalk** thick, cylindrical, black, furrowed, the pigment in granules which are confined to the ridges, the remainder of the stalk ochraceous in transmitted light. **Peridium** singular, membranous, wrinkled when dry, shining but not iridescent, smoky-ochraceous in transmitted light, smooth, with no ornamentation, dehiscing by an irregular apical split. **Columella** and capillitium absent. **Spores** in mass reddish-brown (pale yellow when immature), pale reddish-brown in transmitted light (colourless when immature) 11.5–12.5 μm diam, smooth. **Protoplasmodium** orange. [Fig. 23]

Habitat: bark of living sycamore in moist chamber culture.
Distribution: known only from two separate collections from the same tree in Erddig Park, near Wrexham, north Wales [1].

Notes: this new species is superficially similar to *L. scyphoides* but is twice the size, does not have circumscissile dehiscence or a cup-like base to the sporangium, the spores are quite smooth and uniformly coloured, whereas *L. scyphoides* has minutely roughened spores with a paler area. From other stalked species of the genus it differs in the bright orange plasmodium and young sporangia and the dramatic darkening of the spores on maturity.

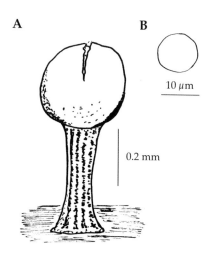

Fig. 23. *Licea erddigensis*:
A: sporangium; B: spore.

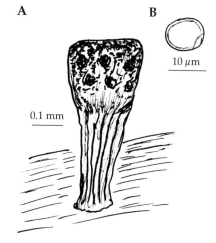

Fig. 24. *Licea eleanorae*:
A: sporangium; B: spore.

Licea eleanorae Ing nov. spec.

Sporangia stipitata, dispersa, ad 0.7 mm alta. Stipes crassus, canaliculatus, furfuraceus, ad 0.4 mm longus, 0.12 mm latus ad basis, ad 0.08 mm sub sporangium. Sporangium 0.2 mm latum et 0.3 mm longum. Apex sporangii obtusus orbiculatusque, cum peridio crasso, ornato, manifestante crystallino luce directo sed sine formae luce transmissa. Operculum nullum, sporangium dehiscente fissurae in apicem. Peridium, luce transmissa, pallido-ochraceum cum maculis obscuris angularibus. Columella nulla. Capillitium nullum. Sporae in cumulo pallido-fuscae, luce transmissa pallido-ochraceae, laeves, cum muris crassis et regione parve, pallido, 8–10 µm in diam. Protoplasmodium flavido-melleum.

HOLOTYPUS: in cortice vivo *Platanus x hispanicae* in camera humida, Cantine di Gandria, Lugano, Ticino, Switzerland, September 1997, legit B. Ing, (**Hb. Ing,** No. 97097).

Other material studied: Buchs, St Gallen, Switzerland, September 1998, Ing (on *Platanus*) No. 98058; St Cyrus, Kincardine, Scotland, September 1997, Ing (on *Ulmus*) No. 97149; Ardrossan, Ayrshire, Scotland, September 1998, Ing (on *Ulmus*) No. 98082.

Sporocarps stalked, scattered, to 0.7 mm tall. **Stalk** thick, furrowed, the surface covered with granular deposits, up to 0.3 mm long, 0.12 mm wide at the base, narrowing to 0.08 mm below the sporangium. **Sporangium** becoming wider towards the apex, twice as wide as the stalk, 0.2 mm wide and 0.3 mm long. The sporangium is blunt at the apex and slightly rounded, thick-walled with deposits which appear frosted and crystalline under low power binocular but amorphous under high power microscope. There is no trace of a lid and dehiscence is by a split in the top. In transmitted light the peridium appears to be mottled with angular dark patches. **Spores** in mass pale brown, under transmitted light pale ochraceous, smooth, with a thick wall and a small pale germination area, 8–10 µm diam. **Protoplasmodium** honey-yellow. [Fig. 24]

Habitat: bare bark of isolated trees, lime in England, elm in Scotland, plane in Switzerland.

Distribution: recently found in Central London (1998), Ayrshire (1998) and Kincardine (1997) [3]. Known elsewhere only from the cantons of St Gallen and Ticino, Switzerland.

Notes: the distinctive shape of the sporangia is sufficient to separate it from non-operculate forms of *L. operculata* which are taller, and the stalk is much longer than in *L. scyphoides*, which in any case dehisces by an equatorial, not terminal, fissure. During development *L. operculata* forms a distinct stalk with a globose blob at the apex, while *L. eleanorae* has a clearly cylindrical blob and is much paler, almost yellow, at this stage. The species is named after my wife, who much admires the distant view of the type locality tree across the waters of the Lake of Lugano.

Licea gloeoderma Döbbeler & Nann.-Bremek.
Z. Mykol. **45**: 235. 1979. Bavaria.

Sporocarps scattered, nearly globose or slightly flattened, 0.13–0.2 mm diam, or sometimes bolster-shaped, then 0.15–0.45 mm long x 0.11–0.2 mm broad x 0.09–0.2 mm high, sessile, with or without as slightly constricted base. **Peridium** of two closely attached layers, the outer gelatinous when moist and attracting waste fragments and algal cells, the inner membranous. Colour varies from dull grey, through bluish-grey to black. Dehiscence irregular with no evidence of pre-formed lines or slits. **Spore** mass creamy white, spores colourless in transmitted light, usually globose, 11.5–12 μm diam, but frequently slightly elliptic, then 11.5–12 x 12.5–18 μm, appearing smooth but under oil immersion seen to be minutely punctate. With the spores are yellow granules, not seen in other species, 1.5–2.5 μm diam, which are also attached to the peridium. **Protoplasmodium** pale yellow. [Fig. 25]

Illustrations: original description.
Habitat: on the liverwort *Frullania dilatata* on the bark of living trees.
Distribution: recorded from Merioneth, south-west and north-west Scotland and Donegal [5, H1]. Elsewhere reported from Germany and Switzerland.

Notes: the small size, almost white spore mass, contained granules and habitat make this inconspicuous species readily identifiable. The original description suggests a close relationship with *L. biforis* but that is always date-stone shaped and pale, whereas *L. gloeoderma* is dark. The lips of the slit in *L. biforis* are thickened and obvious, whereas if there is a slit in *L. gloeoderma* it is not margined.

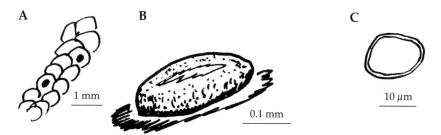

Fig. 25. *Licea gloeoderma*: A: sporangia on *Frullania*; B: sporangium; C: spore.

Licea inconspicua T.E. Brooks & H.W. Keller
Mycologia **69**: 671. 1977. Kansas.

Sporocarps scattered or gregarious, more or less hemispherical, sessile on a broad base, dark brown to black, 0.2–0.3 mm diam. **Peridium** of three closely adherent layers, the outer dark and brittle, the others thin, pale and membranous. Dehiscence irregular. **Spore** mass orange or reddish-orange when fresh, fading to pinkish ochraceous with age. Spores pale yellowish-orange by transmitted light, 14–15.5 μm diam, minutely papillose, forming a faint reticulum. **Protoplasmodium** orange. **Sclerotia** orange. [Fig. 26]

Illustrations: original description.
Habitat: on foliose lichens on the bark of living trees.
Distribution: widely distributed, especially in the west [40, H2, C]. In Europe recorded from Greece, Norway, Switzerland and Yugoslavia; widespread in North America and reported from Chile.

Notes: the orange plasmodium and spore mass, small dark sporangia without peridial plates and the usual occurrence on lichens make this well-named species easy to identify.

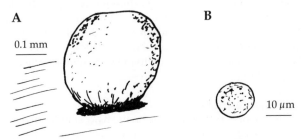

Fig. 26. *Licea inconspicua*: A: sporangium; B: spore.

Licea iridis Ing & McHugh
Proc. R. Irish Acad. **88**B: 102. 1988. Drogheda, Co. Louth.

Sporocarps scattered, globose on a constricted base, bronze-brown, iridescent, 0.2–0.3 mm diam. **Peridium** of two membranous layers, the outer wrinkled, providing the iridescent reflections. **Spore** mass dark grey-brown to almost black, spores dark smoky grey by transmitted light, globose, coarsely warted with no pale area, 10–12 μm diam. **Plasmodium** not seen. [Fig. 27]

Illustrations: original description.
Habitat: bark of living trees.
Distribution: so far known from Sussex, Merioneth, Peebles, Sutherland, Galway and Louth [4, H2]. Recorded from Greece and Spain.

Notes: this is the most iridescent of all *Licea* species and resembles a tiny, sessile *Lamproderma* on the bark. The coarsely warted spores and the double membranous peridium are characteristic.

Fig. 27. *Licea iridis*: A: sporangium; B: spore.

Licea kleistobolus G.W. Martin
Mycologia **34**: 702. 1942. Austria.

Sporocarps scattered or gregarious, discoid, with an obvious flat, recessed operculum, 0.04–0.15 mm diam, black when prematurely dried but shining bronze in ideal conditions. The innerside of the lid has a number of tubular outgrowths. **Spore** mass ochraceous, spores pale yellow or colourless by transmitted light, 9–13 µm diam, densely spinulose with small clusters of larger warts, wall of even thickness. **Protoplasmodium** pale ochraceous. [Fig. 28]

Illustrations: FMI 2: 119; MA: fig. 7; NB: 51.
Habitat: on bare bark of living trees, especially conifers.
Distribution: common and well distributed in the British Isles [62, H13, C]. Probably cosmopolitan.

Notes: the minute bronze discs look like tiny coins on the bark and may be abundant on thin-barked trees and vines, with many hundreds of sporangia in a petri dish of bark. The plasmodium is also very distinctive, looking like a minute blob of pale honey.

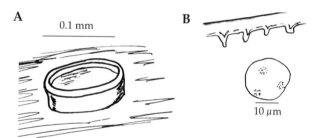

Fig. 28. *Licea kleistobolus*: A: sporangium; B: underside of lid and spore.

Licea marginata Nann.-Bremek.
Acta Bot. Neerl. **14**: 144. 1965. Netherlands.

Sporocarps in groups, flattened discs, 0.1–0.2 mm diam, black, surrounded by a basal black ring. **Peridium** double, the inner membranous, translucent, yellow-brown by transmitted light, the outer gelatinous containing refuse material. Dehiscence irregular or by a split, with the edges curling back. **Spores** in mass dark brown to black, rosy to yellowish-brown in transmitted light, 10–13 µm diam, wall thin, evenly and minutely spinulose. **Protoplasmodium** pale to brown. [Fig. 29]

Illustrations: NB: 49.
Habitat: bark of living trees.
Distribution: well distributed in the British Isles and quite common [61, H11, C]. Widespread in Europe and also recorded from New Zealand, Belize and Kentucky.

Notes: the black basal ring and absence of a lid separate this from small fruitings of *L. parasitica*, with which it often grows. The black ring sometimes seen around the developing lid margin of *L. parasitica* is itself surrounded by sporangial material whereas the ring in *L. marginata* is outside everything else. The spore markings are only clear under the oil immersion lens.

A

50 µm

B

Fig. 29. *Licea marginata*: A: sporangium; B: spore.

Licea microscopica D.W. Mitchell
Bull. Br. Mycol. Soc. **12**: 24. 1978. Glamorgan.

Sporocarps scattered, sessile, subglobose, shining coppery, 0.05–0.15 mm diam, enclosed in a gelatinous sack containing algal cells, the peridium showing through a hole in the top. Dehiscence by fragmentation of the delicate peridium. **Spores** in mass pale, by transmitted light pale yellow maturing to pale brown, smooth, with a pale area, 15–17 µm diam. **Plasmodium** not seen. [Fig. 30]

Illustrations: original description.
Habitat: bark of living ash and elder trees.
Distribution: only known from the type collection from Glamorgan and several gatherings in Sussex [2].

Notes: the small size, very simple structure, algal coat and large, pale spores characterise this species, which is probably very difficult to see in bark cultures.

A

0.05 mm

B

10 µm

Fig. 30. *Licea microscopica*: A: sporangium; B: spore.

Licea minima Fr.
Syst. Mycol. **3**: 199. 1829. Sweden.

Sporocarps scattered or gregarious, dark brown to black, pulvinate, angular, 0.1–0.4 mm diam. **Peridium** of two layers, the inner membranous, the outer horny and split into up to six peridial plates, the inner margins of which are ornamented with a single row of prominent pegs, with a clear band right on the edge. The dry sporangium is angular from the tough plate margins and the face of the plates is sometimes depressed, thus exaggerating the ridges. **Spores** in mass rusty red-brown, olive-brown to ferrugineous in transmitted light, 10–12 μm diam, evenly and minutely warted, with a small area of thin, pale wall. **Protoplasmodium** pale yellowish-brown. [Fig. 31]

Illustrations: DM 1: 151; E: pl. 3; FMI 2: 120; L3: pl. 148; MA: fig. 8; NB: 42.
Habitat: bark of living trees, especially old parkland oaks, less commonly on rotten conifer logs, decaying bracket fungi and living *Cladonia* stems.
Distribution: widely distributed in the British Isles, generally common [90, H4, C]. Probably cosmopolitan.

Notes: the sharp ridges formed as the sporangium dries and the reddish colour of the spore mass make this a distinctive species. The few, large peridial plates separate it from *L. testudinacea* and the spore colour and sporangial dimensions separate it from *L. pygmaea*. Records of this species made before 1965 probably include some of the more recently described platelet species.

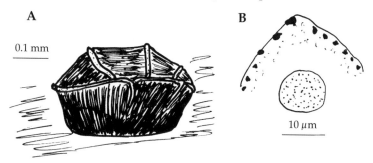

Fig. 31. *Licea minima*: A: sporangium; B: peridial lobe and spore.

Licea operculata (Wingate) G.W. Martin
Mycologia **34**: 702. 1942. Pennsylvania.
Syn. *Licea capitata* Ing & McHugh; *Orcadella operculata* Wingate

Sporocarps long-stalked, shaped like a wine-glass, usually with a well-defined recessed operculum but often with a globose sporangium lacking a lid, total height up to 1.25 mm. **Stalk** grooved, dark, opaque in transmitted light from granular inclusions. **Sporangium** 0.1–0.3 mm diam, the larger size often associated with an absence of the lid. **Peridium** dull, slightly gelatinous when wet, translucent and pale brown in transmitted light, again with granular inclusions, lid membranous with a smooth margin. **Spores** in mass pale yellow, almost colourless in transmitted light, 10–13 μm diam, smooth, thick-walled with prominent pale area. **Protoplasmodium** clear orange-brown. [Fig. 32]

Illustrations: E: pl. 7; FMI 2: 124 (atypical); L3: pl. 149; MA: fig. 9; NB: 50.
Habitat: bark of living trees, and, once, on living *Calluna* stems.
Distribution: widely distributed in the British Isles, apparently increasing [43, H16, C]. Widespread in Europe, the Americas, Australasia and Asia.

Notes: *L. capitata* was based on a lidless form of this species which was characteristically found in western Britain and Ireland. However, extensive studies in the last three years have shown that the operculum develops as the sporangium dries by sinking into the top of the sporangium. When the culture is kept moist no lid is formed – this correlates well with the western distribution of the inoperculate form. In some cultures both forms occur on opposite sides of the same bark sample. There are no microscopic differences between these two forms, the thinner apex of the peridium in *L. capitata* corresponding to the membranous operculum in *L. operculata*. They are therefore synonymised. *L. eleanorae* differs in the thicker stalk, rough thick peridium and different shape of the sporangium; it is also smaller.

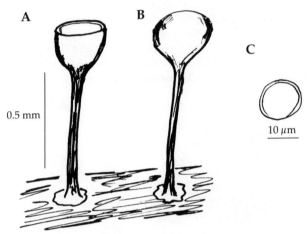

Fig. 32. *Licea operculata*:
A: typical sporangium; B: inoperculate sporangium; C: spore.

Licea parasitica (Zukal) G.W. Martin
Mycologia **34**: 702. 1942. Austria.
Syn. *Hymenobolina parasitica* Zukal

Sporocarps scattered or in large developments, sessile, hemispherical when young, becoming pulvinate with maturity, 0.05–0.2 mm diam, black or dark brown, the lid sometimes paler, rarely absent. **Peridium** tough, gelatinous, lid less gelatinous. **Spores** in mass dark brown, olive-brown in transmitted light, smooth, with a thick wall showing a large, thinner, pale area, 13–15 µm diam. **Protoplasmodium** rich orange-brown, very gelatinous and distinctive. **Microcysts** spherical, pale ochraceous. [Fig. 33]

Illustrations: E: pl. 7; FMI 2: 125; L3: pl. 217; MA: fig. 10; NB: 50.
Habitat: bark of living trees, especially on epiphytic mosses and lichens.
Distribution: common on bark everywhere [108, H39, C]. Cosmopolitan.

Notes: the commonest bark *Licea* and easily recognised by the small, dark pork-pie shaped sporangia. The protoplasmodium is conspicuous as a gelatinous orange-brown blob and this is usually the first species to show when bark is moistened. However, the sporangia may take several days to mature. The development of the lid is often accompanied by a prominent black ring at the apex of the sporangium. This should not be confused with the basal ring on the *outside* of the sporangium of *L. marginata*. Small, spherical, pale amber microcysts are often abundant on the leaves of mosses on the bark.

Fig. 33. *Licea parasitica*: A: sporangium; B: spore.

Licea pedicellata (H.C. Gilbert) H.C. Gilbert
Mycologia **34**: 702, 1942. Iowa.

Sporocarps short-stalked, globose, dark brown to black, 0.075–0.175 mm diam, total height up to 0.5 mm; very occasionally sessile. Stalk dark, furrowed. **Peridium** membranous, on drying forming a network of ridges, these mark the boundaries of irregular plates by which the sporangium dehisces. Spores in mass dark brown, yellow-brown in transmitted light, paler on one side, smooth or very finely spinulose, 11–13 μm diam. **Protoplasmodium** yellow. [Fig. 34]

Illustrations: MA: fig. 11.
Habitat: bark of living trees.
Distribution: scattered in Great Britain, not yet recorded for Ireland [12, C]. Sparsely recorded in Europe, North America, Tunisia, Turkey, India, Sikkim, Australia and Japan.

Notes: the only stalked species with peridial plates.

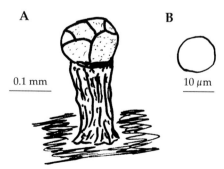

Fig. 34. *Licea pedicellata*: A: sporangium; B: spore.

Licea perexigua T.E. Brooks & H.W. Keller
Mycologia **69**: 674. 1977. Arkansas.

Sporocarps scattered or in small groups, sessile on a narrow base or occasionally with a short stalk, globose, yellowish-olive towards grey tones, shiny, with a marked iridescence, reflecting reds and blues, 0.04–0.11 mm diam. **Peridium** simple, membranous, thin, almost colourless by transmitted light, dehiscing along an equatorial line, leaving the lower portion of the sporangium as a cup. **Spores** in mass olivaceous yellow, pale olivaceous yellow in transmitted light, smooth, with a pale area, 8.5–10.5 μm diam. **Protoplasmodium** clear pale yellow. [Fig. 35]

Illustrations: FMI 2: 127.
Habitat: bark of living trees, especially *Taxus* and *Juniperus*.
Distribution: a rare species scattered across the British Isles [7, H3]. Known from Spain, Switzerland, Yugoslavia, India, Belize and North America.

Notes: the yellow spore mass, smooth spores, short stalk and iridescent peridium make this species fairly distinctive.

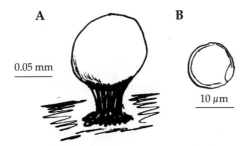

Fig. 35. *Licea perexigua*: A: sporangium; B: spore.

Licea pusilla Schrad.
Nov. Gen Pl.: 19. 1797. Germany.

Sporocarps scattered or gregarious, sessile, brownish-black to black with pale lines separating the peridial plates, 0.3–0.6 mm diam. **Peridium** with outer layer leathery and horny when dry, divided into pre-formed platelets with a single row of pegs on the very edge of the plate margins; inner layer smooth. **Spores** in mass black, olive-brown by transmitted light, minutely and densely warted, wall with a pale area, 15–17 μm diam. **Protoplasmodium** yellow, becoming chestnut as the sporangia mature, with yellow lines separating the peridial plates. [Fig. 36]

Illustrations: E: pl. 4; FMI 2: 128; L3: pl. 149; MA: fig. 12; NB: 44.
Habitat: bark of living trees, especially conifers, and cyanobacterial slime on rotten conifer logs.
Distribution: widely distributed and quite common in the British Isles [51, H5]. Frequent in Europe, North America, Australasia and Japan.

Notes: the large, dark spores and smooth inner peridium distinguish this species. Among those with peridial plates this is the slowest species to mature in moist chamber culture.

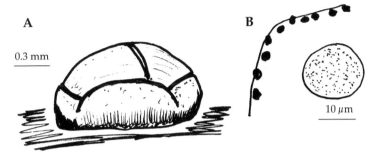

Fig. 36. *Licea pusilla*: A: sporangium; B: peridial lobe and spore.

Licea pygmaea (Meyl.) Ing
Trans. Br. mycol. Soc. **78**: 443. 1982. Switzerland.
Syn. *Licea pusilla* var. *pygmaea* Mey.

Sporocarps sessile, scattered or grouped, black, pulvinate or globose, slightly angular in outline, 0.05–0.4 mm diam. **Peridium** tough, inner layer densely and evenly covered with warts, the outer layer divided into plates whose margins have a single row of pegs at the edge. **Spores** in mass black, greyish-yellow in transmitted light, with a pale area in the thick wall, densely spinulose, 12–13 μm diam. **Protoplasmodium** pale brown. [Fig. 37]

Illustrations: FMI 2: 130; NB: 45.
Habitat: on acidic bark of living trees.
Distribution: scattered in England and Scotland, quite common in Ireland [8, H7]. Widespread in Europe, recorded from New Zealand.

Notes: the small size of the spores and sporangia and the warted inner peridium separate this species from *L. pusilla*; the spore colour from *L. testudinacea*.

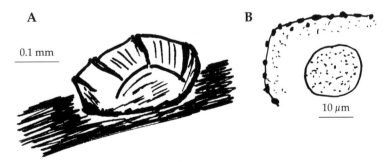

Fig. 37. *Licea pygmaea*: A: sporangium; B: peridial lobe and spore.

Licea scyphoides T.E. Brooks & H.W. Keller
Mycologia **69**: 679. 1977. Ohio.

Sporocarps stalked, scattered, brown. **Sporangium** globose, 0.08–0.12 mm diam.
Stalk 0.08–0.15 mm long, tapering to the apex, opaque and stuffed with refuse.
Peridium membranous, dehiscing by a pre-formed equatorial fissure, leaving the
lower part as a cup. **Spores** in mass golden-brown, pale ochraceous in transmitted
light, minutely roughened, with a pale area to one side, 11.5–13 μm diam.
Protoplasmodium pale ochraceous. [Fig. 38]

Illustrations: original description.
Habitat: bark of living trees.
Distribution: widespread and frequent in damp, western areas, almost absent
from the south-east [32, H21]. Recorded from Spain, Switzerland, France, Greece,
India, Belize and North America.

Notes: this is the only stalked species to have equatorial dehiscence; it is
intermediate in size between *L. operculata* and *L. pedicellata* and may have been
mistaken for either of these in the past.

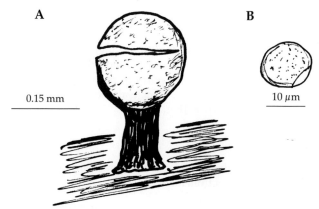

A

B

0.15 mm

10 μm

Fig. 38. *Licea scyphoides*: A: sporangium; B: spore.

Licea synsporos Nann.-Bremek.
Proc. K. Ned. Akad. Wet. C **71**: 42. 1968. Kindrogan, Perthshire.

Sporocarps scattered, sessile, globose on a constricted base, dark brown to black,
0.1–0.2 mm diam. **Peridium** thin, membranous, dehiscing along pre-formed lines,
the lobes (scarcely plates) with thickened but smooth margins. **Spores** in mass
dark brown, yellowish-brown in transmitted light, adhering in clusters 20–30 μm
diam, individual spores 9–12 μm diam, top-shaped, smooth on the faces in
contact, densely and minutely warted on the outer face. **Protoplasmodium** pale
brown. [Fig. 39]

Illustrations: original description.
Habitat: moss on bark of living trees, in Atlantic or montane situations.

Distribution: known from Merioneth, Perthshire, W. Ross and W. Sutherland [5]. Elsewhere recorded from France and Switzerland.

Notes: the only species with clustered spores.

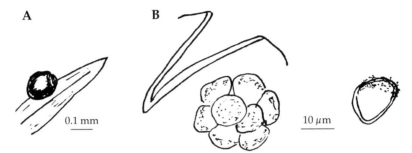

Fig. 39. *Licea synsporos*: A: sporangium on moss leaf; B: peridial lobe and spores.

Licea tenera E. Jahn
Ber. Deutsch. bot. Ges. **36**: 665. 1918. Bavaria.

Sporocarps sessile on a constricted base, globose, shining yellow, darkening with age, 0.2–0.4 mm diam. **Peridium** membranous, dehiscence irregular. **Spores** in mass golden-yellow, pale yellow in transmitted light, smooth, 10–12 μm diam. **Protoplasmodium** bright yellow. [Fig. 40]

Illustrations: E: pl. 6; L3: pl. 219; MA: fig. 13.
Habitat: bark of living trees, reported from herbivore dung but this may refer to a different species.
Distribution: rare, known from the London area, Worcestershire, Perthshire and Bute [6]. Recorded from Germany, Sweden, Switzerland, North America, Brazil, Mexico, India and Japan.

Notes: the smooth, yellow, globose sporangia and yellow spore mass are useful diagnostic features. The species as here interpreted is a corticole. Records from dung may well refer to another species, possibly a *Perichaena*, which often lack a capillitium and have yellow spores.

Fig. 40. *Licea tenera*: A: sporangium; B: spore.

Licea testudinacea Nann.-Bremek.
Acta Bot. Neerl. **14**: 141. 1965. Netherlands.

Sporocarps grouped, pulvinate to slightly flattened, 0.2–0.8 mm diam, dark brown to black with a network of ridges separating the peridial plates. **Peridium** shining on the inside and dull on the outside, divided in a large number of small plates, whose margins are furnished with a single row of large, dark knobs and short ridges. **Spores** in mass dark brown, brownish-grey in transmitted light, with a prominent pale area, minutely warted, 11–13 µm diam. **Protoplasmodium** yellowish-brown. [Fig. 41]

Illustrations: NB: 46.
Habitat: bark of living trees, rarely on leaf litter and rabbit dung.
Distribution: scattered across the British Isles but never common [24, H5]. Widely reported in Europe and known from North America and India.

Notes: the small, numerous, peridial plates with conspicuous marginal ornamentation and the grey spores distinguish this species.

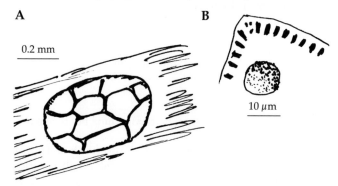

Fig. 41. *Licea testudinacea*: A: sporangium; B: peridial lobe and spore.

Licea variabilis Schrad.
Nov. Gen. Pl.: **18**. 1797. Germany.
Syn. *Licea flexuosa* Pers.

Sporocarps sessile, usually as long, often branched, plasmodiocarps but may be short, bolster-shaped sporangia, tan when young maturing to black, to 10 mm long and 1.0 mm wide. **Peridium** single, persistent, dull, dehiscing by irregular splits. **Spores** in mass pale olive-brown, pale brownish-yellow by transmitted light, densely, evenly but faintly spinulose, with or without a pale area, 12–13 µm diam. **Phaneroplasmodium** pink. [Fig. 42]

Illustrations: DM 1: 155; E: pl. 5; FMI 2: 133; L3: pl. 148; MA: fig. 15; NB: 48.
Habitat: typically on small fallen conifer branches that have lost their bark but also on rotten conifer wood, stumps and even fence posts.

Distribution: widespread and common, increasing with the coniferisation of our forests [106, H4]. Common in Europe, North America, India and Japan.

Notes: the dark plasmodiocarps are easily confused with those of *Enteridium liceoides* and *Dianema corticatum* which share the habitat and also have pink plasmodia. Both are rare and have clustered spores. This species is so different form the other members of the genus that it might be sought elsewhere, such as in *Perichaena*.

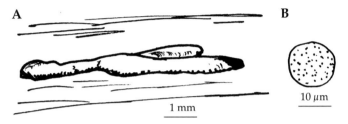

Fig. 42. *Licea variabilis*: A: plasmodiocarp; B: spore.

LISTERELLACEAE E. Jahn (accepted as publ. 1906 in *Regnum Veg*. **126**: 84. 1993)
Ber. Deutsch. Bot. Des. **24**: 541. 1906.

Sporocarps are sessile sporangia, peridium with plates, like a *Licea*, no columella, spore mass dark. The family differs from Liceaceae in the presence of a regularly beaded thread-like pseudocapillitium attached to the inside of the peridium and to the base of the sporangium. A single genus.

Note: the family is clearly close to Liceaceae but has been of uncertain position since its discovery, being placed in the Trichiales for many years.

LISTERELLA E. Jahn
Ber. Deutsch. Bot. Des. **24**: 540. 1906.

With the characters of the family. A single species.

Listerella paradoxa E. Jahn
Ber. Deutsch. Bot. Ges. **24**: 540. 1906. Germany.

Sporocarps sessile sporangia, mostly pulvinate on an expanded base, 0.2–0.3 mm diam, dull blackish-brown, marked with shining yellow ridges along the lines of dehiscence. **Peridium** membranous, covered in dark granular matter except at the edges of the plates. **Capillitium** (or possibly pseudocapillitium) sparse, consisting of dark, flexuous threads attached at the base of the sporangium and to the peridium, smooth near the attachments but elsewhere marked with regular bead-like annulations, giving the appearance of a string of pearls. **Spores** in mass black, pale brownish-grey by transmitted light, paler to one side, faintly spinulose, 7–8 μm diam. **Protoplasmodium** pale brown. [Fig. 43]

Illustrations: DM 1: 159; L3: pl. 191; MA: fig. 61.
Habitat: on pudetia of living *Cladonia* lichens, especially *C. portentosa*, in coastal dunes and shingle beaches. Outside the British Isles this is a moorland species.
Distribution: very rare, only known from Dungeness, Kent and Tentsmuir Point, Fife [2]. Elsewhere recorded from Germany, Scandinavia, Russia and California.

Notes: apart from the capillitium this could easily be mistaken for *Licea minima*, which occasionally occurs in the same habitat. It is very tedious to search *Cladonia* for this myxomycete, several litres of lichen may need to be scanned to find a few sporangia. Search in moorland and lowland heath has not yet been successful in the British Isles.

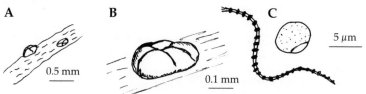

Fig. 43. *Listerella paradoxa*:
A: sporangia on *Cladonia*; B: sporangium; C: capillitium and spore.

CRIBRARIACEAE Corda
Icon. Fung. **2**: 22. 1838.

Sporocarps usually stalked sporangia but may be pseudoaethalia (*Lindbladia*). **Peridium** membranous, with a network of narrow, dark threads which remain as a mesh, connected by thickened nodes containing calcareous *dictydine* granules. The mesh allows escape of mature spores. Capillitium and columella absent. Spore mass varies from bright yellow through ochraceous, shades of brown, red and purple to violet.

KEY TO GENERA

1   Sporocarps stalked sporangia, clustered but always clearly separate; peridium perforated, forming a net   *Cribraria*
–   Sporocarps pseudoaethalia, with occasional sessile sporangia; peridium not perforated   *Lindbladia*

CRIBRARIA Pers.
Neues Mag. Bot. **1**: 91. 1794.

Sporocarps stalked, rarely aggregated, **peridium** with or without a persistent basal cup. Over 40 species, world-wide, the type is *Cribraria rufa* (Roth)Rostaf.

Notes: the basal cup is not always present and this is reflected in the key to species. It is important to view the peridial nodes in optical section as they may be thickened in the plane of the wall – the distinction between flat and thickened nodes is of diagnostic value. The genus is difficult and it is not possible to assign every collection to a known taxon. As accepted in the rest of Europe the genus now includes the species previously in *Dictydium* Schrad.The majority of species are found on coniferous wood, but this is also not an exclusive character.

KEY TO SPECIES

1   Sporocarps intense violet, small, usually on bark   *violacea*
–   Sporocarps shades of yellow, orange, red or brown, not violet   2

2 (1)   Sporocarps with the peridial net more or less reduced to longitudinal ribs, with some connecting threads but lacking nodes, with or without a basal cup   3
–   Sporocarps with the peridial net composed of branching threads, usually with distinct nodes, often thickened, not reduced to longitudinal ribs, with or without a basal cup   6

3 (2)   Ribs 40–50, continued to apex of sporangium, which is indented, like a lobster pot or lampshade, after the spores are dispersed; sporangia nodding, reddish or purplish-brown   *cancellata*
–   Ribs far fewer, globose shape persisting   4

4 (3)   Ribs 20–30, forming an apical net; sporangia metallic reddish-brown
                                                                   mirabilis
–   Ribs fewer, no metallic sheen   5

5 (4)   Ribs 8–15, connected by delicate threads   *splendens*
–   Ribs 3–6, without connecting threads; minute, rare   *paucicostata*

6 (2)   Peridial net fine and inconspicuous, without obvious nodes   7
–   Peridial net well developed, with distinct nodes   8

7 (6)   Sporangia short-stalked, clustered, ochraceous, peridium glistening
                                                                  argillacea
–   Sporangia long-stalked, scattered, orange-red, peridium not glistening
                                                                        rufa

8 (6)   Sporangial cup absent   9
–   Sporangial cup well developed   12

9 (8)   Spore mass dull orange-red; stalk to 20 times height of sporangium
                                                                  microcarpa
–   Spore mass ochraceous; stalk to 10 times height of sporangium   10

10 (9) Peridial nodes in lower part of sporangium elongated, rib-like; in
        hothouses only   *dictydioides*
–   Peridial nodes not forming ribs; in woodland   11

11 (10) Peridial nodes branched, with unattached ends, connected by 5–8 slender
        threads   *intricata*
–   Peridial nodes rounded, unbranched with no free ends, connected by 3–5
        slender threads   *tenella*

12 (8) Nodes of net flat (optical section)   13
–   Nodes distinctly thickened   16

13 (12) Sporangia minute, less than 0.3 mm diam, cup delimited, rare
                                                                 minutissima
–   Sporangia larger   14

14 (13) Sporangial cup perforated above, gradually merging into the net
                                                                  macrocarpa
–   Sporangial cup not perforated, delimited from the net   15

15 (14) Sporangia dull orange-brown   *oregana*
–   Sporangia hazel to purplish-brown   *vulgaris*

16 (12) Spore mass reddish or hazel-brown   17
–   Spore mass yellow or ochraceous   18

17 (16) Sporangia pyriform, stalk expanded at apex   *pyriformis*
–   Sporangia globose, stalk not expanded at apex; rare   *atrofusca*

18 (16) Sporangia bright yellow when fresh, fading ochraceous   *aurantiaca*
–   Sporangia hazel to dusky brown   19

19 (18) Cup well developed; meshes of net triangular or square   *persoonii*
–   Cup not reaching a third of the way up the sporangium   20

20 (19) Peridial nodes branched, with free ends, connected by 5–8 slender threads
     intricata
–   Peridial nodes rounded, without free ends, connected by 3–5 slender
     threads   *tenella*

Cribraria argillacea (Pers.) Pers.
Neues Mag. Bot. **1**: 91. 1794. Europe.

Sporocarps short-stalked sporangia, usually clustered together in large developments and occasionally giving the impression of pseudoaethalia, but the individual sporangia retain complete identity, globose, 0.5–1.0 mm diam, dull ochraceous (clay-coloured). **Stalk** rarely more than 1 mm tall, dark brown to black, furrowed. **Hypothallus** well developed, horn-brown. **Peridium** soon disappearing above except for a thin, weak, dark net, without nodes; lower part remaining as a cup, thicker below, thinner above, marked with ribs and reticulations, the whole peridium often iridescent with bronze or silver reflections. The dark dictydine granules are small, to 1.5 μm diam. **Spores** in mass clay-coloured, very pale by transmitted light, nearly smooth, 6–8 μm in diam. **Plasmodium** shining lead-coloured, resembling freshly made lead shot as the sporangia develop. [Fig. 44]

Illustrations: DM 1: 65; E: pl. 15; FMI 2: L3: pl. 138; MA: fig. 33; NB: 77.
Habitat: more or less confined to rotten trunks and stumps of conifers, but occasionally found on birch and alder.
Distribution: very common in conifer woods, found throughout the British Isles [111, H38, C]. Probably cosmopolitan but in the tropics only on the mountains in temperate forest.

Notes: the striking lead-shot appearance of the freshly emerging plasmodium, the colour, the reduced peridial net, together with the short stalk and large fruitings make this an easy species to identify. It is closely related to *Lindbladia*.

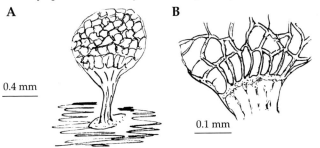

A

B

0.4 mm

0.1 mm

Fig. 44. *Cribraria argillacea*: A: sporangium; B: lower part of net.

Cribraria atrofusca G.W. Martin & Lovejoy
J. Wash. Acad. **22**: 92. 1932. Colorado.
Syn. *Cribraria pyriformis* var. *fuscopurpurea* Meyl.

Sporocarps long-stalked sporangia, gregarious in small groups, 0.3–0.6 mm diam, 1–2.2 mm tall, globose, dark purplish-brown to black, iridescent and shining. **Stalk** dark brown to black, slender, furrowed, to 1.8 mm high arising from a small, undistinguished hypothallus. **Peridium** silvery, persistent, with a well-developed cup about half the height of the sporangium, marked with ribs arising from the top of the stalk and with concentric rings of granules inside and out, the margin of the cup with fine teeth mixed with long thin projections from which the net radiates. Peridial net regular with expanded but hardly thickened nodes, dictydine granules dark, large, to 2.5 μm diam, and connecting thread broad, with few free ends. **Spores** dark reddish-brown in mass, grey-brown in transmitted light, slightly angular, with a fine, broken reticulate pattern of warts, 7–8 μm diam. **Plasmodium** unknown. [Fig. 45]

Illustrations: DM 1: 68; MA: fig. 34.
Habitat: rotten pine wood.
Distribution: only known in the British Isles from a single collection made in November 1927 at Stratton Strawless, Norfolk [1]. Elsewhere known from France, Austria, Norway, Japan, the Philippines and North America.

Notes: this species is close to *C. pyriformis* but differs in the concentric markings on the cup, the larger spores, darker colour, and the narrow tip of the stalk. It is clearly a globally rare species.

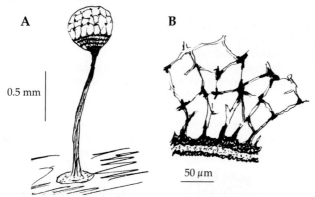

A

0.5 mm

B

50 μm

Fig. 45. *Cribraria atrofusca*: A: sporangium; B: lower part of net.

Cribraria aurantiaca Schrad.
Nov. Gen. Pl.: 5. 1797. Germany.
Syn. *Cribraria vulgaris* var. *aurantiaca* (Schrad.) Pers.

Sporocarps stalked sporangia, globose, bright yellow fading to ochraceous, 0.3–0.6 mm diam, 1–2 mm tall. **Stalk** reddish-brown, often brightly so, and tapering to the tip, sporangia often nodding. **Hypothallus** inconspicuous.

Peridium soon disappearing except for a well-developed cup, which occupies from a quarter to a third of the sporangium, and a net. The margin of the cup is regular with numerous teeth and spines or low triangular projections from which the net begins. Peridial net regular with small meshes, numerous small, rounded nodes, connecting thread with few free ends and dictydine granules which are to 1.5 μm diam. **Spores** in mass bright yellow at first, fading to ochraceous, pale yellow to pallid in transmitted light, nearly smooth, 6–7 μm diam. **Plasmodium** bright leaf green. [Fig. 46]

Illustrations: DM 1: 59; E: pl. 18; FMI 2: 60; L3: pl. 142; MA: fig. 53; NB: 79.
Habitat: on rotten coniferous wood of all kinds, rarely on alder or birch.
Distribution: very common throughout the British Isles [110, H38, C]. Probably cosmopolitan, although only in mountain forests in the tropics.

Notes: the bright yellow colour of the young sporangia and the bright green plasmodium, which persists as the sporangia differentiate, are distinguishing features of this very common species.

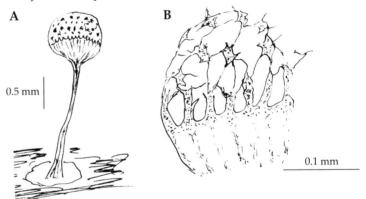

Fig. 46. *Cribraria aurantiaca*: A: sporangium; B: lower part of net.

Cribraria cancellata (Batsch) Nann.-Bremek.
Acta Bot. Neerl. **11**: 22. 1962. Germany.
Syn. *Dictydium cancellatum* (Bastch) T.L. Macbr.
var. **cancellata**

Sporocarps stalked sporangia, often nodding, clustered in large developments, reddish or purple-brown, 0.4–0.7 mm diam. The sporangia are usually nodding and are umbilicate below and often above. **Stalk** tapering, to 4 mm long, dark. **Peridium** disappearing, leaving a system of longitudinal thickened bands, connected by thin transverse threads. Cup absent in the typical form. Dictydine granules large, dark. **Spores** reddish or purplish in mass, pale red by transmitted light, nearly smooth, 5–7 μm diam. **Plasmodium** purple-black. [Fig. 47]

Illustrations: DM 1: 71; FMI 2: 62; L3: pl. 147; MA: fig. 54; NB: 73.
Habitat: mainly on fallen trunks and branches of conifers, but also found

frequently on birch and beech and more rarely on other hardwoods.
Distribution: common throughout the British Isles [111, H39, C]. Probably cosmopolitan.

var. **fusca** (Lister) Nann.-Bremek.
Acta Bot. Neerl. **11**: 22. 1962. Antigua.

Differs from the type variety in possessing a well-marked cup and usually lacking the purple shades; it may also be upright rather than nodding.
Habitat and **distribution** as for the type, though much less common [34, H4].

Notes: the distinctive longitudinal ribs of this elegant species remind one of the lampshades in vogue in the 1960s.

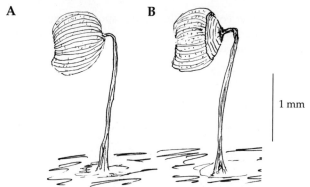

A   B

1 mm

Fig. 47. *Cribraria cancellata*: A: var. *cancellata*; B: var. *fusca*.

Cribraria dictydioides Cooke & Balf. ex Massee
Mon. Myxog.: 65. 1892. South Carolina.
Syn. *Cribraria intricata* var. *dictydioides* (Cooke & Balf. ex Massee) Lister

Sporocarps stalked sporangia, gregarious, nodding, dusky brown, 0.5–0.7 mm diam. **Stalk** slender, tapering, dark brown, up to 2.5 mm high, arising from a conspicuous black hypothallus. **Peridium** disappearing, cup absent, net with prominent, angular nodes, the lower nodes elongated and rib-like, connected to the top of the stalk. **Spores** ochraceous in mass, pale yellow in transmitted light, spinulose, 5–6 μm diam. **Plasmodium** lead-coloured, brown or black. [Fig. 48]

Illustrations: L3: pl. 143.
Habitat: in hothouses, on woody compost in orchid pots.
Distribution: recorded from a few Botanic Gardens, not seen since 1925 [3, H1]. Common in the tropics and possibly confined to these regions, but recorded from Australia and New Zealand.

Notes: this species is very close to *C. intricata* and is included with it by many authors. However, the rib-like lower fused nodes and the tropical distribution suggest that it may well be distinct.

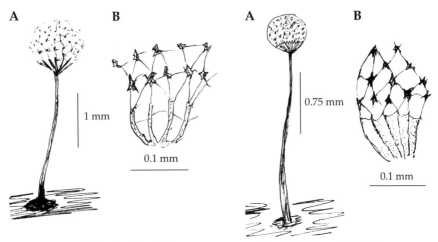

Fig. 48. *Cribraria dictydioides*:
A: sporangium; B: lower part of net.

Fig. 49. *Cribraria intricata*:
A: sporangium; B: lower part of net.

Cribraria intricata Schrad.
Nov. Gen. Pl.: 7. 1797. Germany.

Sporocarps stalked sporangia, gregarious, ochraceous to dark brown, nodding, 0.5–0.7 mm diam. **Stalk** slender, dark, furrowed, arising from a conspicuous brown hypothallus, to 2 mm high. **Peridium** soon disappearing, leaving a network of threads and nodes. **Cup** usually present, occupying up to a third of the sporangium, but sometimes reduced to a basal disc. **Nodes** of the net angular with projections carrying the threads of the net. Usually 5–8 threads connect adjacent nodes and there are several unconnected, loose ends on the nodes. Dictydine granules, brown, small. **Spores** ochraceous in mass, pale yellow by transmitted light, spinulose, 5–6 μm diam. **Plasmodium** greenish-brown. [Fig. 49]

Illustrations: DM 1: 79; E: pl. 18; FMI 2: 68; L3: pl. 143; MA: fig. 38.
Habitat: on dead wood, mostly of conifers but also recorded from birch, oak and sweet chestnut.
Distribution: generally uncommon, scattered [22]. Common in North America, New Zealand and the tropics, less so in Europe.

Notes: the angular nodes with several connecting threads and free ends separate this from the superficially similar *C. tenella*. *C. dictydioides* is similar but has the characteristic ribbed nodes at the base; it is most likely to confused with the forms of *C. intricata* lacking a cup. Most authors unite these species but they are here retained in the hope that more material will be studied.

Cribraria macrocarpa Schrad.
Nov. Gen. Pl.: 8. 1797. Germany.

Sporocarps stalked sporangia, crowded, erect, usually bronze-red and iridescent but may fade to ochraceous, 0.8–1.0 mm diam. **Stalk** stout, furrowed, to 2 mm high, arising from a conspicuous silvery hypothallus, expanding noticeably into the cup of the sporangium. **Peridium** membranous, persisting as a large cup with numerous dark ribs radiating up from the base, iridescent, with many perforations in the upper part of the cup. The margins of the cup irregularly lobed and toothed and merging imperceptibly with the net. **Nodes** dark, with dark dictydine granules 1–2 μm diam, threads slender, sometimes dichotomously branched. **Spores** in mass dull yellow, almost colourless by transmitted light, minutely roughened, 5–7 μm diam. **Plasmodium** slate-coloured. [Fig. 50]

Illustrations: DM 1: 84; E: pl. 17; L3: pl. 141; MA: fig. 42.
Habitat: on dead wood, especially of conifers.
Distribution: uncommon, scattered [14, H1]. Scattered in most parts of the world but nowhere common.

Notes: the large shiny sporangia and the perforated cup are the distinguishing features of this handsome species.

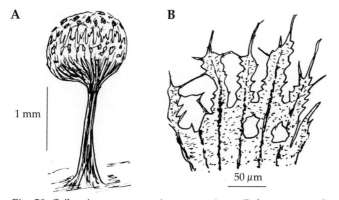

Fig. 50. *Cribraria macrocarpa*: A: sporangium; B: lower part of net.

Cribraria microcarpa (Schrad.) Pers.
Syn. Fungi.: 190. 1801. Iowa.

Sporocarps long-stalked sporangia, 0.1–0.3 mm diam, reddish ochraceous, nodding. **Stalk** long and tapering, to 4 mm high. **Peridium** quickly disappearing, leaving a basal disk or no trace of a cup. **Nodes** small, 10–20 μm diam, connected by delicate threads, giving rectangular or triangular meshes. **Spores** ochraceous in mass, pale yellow by transmitted light, minutely spinulose, 5–7 μm, diam. **Protoplasmodium** at first colourless, becoming white then dull brown. [Fig. 51]

Illustrations: DM 1: 90; E: pl. 21; FMI 2: 70; L3; pl. 145; MA: fig. 43; NB: 84.
Habitat: on rotten conifer logs, usually associated with the liverworts *Lepidozia reptans* and *Nowellia curvifolia*; also on bark in moist chamber or on fallen sticks. In the tropics this is characteristic of bark and refuse such as coconut husks.
Distribution: surprisingly rare in the British Isles, known from a few sites in southern England, north Wales, West Ross and Co. Kerry [6, H1]. Probably cosmopolitan and especially abundant in the tropics.

Notes: the small size of the sporangia, the very long stalks and the regular, small, dark nodes make this a distinctive species. It can most easily be obtained by culturing liverwort-covered conifer wood in a moist chamber.

Cribraria minutissima Schwein.
Trans. Am. Phil. Soc. II **4**: 260. 1832. Pennsylvania.

Sporocarps stalked, minute orange-brown sporangia, sometimes with a coppery tinge, 0.1–0.2 mm diam. **Stalk** brown, tapering, to 0.8 mm high. **Hypothallus** absent. **Peridium** disappearing, often leaving a cup which may be as much as half of the sporangial height, or lacking. **Net** separated from the cup by a slight constriction, but this is not always present; nodes expanded but not thickened in optical section, dictydine granules pale, connecting threads flattened, without free ends. **Spores** yellow in mass, pale by transmitted light, minutely roughened, 6–8 μm diam. **Plasmodium** very dark blue. [Fig. 52]

Illustrations: DM 1: 74; E: pl. 16; FMI 2: 72; L3: pl. 140; MA: fig. 44.
Habitat: fallen branches of oak.
Distribution: known from a single collection from Inchcailloch, Loch Lomond Nature Reserve, in 1966 [1]. Elsewhere widely distributed in the Americas, Asia, New Zealand and Europe.

Notes: the small size, short stalk and flattened net make this rare species fairly distinctive. As Martin & Alexopoulos (1969) state, the forms with or without a cup are constant and could well be regarded as distinct species.

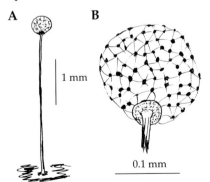

Fig. 51. *Cribraria microcarpa*:
A: sporangium; B: net.

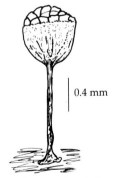

Fig. 52. *Cribraria minutissima*

Cribraria mirabilis (Rostaf.) Massee
Mon. Myxog.: 60. 1892. Germany.
Syn. *Dictydium mirabile* (Rostaf.) Meyl.; *D. cancellata* var. *alpinum* Lister

Sporocarps stalked, erect, gregarious, iridescent purplish-brown, 0.5–0.8 mm diam. **Stalk** to 1.5 mm high. **Peridium** remaining as a basal cup and as membranous, iridescent expansions between the 30 or more longitudinal ribs, which are connected by a branching network in the upper half of the sporangium. **Nodes** lacking, but the ribs bearing dark dictydine granules up to 2 μm diam. **Spores** reddish-brown in mass, transparent reddish-brown in transmitted light, often bearing dictydine granules, 5.5–7 μm diam. **Plasmodium** purple-brown. [Fig. 53]

Illustrations: DM 1: 93; FMI 2: 74; L3: pl. 147; MA: fig. 55; NB: 74.
Habitat: on rotten logs and stumps of conifers, mostly in mountain forests.
Distribution: scattered in the British Isles, mostly northern and western but generally rare [15, H4]. Elsewhere known from the mountainous parts of Europe, New Zealand and North America.

Notes: although closely related to *C. cancellata* it may be readily separated by the larger, erect sporangia and the prominent cross-connections and network in the upper half of the sporangium. The metallic reflections are usually strong.

Cribraria oregana H.C. Gilbert
in Peck & Gilbert. *Am. J. Bot.* **19**: 142. 1932. Oregon.
Syn. *Cribraria vulgaris* var. *oregana* (H.C. Gilb.) Nann.-Bremek. & Lado

Sporocarps stalked sporangia, dull orange-brown to dark brown, 0.2–0.4 mm diam. **Stalk** wrinkled, tapering, dark at base, sporangial colour at tip, to 1 mm high. **Hypothallus** inconspicuous. **Peridium** remaining as a cup, up to half the sporangial height, with the margin irregularly toothed, the cup portion faintly ribbed, bearing numerous dark dictydine granules, to 2 μm diam. **Net** and **nodes** variable in size, the latter flat and expanded, scarcely thickened. Connecting thread either slender or, between the larger nodes, broader and filled with granules. **Spores** orange-brown in mass, dull yellow or brownish-yellow by transmitted light, more or less globose but slightly angular, especially in optical section, marked with a faint reticulum of minute warts, 7–8.5 μm diam, occasionally slightly oval. **Plasmodium** dark grey, becoming white before fruiting. [Fig. 54]

Illustrations: DM 1: 95; FMI 2: 78; MA: fig. 45.
Habitat: rotten coniferous wood.
Distribution: known only from the Isle of Wight, Northumberland and Aberdeenshire [3]. Scattered in Europe, e.g. Germany and Spain, otherwise known from North America.

Notes: this is closest to *C. vulgaris*, from which it can be distinguished by the smaller size of the sporangia and the larger and darker spores.

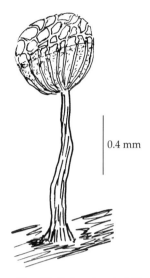

Fig. 53. *Cribraria mirabilis*

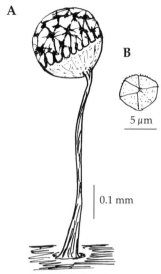

Fig. 54. *Cribraria oregana*:
A: sporangium; B: spore.

Cribraria paucicostata Nann.-Bremek.
Proc. K. Ned. Akad. Wet. C **74**: 356. 1971. France.

Sporocarps minute, stalked sporangia, ochraceous or cinnamon, to 0.2 mm in diam. **Stalk** hollow, furrowed, ochraceous, translucent, up to 0.7 mm high. **Hypothallus** absent. **Peridium** reduced to 3–6 thickened, purple-ochraceous ribs, filled with minute dictydine granules to 1 µm diam; the ribs are usually simple but may be branched in the upper part, rarely connected by thin threads. **Cup** absent. **Spores** in mass pale orange, pale ochraceous by transmitted light, minutely roughened, 6.5–8 µm diam. Plasmodium hyaline. [Fig. 55]

Illustrations: original description.
Habitat: rotten conifer stump.
Distribution: known from a single collection from Lyminge Forest, Kent, 1973 [1]. Elsewhere only known from France.

Notes: this is the smallest and simplest member of the genus and suggests a ribbed *Echinostelium*. Its small size means that it must be sought in moist chamber cultures.

Cribraria persoonii Nann.-Bremek.
Proc. K. Ned. Akad. Wet. C **74**: 353. 1971. France.

Sporocarps stalked sporangia, gregarious, hazel-brown, 0.7–1.0 mm diam. **Stalk** tapering, to 1.5 mm high, darker at the base, arising from a conspicuous dark brown hypothallus. **Peridium** leaving a well-marked cup, to a third of the sporangial height, which has a series of concentric wrinkles, especially in the upper part; cup margin with close set, even teeth; dictydine granules dark, to 1 μm diam, situated on the wrinkles and margin of the cup. **Net** with small meshes and small **nodes**, which are thickened, with 3–6 radiating threads with few free ends. **Spores** in mass hazel-brown, pale buff by transmitted light, 6.5–7.5 μm diam, minutely and densely warted, the warts pale and inconspicuous, when dry wrinkled. **Plasmodium** grey. [Fig. 56]

Illustrations: DM 1: 96; FMI 2: 80; L3: pl. 142 (as *vulgaris*); NB: 81.
Habitat: on rotten coniferous wood.
Distribution: frequent throughout the British Isles [75, H5]. Common in Europe and reported from North America and New Zealand.

Notes: differs from *C. tenella* in the larger sporangia and shorter stalk, from *C. intricata* by the small number of free ends in the net; from *C. aurantiaca* by the colour, the wrinkles on the cup, the pale warts on the spores and the plasmodial colour; and from *C. vulgaris*, under which name it has been most frequently misidentified in the past, by the smaller, thickened nodes, regular cup margin and lack of spore reticulation.

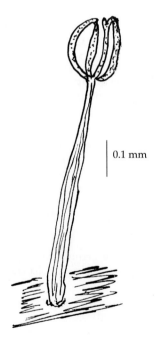

0.1 mm

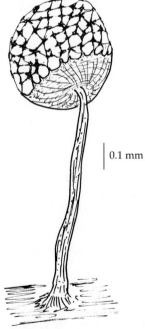

0.1 mm

Fig. 55. *Cribraria paucicostata*   Fig. 56. *Cribraria persoonii*

Cribraria pyriformis Schrad.
Nov. Gen. Pl.: 4. 1797. Germany.
Syn. var. *notabilis* Rex

Sporocarps stalked sporangia, gregarious, 0.3–0.6 mm diam, globose, or more often pear-shaped, purplish-brown. **Stalk** purple or brown, furrowed, expanded just below the sporangium. **Hypothallus** inconspicuous. **Peridium** leaving a well-defined cup, one third of the sporangial height, ribbed and marked with lines of granules, dusky brown, margin narrowly toothed. **Net** with large triangular meshes, **nodes** thickened, dark, filled with large dictydine granules to 2.5 μm diam. **Spores** on mass dull yellow-brown, pale ochraceous or with a pinkish tinge by transmitted light, covered with distinct pale warts, 6–8 μm diam. **Plasmodium** slate-grey. [Fig. 57]

Illustrations: DM 1: 98; E: pl. 20; FMI 2: 83; L3: pl. 144; MA: fig. 46.
Habitat: on rotten conifer wood and sawdust.
Distribution: widespread in the British Isles but only really common in the native pinewoods of Scotland [37, H2]. Widespread throughout the temperate regions, perhaps more commonly in mountain forests.

Notes: the var. *notabilis*, with more prominent nodes to the peridial net, is connected to the typical form by transitional forms and is not worthy of recognition. The features of this species are the pyriform sporangia, hazel-brown colour and stalk expanded just below the sporangium. The frequent spelling of the name as 'piriformis' is incorrect (the original was spelt with a 'y').

Cribraria rufa (Roth) Rostaf.
Mon.: 232. 1875. Germany.

Sporocarps stalked sporangia, 0.4–0.7 mm diam, bright orange-red. **Stalk** black, to 2 mm high. **Peridium** remaining as a cup, up to half the sporangial height, the margin toothed, the wall ribbed and continuing directly into the open, wide-meshed net. The **net** consisting of flattened orange threads with flattened, not thickened, **nodes** which are small and often imperceptible. Dictydine granules large, to 2 μm diam, pale. **Spores** orange to dull red in mass, dull yellow by transmitted light, 7–9 μm diam, slightly angular, with a very faint reticulation of small warts. **Plasmodium** white. [Fig. 58]

Illustrations: DM 1: 103; E: pl. 16; FMI 2: 86; L3: pl. 140; MA: fig. 49; NB: 78.
Habitat: rotten wood of conifers.
Distribution: widespread and increasingly common throughout the British Isles [94, H7]. Widely distributed throughout temperate coniferous forests and in mountains in the tropics.

Notes: the bright orange sporangia and the black stalks, together with a net usually lacking nodes, are the hall-marks of this species which is now much commoner in the British Isles than it was 50 years ago. The spread of coniferous plantations is the obvious reason for its increase.

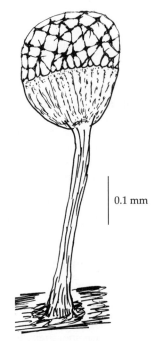

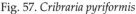

Fig. 57. *Cribraria pyriformis*

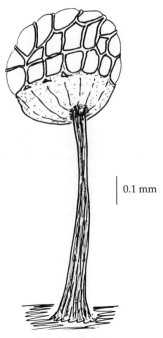

Fig. 58. *Cribraria rufa*

Cribraria splendens (Schrad.) Pers.
Syn. Fung.: 191. 1801. Germany.

Sporocarps stalked sporangia, gregarious, 0.3–0.7 mm diam, brown when empty, ochraceous when full of spores. **Stalk** tapering, purple-brown, to 1.5 mm high. **Hypothallus** inconspicuous. **Peridium** quickly disappearing, leaving an open, brown net with large meshes. **Cup** absent, replaced by 8–15 distinct ribs radiating from the top of the stalk and supporting the net, sometimes with fragments of membrane connecting the basal parts of adjacent ribs. **Nodes** irregular, flattened, connecting threads flattened, dictydine granules small, to 1 μm diam. **Spores** ochraceous in mass, colourless by transmitted light, nearly smooth, 6–7 μm diam. **Plasmodium** lead-coloured. [Fig. 59]

Illustrations: DM 1: 105; E: pl. 19; L3: pl. 141; MA: fig. 50.
Habitat: on rotten wood of conifers.
Distribution: rare, known only from Sussex, Warwickshire, Merioneth, Perthshire and West Ross [5]. Widely distributed in temperate America, Europe, New Zealand and Asia.

Notes: the ribs which replace the cup and the large meshes of the net make this a readily recognised species. Its rarity in the British Isles is difficult to explain.

Cribraria tenella Schrad.
Nov. Gen. Pl.: 6. 1797. Germany.

Sporocarps long-stalked sporangia, gregarious, 0.3–0.5 mm diam, ochraceous.
Stalk slender, to 3 mm high. **Peridium** leaving a shallow cup, ribbed but not
toothed; cup frequently lacking. **Net** small, regular, with prominent, small, round,
dark nodes connected by 3–6 transparent threads with few free ends. Dictydine
granules brown, to 2 μm diam. **Spores** olivaceous or ochraceous in mass, pale
yellow by transmitted light, almost smooth, 5–7 μm diam. **Plasmodium** said to be
either brown or colourless. [Fig. 60]

Illustrations: DM 1: 109; E: pl. 19; L3: pl. 143; MA: fig. 51; NB: 83.
Habitat: rotten wood, including oak and beech as well as conifers.
Distribution: uncommon and scattered through the British Isles with no obvious
pattern [16, H6]. Cosmopolitan.

Notes: this uncommon species is characterised by a neat net with few free ends,
relatively long stalk and, at least in the British Isles, its occurrence on hardwood.

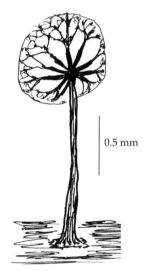

0.5 mm

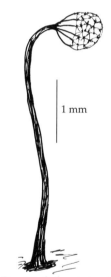

1 mm

Fig. 59. *Cribraria splendens*   Fig. 60. *Cribraria tenella*

Cribraria violacea Rex
Proc. Acad. Nat. Sci. Philad. **43**: 393. 1891. Pennsylvania.

Sporocarps minute, stalked, intense violet in colour, often with metallic
reflections, 0.1–0.3 mm wide, to 1.5 mm high, most of which is the stalk. **Peridium**
persistent as a cup which occupies most of the sporangium, net with few, open
meshes with few, thickened, nodes. **Spores** bright violet in mass, lilac by
transmitted light, minutely warted, 7–8 μm diam. **Protoplasmodium** purplish-
black. [Fig. 61]

Illustrations: DM 1: 111; E: pl. 22; FMI 2: 88; L3: pl. 146; MA: fig. 52; NB: 87.
Habitat: bark of living trees, especially elm; occasionally on fallen sticks.
Distribution: scattered and widespread but never common [25, H4]. Cosmopolitan, especially common in North America and Switzerland.

Notes: the small size, bright violet colour and habitat make this an easy species to identify.

Cribraria vulgaris Schrad.
Nov. Gen. Pl.: 5. 1797. Germany.

Sporocarps stalked sporangia, nut-brown, 0.4–0.7 mm diam. **Stalk** tapering, to 1.5 mm high. **Peridium** remaining as a well-marked cup, marked by delicate radiating veins, the margin with coarse, angular, irregular teeth. **Net** irregular with pale nodes which are broad, flat, branching and angular, connecting threads slender, with few free ends. **Spores** ochraceous in mass, colourless by transmitted light, 5–6 μm diam, marked with a faint reticulation of minute warts, angular when dry. **Plasmodium** slate-grey. [Fig. 62]

Illustrations: DM 1: 113; FMI 2: 91; NB: 86.
Habitat: rotten wood of conifers.
Distribution: rare, known from Wiltshire, Dorset, Sussex, Warwickshire and Aberdeenshire [5]. World distribution unclear because of confusion with *C. persoonii* and *C. oregana*, but known from several parts of Europe, Asia, Australasia and North America.

Notes: this species is closest to *C. oregana* but is larger, with smaller, paler spores. The name has been applied to material now included in *C. persoonii* but that species has thickened nodes, a regular cup margin and lacks the spore reticulation.

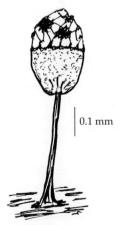

Fig. 61. *Cribraria violacea*

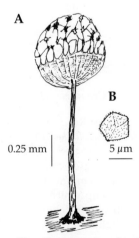

Fig. 62. *Cribraria vulgaris*:
A: sporangium; B: spore.

LINDBLADIA Fr.
Summa Veg. Scand.: 449. 1849.

Sporocarp an aethalium or pseudoaethalium, or of sessile sporangia. **Peridium** persistent, mostly lacking any development of the net. Dictydine granules present but not differently coloured from the peridium. **Hypothallus** well developed, thick and spongy. Spores dark brown in mass. Two species of which we have *L. tubulina* Fr., the type.

Lindbladia tubulina Fr.
Summa Veg. Scand.: 449. 1849. Germany.
Syn. *Lindbladia effusa* (Ehrenb.) Rostaf.

Sporocarp a pseudoaethalium or aethalium, to 20 cm long and 1 cm thick, dark khaki-brown to nearly black, consisting of numerous sporangial units and covered with a common cortex, which is thick and may be marked with more or less octagonal shapes which correspond to the individual sporangia. The sporangial walls may remain as membranous sheets, often shredded, which suggest a pseudocapillitium. **Dictydine** granules present in these membranes and in the cortex. No network develops except in rare sporangiate forms, even then it is not perforated. **Spores** khaki-brown in mass, pale yellow by transmitted light, faintly warted, 6–7.5 µm diam. **Plasmodium** black, like tar. [Fig. 63]

Illustrations: DM 1: 116; E: pls. 14 & 15; FMI 2: 136; L3: pl. 137; MA: fig. 32; NB: 70.
Habitat: on stumps, logs and sawdust of conifers; in parts of central Europe on hardwood debris.
Distribution: uncommon, scattered in England, rare in Wales, commonest in the native pinewoods of Scotland [28]. Widespread in temperate coniferous forests, in the tropics more or less confined to the mountains.

Notes: the distinctive colour of the aethalia and the plasmodium and the frequent habitat of pine sawdust make this a distinctive enough species. It is closely related to *Cribraria argillacea* and forms a link between that species and the *Lycogalaceae*.

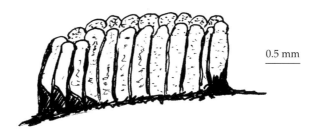

0.5 mm

Fig. 63. *Lindbladia tubulina*: aethalium.

DICTYDIAETHALIACEAE Nann.-Bremek. ex Neubert, Nowotny & Baumann
in Die Myxomyceten **1**: 117. 1993.

Sporocarp an aethalium or pseudoaethalium, consisting of a large number of tall, narrow sporangia closely appressed, their walls disappearing during maturation, leaving behind narrow T-shaped corner pieces, the upper surface of the sporocarp is marked by hexagonal plates which are the peridia of the individual sporangia. **Pseudocapillitium** consists of threads hanging down from the plates, hardly, or not at all, connected at the base. A single genus.

DICTYDIAETHALIUM Rostaf.
Vers. Syst. Mycet.: 5. 1873.

With the characters of the family. Four species, of which ours, *D. plumbeum* (Schum.) Rostaf. is the type.

Dictydiaethalium plumbeum (Schum.)Rostaf.
Vers. Syst. Mycet.: 5. 1873. Denmark.

Sporocarp an aethalium or pseudoaethalium, strongly flattened, to 5 cm long and up to 1 mm thick, surface smooth but marked with the hexagonal plates of the constituent peridia, grey when fresh, becoming brownish then yellow, surrounded by a rim of silvery white hypothallus. **Pseudocapillitium** of vertical strands, T-shaped in cross-section, pale brown or yellow, often fringed with hairs. **Spores** in mass ochraceous or yellow, pale yellow in transmitted light, 8–10 μm diam, spiny, the spines reaching 1 μm in length. **Plasmodium** bright rose-pink. [Fig. 64]

Illustrations: DM 1: 119–121; E: pl. 12; FMI 2: 94; L3: pl. 152; MA: fig. 21; NB: 68.
Habitat: mainly on fallen trunks, especially of beech, but occasionally on small branches and twigs.
Distribution: common and widespread in the south of England, thinning out northwards and not yet found north of Aviemore, less common in Ireland [75, H6]. Cosmopolitan.

Notes: the vertical rows of compressed sporangia in the flat aethalium and the distinctive pseudocapillitium make this an easy species to identify. The other three species are closely similar, largely differing in spore colour, markings or size.

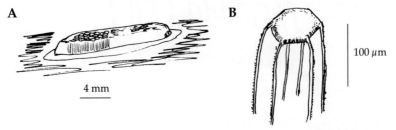

A

B

100 μm

4 mm

Fig. 64. *Dictydiaethalium plumbeum*: A: pseudoaethalium; B: pseudocapillitium.

LYCOGALACEAE Corda
Icones **2**: 41. 1838.

Sporocarp an aethalium or pseudoaethalium. **Capillitium** absent but pseudocapillitium, from the remains of component sporangial walls, usually well developed. **Spore** mass shades of pink or brown, rarely greyish. Three genera.

KEY TO GENERA

1	Sporocarp a pseudoaethalium with component sporangia easily discernible, spore mass pinkish-brown, no pseudocapillitium or capillitium (in the British species)	*Tubifera*
–	Sporocarp a true aethalium with only the tops of the sporangia suggested, spore mass shades of brown, pink or olivaceous grey, pseudocapillitium obvious	2

2 (1)	Spore mass brown, pseudocapillitium of frayed or perforated plates	*Enteridium*
–	Spore mass shades of pink, olivaceous or grey, pseudocapillitium of ornamented tubes	*Lycogala*

ENTERIDIUM Ehrenb.
Jahrb. Gewächsk. **1(2)**: 55. 1819.
Syn. *Reticularia* Bull.

Sporocarps true aethalia, **pseudocapillitium** of frayed threads or perforated plates, spore mass olive-brown to red-brown, **spores** often clustered and reticulated. Eight species, the type is *E. olivaceum* Ehrenb.

KEY TO SPECIES

1	Spores in clusters	2
–	Spores free	5

2 (1)	Aethalia linear, resembling plasmodiocarps, pseudocapillitium scanty, of vertical pillars	*liceoides*
–	Aethalia flattened or pulvinate, with abundant pseudocapillitium	3

3 (2)	Aethalia flattened, olive-brown	*olivaceum*
–	Aethalia pulvinate, lacking olive shades	4

4 (3)	Aethalia large, pseudocapillitium arising from base of aethalium, of flat plates frayed into branching threads, spores in large clusters	*lycoperdon*
–	Aethalia minute, pseudocapillitium of perforated plates, spores in clusters of two or three	*minutum*

5 (1)	Aethalia minute, clustered, shining chestnut-brown	*lobatum*
–	Aethalia larger, not clustered, olive or red-brown	6

6 (5)	Aethalia flattened, olive-brown	*simulans*
–	Aethalia pulvinate, reddish-brown	7

7 (6)	Pseudocapillitium of perforated plates	*splendens*
–	Pseudocapillitium of slender, branching threads	*intermedium*

Enteridium intermedium (Nann.-Bremek.) M.L. Farr
Taxon **25**: 514. 1976. Netherlands.
Syn. *Reticularia intermedia* Nann.-Bremek.

Sporocarp an aethalium, reddish-brown, solitary, 5–20 mm diam. **Hypothallus** forming a white ring around the base of the aethalium. Wall thin, transparent, tearing easily and not persisting. **Pseudocapillitium** a dense mass of slender, branched threads, some loose, others connected to the wall. **Spores** in mass cocoa-brown, pale rusty brown in transmitted light, 7–9 μm diam, with a fine reticulum of ridges, with a clear germination area. **Plasmodium** white. [Fig. 65]

Illustrations: MA: fig. 26; NB: 63.
Habitat: on rotten wood.
Distribution: scattered across Great Britain but nowhere common [25]. Recorded from several countries in Europe and also from North America.

Notes: this species could easily be passed over for delicate forms of *E. lycoperdon* but the filamentous pseudocapillitium is very distinctive. The sporocarp is very fragile and difficult to mount for the hebarium.

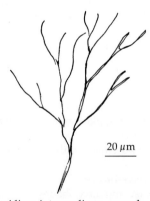

20 μm

Fig. 65. *Enteridium intermedium*: pseudocapillitium.

Enteridium liceoides (Lister) G. Lister
Guide Br. Mycet. edn 4: 48. 1909. Alderbury, Wiltshire.
Syn. *Reticularia liceoides* (Lister) Nann.-Bremek.

Sporocarp an aethalium which resembles a plasmodiocarp, worm-shaped, sometimes forming a ring or branched, 1–10 mm long, 0.5 mm wide, dark brown, often shining. **Hypothallus** inconspicuous. **Pseudocapillitium** sparse, consisting of flat pillar-like structures, wider at top and bottom and joined to the base and top of the aethalium. **Spores** in mass dark brown, yellow by transmitted light, clustered, minutely warted on the outer faces of the cluster, smooth on the inside; spores, when separated, are top-shaped, 10–12 μm diam. **Plasmodium** pink. [Fig. 66]

Illustrations: FMI 2: 100; L3: pl. 153; NB: 66.
Habitat: on fallen branches and sticks of conifers, also stumps, often rather dry.
Distribution: rare, scattered, commoner in the native pine forests of Scotland [21]. Elsewhere found widely in Europe and probably in North America, although not differentiated there; recorded from New Zealand.

Notes: this species resembles *Licea variabilis* (hence the name) and *Dianema corticatum* in the field, and occupies the same habitat. Under the microscope the clustered spores separate it from *L. variabilis* and the pillar-like pseudocapillitium from *D. corticatum*. When, as often happens, the pseudocapillitium is scanty, separation is more difficult; however, the *Dianema* usually has its own capillitial threads, which allow identification.

Fig. 66. *Enteridium liceoides*: A: aethalia; B: spores.

Enteridium lobatum (Lister) M.L. Farr
Taxon **25**: 514. 1976. Wanstead Park, Essex.
Syn. *Liceopsis lobata* (Lister) Torrend; *Reticularia lobata* Lister

Sporocarps groups of small, sporangium-like aethalia, sometimes with the suggestion of membranous stalks, shining chestnut-brown, often iridescent, 0.4–1.1 mm diam. **Hypothallus** membranous, sometimes providing the stalk-like base. **Pseudocapillitium** usually scanty, of perforated plates and strands. **Spores** in mass rust-brown, ochraceous in transmitted light, 7–8 μm diam, covered in a bold reticulum of thin bands to 1 μm high, with a germination area which may be smooth or bearing a few long warts. **Plasmodium** white, becoming colourless just before fruiting. [Fig. 67]

Illustrations: FMI 2: 100; L3: pl. 154; MA: fig. 28; NB: 67.
Habitat: under the bark of pine stumps, often just below soil surface; less often on pine sticks.
Distribution: scattered and uncommon (but perhaps just hard to find!) only in Co. Dublin in Ireland [35, H1]. Not uncommon in Europe, rare elsewhere.

Notes: the small clusters of iridescent chestnut aethalia, resembling sporangia, and the unusual habitat are valuable aids to identification.

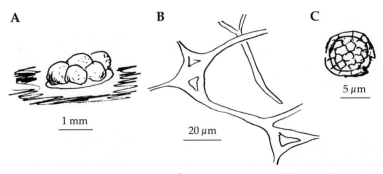

Fig. 67. *Enteridium lobatum*: A: aethalia; B: pseudocapillitium; C: spore.

Enteridium lycoperdon (Bull.) M.L. Farr
Taxon **25**: 514. 1976. France.
Syn. *Reticularia lycoperdon* Bull.

Sporocarp a large, pulvinate aethalium to 10 cm diam, often irregular in shape, when young covered in a thick silvery white cortex, later brown from the spore mass. **Hypothallus** conspicuous, white. **Pseudocapillitium** arising from the thick base of the aethalium as a series of flat plates whose ends and margins fray into strands and threads which may branch. **Spores** in mass dull cocoa-brown, pale reddish-brown in transmitted light, in clusters of up to 80 spores, covered with a fine reticulum of ridges, with a smooth or slightly spinulose germination area, 8–9 μm diam. **Plasmodium** white, becoming creamy on emergence – the so-called 'buttermilk' stage. [Fig. 68]

Illustrations: DM 1: 126; E: pl. 10; FMI 2: 103; L3: pl. 154; MA: fig. 29; NB: 62.
Habitat: typically on dead standing trees in spring, especially alder, where it often emerges from beetle exit holes, but also on fallen wood, usually large branches or trunks, mostly in the first half of the year. Also common on worked timber, such as door and window frames in houses.
Distribution: common everywhere [112, H37, C]. Cosmopolitan.

Notes: the large aethalia with frayed plates in the pseudocapillitium are the important diagnostic characters. The British form is var. *lycoperdon*; var. *americana* Nann.-Bremek. has free spores.

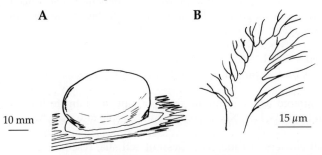

Fig. 68. *Enteridium lycoperdon*: A: aethalium; B: pseudocapillitium.

Enteridium minutum Sturgis
Mycologia **9**: 329. 1917. Colorado.

Sporocarp a minute, pulvinate aethalium, dull brown, 0.7–2 mm diam. **Pseudocapillitium** of plates with large perforations, the margins sometimes frayed. **Spores** in mass pale yellowish-brown, paler in transmitted light, adhering in loose clusters of two or three, minutely warted, subglobose and slightly flattened, 10–11 x 12–13 µm. **Plasmodium** not seen. [Fig. 69]

Illustrations: L3: pl. 220.
Habitat: on rotten branch.
Distribution: known only from a specimen collected at Thearne, in south-east Yorkshire, in 1904 [1]. Otherwise known only from the type.

Notes: several authors have synonymised this species with *E. olivaceum* but it is pulvinate rather than flattened and probably overlooked and very rare. The Yorkshire material was checked by Gulielma Lister who considered it sufficiently distinct to include the species in her 1925 *Monograph*.

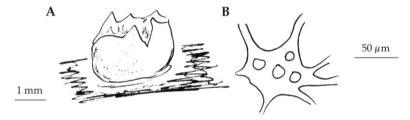

Fig. 69. *Enteridium minutum*: A: aethalium; B: pseudocapillitium.

Enteridium olivaceum species group

Two species are included here which previously have been regarded as varieties of a single species. The species are not distinguishable macroscopically and sometimes occur together. The species group is widespread and frequent, except in Ireland [51, H2]. It is widely distributed in Europe, North America, Australia and Asia.

Enteridium olivaceum Ehrenb.
Jahrb.Gewachsk. **1**: 57. 1819. Germany.
Syn. *Reticularia olivacea* (Ehrenb.)Fr.

Sporocarps flattened or very slightly rounded aethalia, usually oval in outline but sometimes irregularly effused, up to 50 mm diam and up to 3 mm thick, dark olive in colour, slightly shiny, the top pock-marked with small pits and grooves. **Hypothallus** remaining as a white rim around the aethalium. **Pseudocapillitium** pale brown, shining, spongy, persistent, consisting of perforated plates with the consistency of paper. **Spores** in mass olive, paler in transmitted light, in clusters of 5–25, top-shaped, covered with long spines on the outside of the cluster, almost smooth inside, 10–13 μm diam. **Plasmodium** pink. [Fig. 70]

Illustrations: DM 1: 127; E: pl. 13; FMI 2: 105; L3: pl. 153; MA: fig. 38; NB: 65.
Habitat: usually on sticks and branches.
Distribution: only a few of the aggregate records are supported by specimens so the British distribution is unclear [8]. Elsewhere it is probably frequent and widespread.

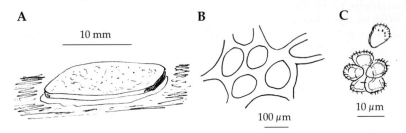

Fig. 70. *Enteridium olivaceum:* A: aethalium; B: pseudocapillitium; C: spores.

Enteridium simulans Rostaf.
Mon. App. 30. 1876. Finland

Sporocarps flattened or very slightly rounded aethalia, usually oval in outline but sometimes irregularly effused, up to 50 mm diam and to 3 mm thick, dark olive in colour, slightly shiny, the top pock-marked with small pits and grooves. **Hypothallus** remaining as a white rim around the aethalium. **Pseudocapillitium** pale brown, shining, spongy, persistent, consisting of perforated plates with the consistency of paper. **Spores** in mass olive, paler in transmitted light, globose, free, evenly and minutely spinulose, 10–13 μm diam. **Plasmodium** pink. [Fig. 71]

Illustrations: DM 1: 129; NB: 65.
Habitat: more often on fallen bark.
Distribution: only a few of the aggregate records are supported by specimens so the British distribution is unclear [5]. Elsewhere it is probably frequent and widespread.

10 μm

Fig. 71. *Enteridium simulans* spore.

Enteridium splendens var. **juranum** (Meyl.) Härkönen
Karstenia **19**: 5. 1979. Switzerland.
Syn. *Reticularia jurana* Meyl.; *R. lycoperdon* var. *juranum* (Meyl.) G. Lister

Sporocarps aethalia which are often in small groups, pulvinate, 2.5–25 cm diam, reddish-brown or copper-brown. **Hypothallus** leaving a white rim around the aethalium, loosely attached to the substrate. **Cortex** thin and often marbled with a pattern reflecting the tops of the constituent sporangia. **Pseudocapillitium** spongy, pale brown, of perforated plates, soft but persistent. **Spores** in mass rust-brown, pale reddish-brown in transmitted light, free, marked with a fine reticulum of thin ridges, with a smooth, pale germination area, 6–8 μm diam. **Plasmodium** white, then pink, becoming reddish-brown as the aethalium matures. [Fig. 72]

Illustrations: DM 1: 131; E: pl. 14; FMI 2: 107; MA: fig. 27; NB: 64.
Habitat: on fallen sticks and small branches, especially of oak, usually in summer and autumn.
Distribution: common and widespread [88, H17]. The variety is frequent in Central and northern Europe, especially in mountain forests. Elsewhere the var. *splendens* is more likely to be found.

Notes: separated from var. *splendens* largely on size of aethalia and more obvious spore reticulations. This is smaller than *E. lycoperdon* and has a very different pseudocapillitium; moreover, it occurs on smaller branches and appears later in the season.

A   B

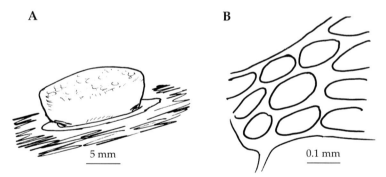

Fig. 72. *Enteridium splendens*: A: aethalium; B: pseudocapillitium.

LYCOGALA Adans.
Fam. Pl. **2**: 7. 1763.

Sporocarps aethalia, always well rounded, not flattened. Cortex often marked with scale-like vesicles. Pseudocapillitium of hollow branched tubes with ornamented walls. **Spores** in mass shades of grey or pink, covered with a fine reticulation. Eight species, *L. epidendrum* (L.) Fr. is the type.

KEY TO SPECIES

1	Cortex smooth, without scales, spore mass whitish-grey	*flavofuscum*
–	Cortex with scales or warts, spore mass pink or olivaceous	2
2 (1)	Aethalium conical, taller than broad	*conicum*
–	Aethalium pulvinate, broader than tall	3
3 (2)	Cortical scales in clusters, forming a reticulate pattern, or, if single, divided internally, spores less than 6 μm diam, width of pseudocapillitium less than 8 m	4
–	Cortical scales not in clusters, nor divided internally, spores more than 6 μm diam, width of pseudocapillitium more than 8 μm	5
4 (3)	Aethalia 1–3 mm in diam, dark, scales clustered, internal walls of scales smooth, pseudocapillitium thin, flexible, 4–6 μm diam	*exiguum*
–	Aethalia 2–10 mm diam, dark or pale, scales in rows or in a reticulate pattern, internal walls of scales wrinkled, pseudocapillitium thick, rigid, 6–8 μm diam	*confusum*
5 (3)	Plasmodium pure red or carmine, without orange tints, aethalia dark grey, rough, 4–7 mm diam, cortex scales dark, lobed, spore mass grey fading to olivaceous, pseudocapillitium fragile, less than 12 μm diam	*epidendrum*
–	Plasmodium orange, peach, pink or vermilion, rarely cream, without red tints, aethalia rose or buff, 5–15 mm (or larger) in diam, cortex scales pale, branched, spore mass pink, peach or salmon, fading to ochraceous, never with olivaceous tints, pseudocapillitium flexible, more than 12 μm diam	*terrestre*

Lycogala conicum Pers.
Syn. Fung. 159. 1801. Germany.

Sporocarps aethalia, usually clustered, conical or ovoid, to 3 mm high and 1.5 mm diam, pinkish-buff but appearing darker above because of the dark scales which form a network on the surface. **Hypothallus** inconspicuous. **Pseudocapillitium** consisting of tubes of various shapes, 3–10 μm diam, smooth or very finely warted. **Spores** in mass bright pink, fading to yellowish-grey, almost colourless in transmitted light, finely reticulate, 5–7 μm diam. **Plasmodium** pink. [Fig. 73]

Illustrations: DM 1: 133; E: pl. 11; FMI 2: 141; L3: pl. 157; MA: fig. 22; NB: 59.
Habitat: on rotten, fallen trunks, especially of oak and beech; characteristic of ancient woodland.
Distribution: rare in England and Wales, only recorded from Skye in Scotland [10]. Widely distributed in temperate and tropical regions but never a common species.

Notes: the shape of the aethalium is quite sufficient to identify this elegant species.

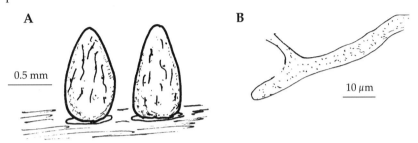

Fig. 73. *Lycogala conicum*: A: aethalia; B: pseudocapillitium.

Lycogala epidendrum species group

Two species are included which were previously treated as one. Both species are abundant and need to be carefully examined, the colours of plasmodium and spore mass are easily used but the microscopic characters *should* be checked.

Illustrations: FMI 2: 143; L3: pl. 156; MA: fig. 23; NB: 57 (none can be assigned to a segregate species.)
Distribution: the aggregate is one of the most frequently recorded myxomycetes [112, H40, C]. Cosmopolitan.

Lycogala epidendrum (L.) Fries.
Syst. Mycol. **3**: 80. 1829. Europe.

Sporocarps aethalia, usually clustered, pulvinate, 4–7 mm diam, dark grey. **Cortex** rough, with dark, lobed scales. **Pseudocapillitium** tubes wrinkled, surface smooth or finely spinulose, fragile, easily breaking when prepared for microscopic examination, 8–12 μm diam. **Spore** mass grey when fresh, fading to olivaceous grey, in transmitted light colourless, 6–7.5 μm diam, finely reticulate. **Plasmodium** carmine red or carmine pink, always with bright, dark red shades. [Fig. 74]

Illustrations: DM 1: 135; E: pl. 11.
Habitat: on fallen branches and stumps.
Distribution: most of the records for the aggregate cannot be checked but this segregate is widespread and common [33, H1]. Because of the recent separation of

these taxa the world distribution is uncertain, but this species seems to be the commoner of the two in the tropics; probably cosmopolitan.

Notes: the combination of red plasmodium, dark grey aethalia and grey spore mass separate this species in the field.

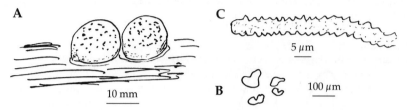

Fig. 74. *Lycogala epidendrum*:   A: aethalia;   B: cortical scales;   C: pseudocapillitium.

Lycogala terrestre Fries.
Symb. Gast.: 10. 1817. Europe.

Sporocarps aethalia, usually clustered, pulvinate, 5–20 mm diam, pale buff or pink. **Cortex** smooth, covered with pale, branching scales. **Pseudocapillitium** tubes flexible, not fragile, 12–25 μm diam. **Spores** in mass pink, retaining pink shades after many years, in transmitted light colourless, 6–7.5 μm diam, finely reticulate. **Plasmodium** usually salmon-pink but occasionally creamy-white or pale orange, never with bright red shades. [Fig. 75]

Habitat: as well as fallen wood this species also occurs on dead standing tree trunks, soil and debris next to fallen wood, and has been collected from the surface of *Sphagnum* patches in woodland.
Distribution: appears to be commoner than *L. epidendrum* in the British Isles [68, H3]. Probably cosmopolitan.

Notes: the combination of pink plasmodium, pale aethalia and pink spore mass separate this species in the field.

Lycogala exiguum species group

Two species are included here which have previously been regarded as a single more variable species, *L. exiguum*. The variety *tessellatum* Lister of *L. epidendrum* has been variously treated as a synonym of *L. exiguum* or as a separate variety. It is here redescribed as a separate species. This pair of species is not common in the British Isles [32, H2] but is widely reported from elsewhere and is especially common in the tropics.

Lycogala exiguum Morgan
J. Cinc. Soc. Nat. Hist. **15**: 134. 1893. Ohio

Sporocarps aethalia, pulvinate, dark pinkish-buff, 1–3 mm diam. **Cortical** scales in clusters, divided into compartments, internal walls smooth. **Pseudocapillitium** tubes wrinkled, thin, soft and flexible, 4–6 μm diam. **Spores** in mass pink, colourless by transmitted light, marked with a faint reticulation of warts, 4.5–5.5 μm diam. **Plasmodium** pink. [Fig. 76]

Illustrations: E: pl. 11; MA: fig. 24.
Habitat: on fallen trunks, usually when well-rotted, especially of beech.
Distribution: the segregate has been identified in southern England, the Midlands, the Highlands of Scotland and Ireland, but appears to be rarer than the next [8, H1]. The exact distribution is unknown because of the segregation of the aggregate.

Notes: the clustered, divided scales, smaller size, more delicate pseudocapillitium and less obviously reticulate spores distinguish this species from the next.

Lycogala confusum Nannenga-Bremekamp ex Ing **nov. spec.**
Syn. *Lycogala epidendrum* var. *tesselatum* Lister

Aethalium pallidum aut obscurum, pulvinatum, 2–10 mm in diam. Cortex cum squamis ordinatis in lineis aut reticule, indivisis, muris internis rugosis. Pseudocapillitium cum tubis rugosis, crassis rigidisque, ornatis verrucis teneris, 6–8 μm in diam. Sporae reticulatae, 5.5–6.5 μm in diam. Plasmodium roseum. Habitat in ligno putrido.
HOLOTYPUS: in ligno putrido Fagus sylvaticae, Coed Dolgarrog National Nature Reserve, north Wales, 8 September 1993, legit M. Härkönen, (**Hb. B. Ing** No. 92077).

Aethalium dark or pale, 2–10 mm diam. **Cortical** scales in rows or forming a reticulate pattern, not divided into compartments, internal walls wrinkled. **Pseudocapillitium** tubes wrinkled, thick, rigid, 6–8 μm diam. **Spores** in mass pink, colourless in transmitted light, finely banded-reticulate, 5.5–6.5 μm diam. **Plasmodium** pink. [Fig. 77]

Illustrations: NB: 58.
Habitat: on fallen trunks, usually when well-rotted, especially of beech.
Distribution: as with the previous species, older records of the aggregate cannot now be assigned, but this segregate has been recorded from all regions of Great Britain and from Co. Mayo [20, H1]. Elsewhere known with certainty only from the Netherlands, Switzerland and Gomera, Canary Islands, but likely to be widespread.

Notes: larger aethalia, scale pattern and robust pseudocapillitium separate this from *L. exiguum*. It was Nannenga-Bremekamp's intention to publish this species but her untimely death intervened. I therefore wish the species to be credited to her. The uncertainty surrounding Lister's variety, for long equated with *L. exiguum*, is clarified by the erection of this species. As with the *L. epidendrum* group it is unfortunate that such well-known organisms exhibit discontinuous variation, thus requiring name changes.

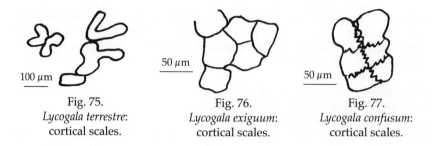

Fig. 75.
Lycogala terrestre:
cortical scales.

Fig. 76.
Lycogala exiguum:
cortical scales.

Fig. 77.
Lycogala confusum:
cortical scales.

Lycogala flavofuscum (Ehrenb.) Rostaf.
in Fuckel, *Jahr. Nass. Ver. Nat.* **27–28**: 68. 1873. Germany.

Sporocarp solitary, an aethalium, subglobose, hemispherical, or when on a vertical surface, mis-shapen and sagging, 20–50 mm diam, or up to 100 mm long (vertical). **Cortex** smooth, pale grey or buff, with a silvery sheen. **Pseudocapillitium** of variously shaped tubes, wrinkled and minutely spinulose, 10–30 μm diam, pale beige. **Spores** in mass pale beige or pale grey, almost colourless in transmitted light, finely reticulate, 5–6 μm diam. **Plasmodium** white. [Fig. 78]

Illustrations: DM 1: 138; E: pl. 10; FMI 2: 146; L3: pl. 155; MA: fig. 25; NB: 60.
Habitat: on the inside of hollow trunks, on the outside of dead standing trunks and occasionally on prepared timbers, even shop fronts.
Distribution: a southern species, absent from Ireland and with a single, old record for Wales, in Scotland two records, from Edinburgh and Pitlochry, both modern [25]. It is widespread in the temperate regions of the world, but nowhere common.

Notes: when emerging from rot holes on trees it strongly resembles a puff-ball or *Enteridium lycoperdon*, but is easily distinguished by its pale spore mass.

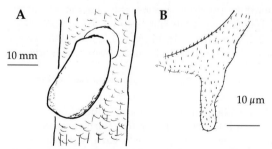

Fig. 78. *Lycogala flavofuscum*: A: aethalium; B: pseudocapillitium.

TUBIFERA J.F. Gmel.
Syst. Nat. **2**: 1472. 1792.

Sporocarp a pseudoaethalium of closely appressed, cylindrical sporangia, resting on a thick, spongy hypothallus. **Peridium** of separate sporangia persistent, often iridescent. **Capillitium** and **pseudocapillitium** absent. **Spores** in mass pinkish brown. Eight species, of which ours, *T. ferruginosa* (Batsch) J.F. Gmel. is the type.

Tubifera ferruginosa (Batsch.) J.F. Gmel.
Syst. Nat. **2**: 1472. 1791. Germany.

Sporocarp a pseudoaethalium of cylindrical sporangia, to 50 mm long and 20 mm wide, to 1 cm tall, pinkish-brown, fading to dull brown. Individual **sporangia** to 5 mm high and 0.3 mm diam. **Hypothallus** white, spongy, in layers below the sporocarp. **Peridium** thin, iridescent, often with mother-of-pearl reflections. **Pseudocapillitium** usually absent but occasionally there are a few horizontal tubes connected to the peridium, rather like the thickening in xylem vessels in plants. **Spores** in mass pinkish-brown, red-brown in transmitted light, free, with a small-meshed reticulation, 6–8 μm diam. **Plasmodium** orange, apricot or pink, or white, then pink, in all cases darkening as the sporocarp matures. The plasmodium's resemblance to a strawberry is very characteristic. [Fig. 79]

Illustrations: DM 1: 143; E: pl. 8; FMI 2: 150; L3: pl. 150; MA: fig. 18; NB: 54.
Habitat: characteristic of rotten conifer logs and stumps, but also found on alder and, more rarely, birch; found in late summer and early autumn.
Distribution: very common throughout the British Isles [111, H38, C]. Cosmopolitan.

Notes: there are no other species to confuse with this in the British Isles; it can be identified as soon as it emerges from the wood.

4 mm

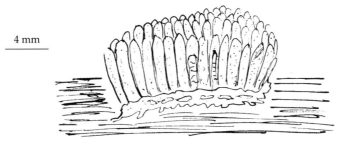

Fig. 79. *Tubifera ferruginosa*: pseudoaethalium.

TRICHIALES T. Macbr.
N. Am. Slime-Moulds, edn. 2: 237. 1922

Sporocarps usually sporangia or plasmodiocarps, rarely aethalia, columella absent, true capillitium present, tubular, often branched, smooth or ornamented. Spore mass usually pale, with shades of yellow and red predominating, rarely brown and never with lilac or purple tones. If calcium is present it is as oxalate, not carbonate. **Plasmodium** of the intermediate type. Four families, all represented in the British Isles.

Notes: Nannenga-Bremekamp (1982) used birefringence under polarised light as a character in separating families in this order. The chemical basis for birefringence is not clear and its origin is certainly not uniform. It is not used in this work.

DIANEMATACEAE T. Macbr.
N. Am. Slime-Moulds: 180. 1899.

Sporocarps sessile sporangia or plasmodiocarps. **Capillitium** of solid, sparsely ornamented threads, often with expanded regions. **Spore** mass greyish-pink or yellow. Two genera.

KEY TO GENERA

1   Capillitial threads, stout, rigid, attached to the sporangium wall   *Dianema*
–   Capillitial threads, slender, coiled, hardly attached to the peridium
                                                                    Calomyxa

CALOMYXA Nieuwl.
Am. Midl. Nat. **4**: 335. 1916.

Sporocarps sporangia, usually sessile, or short plasmodiocarps. **Peridium** membranous, iridescent. Capillitium of simple, flexuous, coiled, solid threads. Two species, of which our *C. metallica* (Berk.) Nieuwl. is the type.

Calomyxa metallica (Berk.) Nieuw.
Am. Midl. Nat. **4**: 335. 1916. Batheaston, Somerset.
Syn. *Margarita metallica* (Berk.) Lister

Sporocarps sessile sporangia or short, curved plasmodiocarps. **Sporangia** globose with a constricted base, solitary or gregarious, coppery or pearly pinkish-grey with a brilliant iridescence, with bronze, gold and red reflections, 0.5–1 mm diam. **Plasmodiocarps** similar, 0.5 mm wide and to 3 mm long. **Peridium** single, membranous. **Capillitium** an abundant web of long, uniform, grey or yellow threads, 0.5–1 μm, exceptionally 2 μm in diam, coiled, minutely warted, scarcely branched and with few attachments to the peridium. **Spores** in mass pinkish-yellow or olivaceous, pale yellow to colourless in transmitted light, minutely warted, 10–11 μm diam. **Plasmodium** watery-white or clear, translucent peachy pink. [Fig. 80]

Habitat: mainly on the bark of large, broad-leaved trees but also on litter, such as petioles, leaves and twigs of broad-leaved woody plants.

Distribution: widely distributed in the British Isles and quite common [76, H22]. Probably cosmopolitan.

Notes: the pinkish-olive spore mass, iridescent peridium and coiled, simple threads make this an easy species to identify. The superficially similar *Prototrichia metallica* has capillitial threads marked with spiral bands.

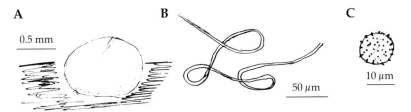

Fig. 80. *Calomyxa metallica*: A: sporangium; B: capillitium; C: spore.

DIANEMA Rex
Proc. Acad. Nat. Sci. Philad. **43**: 397. 1891.

Sporocarps sessile sporangia or plasmodiocarps, often closely aggregated but hardly forming pseudoaethalia. **Capillitium** of more or less straight, smooth threads, attached at both ends. **Spore** mass pink at first, rapidly fading to yellow. Eight species, the type is *D. harveyi* Rex.

KEY TO SPECIES

1	Spores clustered	2
–	Spores free	3
2 (1)	Peridium thick, capillitial threads without expansions; on rotten conifer wood	*corticatum*
–	Peridium thin, capillitial threads with membranous expansions; on bark of living trees	*repens*
3 (1)	Sporangia flattened, lilac-grey, clustered, spores reticulate	*depressum*
–	Sporangia pulvinate, spores not reticulate	4
4 (3)	Sporangia red, iridescent, capillitium sparsely branched; on rotten wood; lowland	*harveyi*
–	Sporangia yellowish, iridescent, capillitium richly branched; on grass and twigs, in meadows and forests on mountains, close to melting snow	*nivale*

Dianema corticatum Lister
Mycet.: 205. 1894. Norway.

Sporocarps usually plasmodiocarps, simple, branched or forming small rings or nets, less commonly pulvinate sporangia, when they are 0.3–1 mm diam, dull purplish-brown. **Peridium** of two layers, the outer cartilaginous, wrinkled, granular, the inner membranous. **Capillitium** sparse, of simple, rarely branched, threads, 1.5–2.5 μm diam, beaded and spirally twisted. **Spores** in mass pinkish-yellow, paler or colourless in transmitted light, subglobose to ellipsoid, clustered in groups of 2–6, spiny on the outside of the clusters, 10–15 x 8–10 μm. **Plasmodium** pink. [Fig. 81]

Illustrations: DM 1: 219; FMI 2: 205; L3: pl. 193; MA: fig. 63.
Habitat: on rotten conifer wood, including fence posts.
Distribution: scattered and generally rare, commonest in the native pine forests in Highland Scotland [13, H3]. Reported widely in Europe, North America, New Zealand and Australia, but nowhere common.

Notes: separated by the thread-like capillitium and clustered spores from the superficially similar *Licea variabilis* and *Enteridium liceoides* which share the same habitat. British material is usually sporangiate.

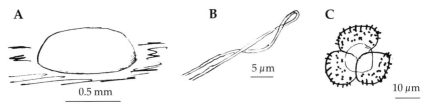

Fig. 81. *Dianema corticatum*: A: sporangium; B: capillitium; C: spore.

Dianema depressum (Lister) Lister
Mycet.: 204. 1894. Batheaston, Somerset.

Sporocarps flattened sporangia to broad plasmodiocarps, frequently gregarious and angled where they meet, 2–10 mm long, very thin, no more than 0.3 mm high, lead-grey to greyish-brown, glossy with a purplish-lilac reflection. **Peridium** membranous, smooth or marked with a pattern of wrinkles forming a network. **Capillitium** abundant, of pale yellowish-grey threads, 1–2 μm thick, triangular in section, on the angles bearing a row of minute tubercles, the threads united into bunches of 2–6, when old breaking free and forming an elastic web. **Spores** in mass lilac-grey, pale yellowish in transmitted light, with a fine reticulation covering most of the surface, 7–9 μm diam. **Plasmodium** white or pink. [Fig. 82]

Illustrations: DM 1: 220; E: pl. 24; FMI 2: 208; L3: pl. 190; MA: fig. 64; NB: 91.
Habitat: on rotten wood, especially on ash on calcareous soils.
Distribution: mostly southern, recorded from England, not from Wales or Ireland, with three records from Scotland, reaching Orkney [28]. Widespread, but not common, in Europe, North America , Japan, New Zealand and Australia.

Notes: the flattened, angular sporangia with a distinctly metallic leaden sheen and lilac spore mass make this unmistakable.

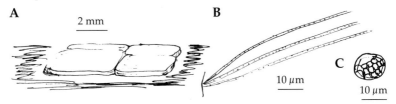

Fig. 82. *Dianema depressum*: A: sporangium; B: capillitium; C: spore.

Dianema harveyi Rex
Proc. Acad. Nat. Sci. Philad. **43**: 397. 1891. Maine.

Sporocarps gregarious sporangia, sessile, pulvinate or shortly plasmodiocarpous, ochraceous to, usually, red or reddish-brown, iridescent, 0.5–2 mm diam. **Peridium** thin, membranous, translucent. **Capillitium** of smooth, rigid threads without clustered ends or forks, rising from the base and attached to the top of the peridium. **Spores** in mass yellow, paler in transmitted light, spiny, 8–10 μm diam. **Plasmodium** white. [Fig. 83]

Illustrations: DM 1: 221; E: pl. 25; FMI 2: 210; L3: pl. 191; MA: fig. 65; NB: 90.
Habitat: on fallen twigs, occasionally on the bark of living trees, mostly in winter.
Distribution: scattered, mostly southern but reaching Orkney, not in Wales [13, H4]. Widely recorded in Europe, North America, Chile, New Zealand and Japan, but not common.

Notes: the reddish, thin, iridescent peridium, the yellow spore mass and the sparsely branched capillitium are good distinguishing features.

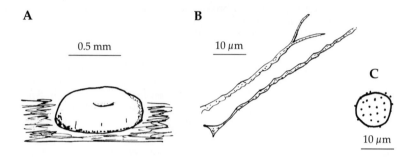

Fig. 83. *Dianema harveyi*: A: sporangium; B: capillitium; C: spore.

Dianema nivale (Meyl.) G. Lister
Mycet. edn 2: 258. 1911. Switzerland.

Sporocarps sessile sporangia, pulvinate, usually solitary but occasionally in small groups, copper-coloured, iridescent with green or golden reflections, 0.5–1.5 mm diam. **Peridium** membranous, translucent. **Capillitium** abundant, of yellow threads radiating from the base, thicker below and branching and forming a web, attached to the peridium by slender tips. **Spores** in mass at first greyish-pink, fading to yellow, very pale yellow in transmitted light, minutely closely warted, 8–12 μm diam. **Plasmodium** not seen. [Fig. 84]

Illustrations: Meyer, M. in *Bull. Fed. Mycol. Dauph. Savoie* **125**: 25. 1992.
Habitat: on grasses, plant litter, including twigs, in alpine meadows and montane forests, close to the edge of melting snow in the spring.
Distribution: known from Perthshire, Aberdeenshire and the Cairngorms, rare [3]. Reported from France, Switzerland, British Columbia and India, always alpine.

Notes: the thin, golden, iridescent peridium and the habitat make this beautiful species easy to identify.

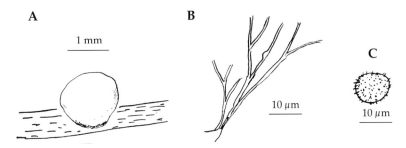

Fig. 84. *Dianema nivale*: A: sporangium; B: capillitium; C: spore.

Dianema repens *in* G. Lister & Cran
Mycet. edn 3: 255. 1925. Lesmoir, Aberdeenshire.

Sporocarps simple, rarely branched, 0.3 mm wide and to 1.5 mm long, dull purplish-brown. **Peridium** membranous, wrinkled, covered with a thin layer of granular material. **Capillitium** sparse, of brown threads, 2–3 μm diam, branching, with membranous expansions where they branch. **Spores** in mass rose-pink, paler in transmitted light, in clusters of 4–12, globose or ovate, minutely warted on outer surface of clusters, 10–11 μm diam. **Plasmodium** rose. [Fig. 85]

Illustrations: none.
Habitat: on *Parmelia* lichens and *Metigera* liverworts on the bark of living trees.
Distribution: known from two collections from Lesmoir, from Porlock, Somerset, from Teesdale, Co. Durham and Orkney [4]. The last two collections are recent. The species appears to be endemic to the British Isles.

Notes: the habitat, clustered spores and membranous expansions in the capillitium separate this rare species.

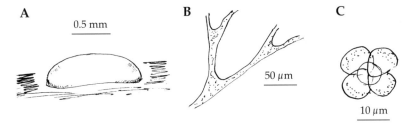

Fig. 85. *Dianema repens*: A: sporangium; B: capillitium; C: spore.

MINAKATELLACEAE Nann.-Bremek. ex Neubert, Nowotny & Baumann
in Die Myxomyceten **1**: 160. 1993.

Sporocarps forming a pseudoaethalium of densely clustered sporangia, usually sessile, but occasionally with a short, common stalk. **Capillitium** of smooth, simple, coiled, flattened threads. **Spore** mass dull reddish-brown. A single genus and species.

MINAKATELLA G. Lister
J. Bot., Lond. **59**: 92. 1921.

With the characters of the family. Type species *M. longifila* G. Lister.

Notes: this genus has been placed in *Dianemataceae* and *Arcyriaceae* by various authors and the family has been placed in the *Liceales* by others. The smooth capillitium rather precludes *Arcyriaceae*, the red spore colour and pseudoaethalial habit do not suggest *Dianemataceae* and the presence of true capillitium and red spores should rule out *Liceales*. It is retained in a separate family in Trichiales pending further study of the only, rare, species.

Minakatella longifila G. Lister
J. Bot., Lond. **59**: 92. 1921. Japan.

Sporocarps sessile, subglobose sporangia, 0.3–0.4 mm diam, closely heaped and forming pseudoaethalia up to 2 mm diam, dull brownish-pink. **Peridium** membranous, iridescent. **Capillitium** of coiled, pale red threads, 1.5–2 μm diam, hardly branched and with a few swollen free ends, one side of the thread bordered by a low ridge or wing. **Spores** in mass dull reddish-brown, pale red by transmitted light, usually adhering in clusters of 8–14 but may also be free, 10–11 μm diam, evenly warted when free, with more distinct warts on the outer surface when clustered. **Plasmodium** watery pink. [Fig. 86]

Illustrations: E: pl. 123; L3: pl. 206.
Habitat: on lichens on the bark of living trees.
Distribution: known only from Warwickshire and Co. Wicklow [1, H1]. Elsewhere from Japan, Kentucky and Taiwan.

Notes: the small pinkish pseudoaethalia and the peculiar winged capillitium threads are unique. It could perhaps be mistaken for *Arcyodes incarnata* but this is larger, has different capillitium and a very different habitat. The Warwickshire collection differs from the type in having free spores. Whether this should be regarded as a distinct species is doubtful, although it may merit varietal rank.

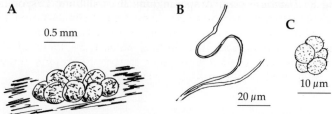

Fig. 86. *Minakatella longifila*: A: pseudoaethalium; B: capillitium; C: spores.

ARCYRIACEAE Rostaf. ex Cooke
Contr. Mycol. Br.: 69. 1877.

Sporocarps sporangiate, plasmodiocarpous, or rarely pseudoaethalial (in the non-European *Arcyriatella congregata*). **Capillitium** of tubular threads, often branching into an elastic network, marked with spines, warts, cogs, ridges or rings but never with spiral bands (in contrast with *Trichiaceae* where spiral bands are the norm). **Spore** mass yellow or red shades or white, rarely other colours. The presence or absence of birefringent capillitium cuts across the morphological characters, is not well based chemically and not used here. Five genera are recognised here, including the Brazilian *Arcyriatella*.

KEY TO GENERA

1	Capillitium of free elaters which may be branched but do not unite to form a net	*Perichaena*
–	Capillitium of branching threads united to form an elastic net	2
2 (1)	Peridium quickly disappearing, sporangia stalked with a well-developed basal cup	*Arcyria*
–	Peridium persistent, sporangia sessile, without a basal cup	3
3 (2)	Capillitium marked with warts or spines, sporangia heaped	*Arcyodes*
–	Capillitium with prominent rings, sporangia not heaped	*Cornuvia*

ARCYODES O.F. Cook
Science, ser. II, **15**: 151. 1902.

Sporocarps sessile sporangia, clustered, often in heaps. **Capillitium** a loose, inelastic network of threads which are ornamented with warts, spines or an irregular net, arising from the cup-like base of the sporangium and attached to the peridium at several points. **Spore** mass pink or pale ochraceous. A single species, *A. incarnata* (Alb. & Schwein.) O.F. Cook.

Arcyodes incarnata (Alb. & Schwein.) O.F. Cook
Science **15**: 651, 1902. Germany.
Syn. *Lachnobolus congestus* (Sommerf.) Lister

Sporocarps sessile, crowded, even heaped, sporangia, pale copper-coloured, fading to ochraceous, 0.4–0.8 mm diam. **Hypothallus** common to cluster but inconspicuous. **Peridium** membranous, opalescent, marked with minute warts and ridges. **Capillitium** an abundant, inelastic network of branching and anastomosing threads, 3–4 μm diam, with frequent swellings, marked with warts and spines, ochraceous in mass, paler in transmitted light. **Spores** in mass pale pink or ochraceous, pale in transmitted light, smooth except for a few scattered warts, 6–8 μm diam. **Plasmodium** white or pink. [Fig. 87]

Illustrations: DM 1: 163; E: pl. 27; L3: pl. 183; MA: fig. 97; NB: 98.

Habitat: on wet fallen branches, especially of willow, in carr, marshes and dried-up ponds.

Distribution: scattered and uncommon, not recorded from Wales and with only three records from Scotland and two from Ireland [31, H2]. Widespread but never common in the temperate regions of the world.

Notes: the dull colours make this an inconspicuous species but the heaped sporangia and capillitium are good markers. The habitat is insufficiently studied by mycologists in spite of its richness.

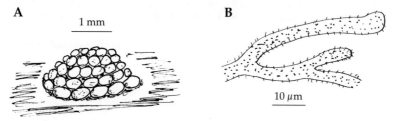

Fig. 87. *Arcyodes incarnata*: A: sporangium; B: capillitium.

ARCYRIA F.H. Wigg.
Prim. Pl. Holsat.: 109. 1780.

Sporocarps stalked sporangia, globose through ovoid to cylindrical, sometimes recumbent when long. **Peridium** thin, quickly disappearing in most species but leaving a well-marked cup or calyculus. **Stalk** often packed with large globose cells, like spores but larger. **Capillitium** an elastic network of sculptured, branching and anastomosing threads, expanding on maturity, the expanded structure often resembling a loofah. The ornamentation of the threads consists of spines, warts, cogs, rings and ridges, the last sometimes arranged in a reticulate pattern. The capillitium is either firmly attached to the cup or so loosely that it breaks away as a single unit at the slightest breath of wind. **Spore** colour follows that of the sporangium. About 40 species world-wide, 12 in the British Isles; the type is *A. denudata* (L.) Wettst.

KEY TO SPECIES

1	Peridium disappearing except at the base where it forms a well-defined cup	2
–	Peridium persistent above, sporangia copper-coloured, closely massed	*stipata*
2 (1)	Capillitium loosely attached to centre of cup, easily blown away as a mass by a gentle puff	3
–	Capillitium firmly attached, not blown away	8
3 (2)	Sporangia yellow, drooping, loofah-like	*obvelata*
–	Sporangia red or pink	4
4 (3)	Spores 9–11 µm diam, sporangia rusty red, occasionally yellow, but then never drooping	*ferruginea*
–	Spores less than 9 µm diam, sporangia bright red or pink	5
5 (4)	Sporangia long and drooping, bright red	6
–	Sporangia short, upright, pink or coral-red	7
6 (5)	Capillitium marked with spines, warts, rings and ridges	*affinis*
–	Capillitium marked only with spines	*oerstedtii*
7 (5)	Capillitium completely free from cup, sporangia pink	*incarnata*
–	Capillitium fragile, blowing away but leaving broken tubes attached to the cup, sporangia coral-red	*major*
8 (2)	Sporangia white, yellow or ochraceous	9
–	Sporangia shades of red	10
9 (8)	Sporangia cylindrical to ovate, usually white or grey but occasionally ochraceous, inside surface of cup smooth or marbled	*cinerea*
–	Sporangia globose to ovate, bright ochraceous, inside surface of cup warted or with a network of raised markings	*pomiformis*

10 (8)   Capillitium with blunt cogs, sporangia ovoid to short cylindrical, flat-topped, pale pink to rose, spores 8–10 μm diam   *minuta*
–   Capillitium with other markings, not cogs, sporangia cylindrical, round-topped, bright red, spores less than 8 μm diam   11

11 (10)   Sporangia 0.5–1.5 mm tall, scattered, rose-pink   *insignis*
–   Sporangia 2–6 mm tall, clustered, bright red   *denudata*

Arcyria affinis Rostaf.
Sluzowce Mon.: 276. 1875. Sweden.
Syn. *Arcyria incarnata* var. *fulgens* Lister

Sporocarps stalked sporangia, crowded, 1.5–2.5 mm tall, 3–4 mm when the capillitium is fully expanded, bright red, usually drooping at maturity. **Hypothallus** common to a cluster, thin, membranous, colourless. **Stalk** to 0.7 mm long, often eccentrically attached to base of sporangium, red to dark brown, rather shining, filled with rounded cells, 10–16 μm diam. **Peridium** single, membranous, leaving a deep funnel-shaped **cup**, bright red and smooth on the outside, paler on the inside and marked with small warts or papillae, connected by a faint net. **Capillitium** tubular, elastic, threads 4–8 μm diam, branched and anastomosed, decorated with warts, cogs, spines and ridges, sometimes connected by a faint net; when the capillitium blows away the remnants of the fragile, broken tubes are left attached to the inside of the cup. **Spores** in mass red, pale yellow or colourless by transmitted light, 7–9 μm diam, very slightly warted, with a few groups of larger warts. **Plasmodium** white. [Fig. 88]

Illustrations: DM: 169; FMI 2: 162; NB: 105,106.
Habitat: on rotten wood, especially beech in calcareous districts.
Distribution: frequent in southern England, north to Cheshire, absent from Wales, only in Perthshire in Scotland and rare in Ireland [24, H5]. Not uncommon in Europe but its distribution elsewhere is unclear because of confusion with other species, but there are definite records from Australia and New Zealand.

Notes: the elastic, bright red capillitium falling over the substrate resembles *A. oerstedtii* but the markings are different. *A. major* may approach the floppiness of this species but has broken tubes remaining attached to the cup.

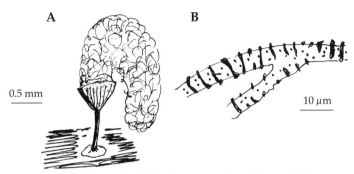

Fig. 88. *Arcyria affinis*: A: sporangium; B: capillitium.

Arcyria cinerea (Bull.) Pers.
Syn. Fung.: 84. 1801. France.

Sporocarps stalked sporangia which may be in groups or solitary, sometimes with several sporangia joined by their confluent stalks, 0.5–2.5 mm high, milky white to pale grey, sometimes with a yellowish tint, often fading to pale ochraceous. **Hypothallus** membranous, either discoid with solitary sporangia or forming a sheet under groups, inconspicuous. **Stalk** to 1 mm long, usually darker than the sporangium, filled with round cells 14–24 μm diam, especially at the base of the stalk. **Peridium** membranous, leaving a cup which is conical or saucer-shaped, with radial pleats on the outside, the inside nearly smooth or with a greyish marbling. **Capillitium** of white to colourless threads, 3–6 μm diam, strongly attached to the cup, the basal tubes are nearly smooth, those in the upper part of the sporangium are strongly spiny and there may also be a few cogs. **Spores** in mass yellowish-white to yellowish-grey, colourless in transmitted light, 6–8 μm diam, smooth or with a few groups of prominent warts, seen under oil immersion. **Plasmodium** white, usually developing a pinkish tinge before the sporangia are fully formed. [Fig. 89]

Illustrations: DM 1: 171,172; E: pl. 31; FMI 2: 169; L3: pl. 176; MA: fig. 80; NB: 117.
Habitat: on well-rotted wood, especially of hardwoods, often on mosses, and on the bark of living trees, especially oak, less often in areas of acid deposition.
Distribution: very common throughout the British Isles [111, H40, C]. Cosmopolitan.

Notes: this is a distinctive species and normally presents no problems with identification. However, in bark cultures the solitary, ovoid, ochraceous forms of this species could be mistaken for *A. pomiformis*. The plasmodium of the latter, however, develops a yellow tinge during final development contrasting with the pinkish tinge of *A. cinerea*. The characters of the cup decoration are important but not always easy to see. The apex of the sporangium is nearly always obviously acute, not rounded as in *A. pomiformis*. The confluent, so-called digitate form is especially common in the tropics but may occasionally occur in bark cultures in the British Isles. It does not merit a name.

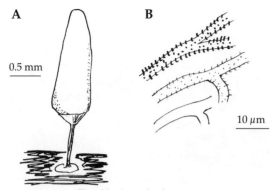

Fig. 89. *Arcyria cinerea*:
A: sporangium; B: capillitium; top: outer, middle: middle, bottom: basal.

Arcyria denudata (L.) Wettst.
Verh. Zool.-bot. Ges. Wien **35**: 535. 1886. Italy.

Sporocarps stalked, gregarious sporangia, cylindrical with rounded or acute apices, 2–6 mm high, bright red. **Stalk** dark red to black, to 1.5 mm high, the lower part filled with round cells to 15 μm diam. **Hypothallus** common to the group, thin, shining, reddish-brown with a silvery sheen. **Peridium** disappearing except for the cup, which is bright red and shiny. **Capillitium** firmly attached to the cup, an elastic network of pink to pale red threads, 3–5 μm diam, marked with prominent transverse ridges, often connected by oblique, thinner ridges giving the suggestion of a net, the oblique ridges not, however, forming spiral bands. **Spores** bright red in mass, almost colourless in transmitted light, minutely and evenly warted, 6–8 μm diam. **Plasmodium** white. [Fig. 90]

Illustrations: DM 1: 173,174; E: pl. 30; FMI 2: 172; L3: pl. 174; MA: fig. 82; NB: 115.
Habitat: on fallen trunks and stumps, especially of hardwoods.
Distribution: very common throughout the British Isles [112, H37, C]. Cosmopolitan.

Notes: the bright red, upright sporangia with a non-dehiscent capillitium make this common and beautiful species easy to recognise.

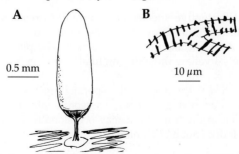

Fig. 90. *Arcyria denudata*: A: sporangium; B: capillitium.

Arcyria ferruginea Saut.
Flora **24**: 36. 1841. Austria.

Sporocarps stalked sporangia, gregarious, short-cylindric before expansion, 1–2 mm tall, expanding little, dull orange-brown, brick red or rust-coloured, exceptionally bright ochraceous yellow. **Hypothallus** membranous, continuous below groups of sporangia, yellow-brown. **Peridium** remaining as a large, wide cup, the inside nearly smooth or reticulate. **Capillitium** weakly attached to the cup, easily blown away, threads coarse, 5–8 μm diam, marked with transverse bars, ridges, warts often forming a distinct net. **Spores** rusty red in mass, pale ochraceous by transmitted light, minutely warted, 9–12 μm diam. **Plasmodium** rose-red or creamy white. [Fig. 91]

Illustrations: DM 1: 176,177; E: pl. 29; FMI 2: 174; L3: pl. 173; MA: fig. 83; NB: 101.
Habitat: rotten trunks and stumps, especially during the winter months.
Distribution: frequent in the south and east, thinning out to the north and west [72, H4]. Widespread in temperate regions but less common in the tropics.

Notes: the normal rusty-red colour, larger spores and reticulate pattern on the capillitium are good pointers. The yellow form is much less common and may be a response to cold conditions; the colour is brighter than in our other yellow species and the shape is intermediate between *A. obvelata* and *A. pomiformis*.

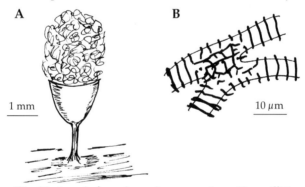

A

B

1 mm

10 μm

Fig. 91. *Arcyria ferruginea*: A: sporangium; B: capillitium.

Arcyria incarnata (Pers.) Pers.
Obs. Myc. **1**: 58. 1796. Germany.

Sporocarps short-stalked sporangia, 1–2 mm tall before expansion, to 5 mm afterwards, cylindric, pale pink to pale crimson, weathering to a dull reddish-brown. **Hypothallus** inconspicuous, dull red. **Stalk** short, to 0.6 mm high, pink or pale red, filled with round cells. **Peridium** leaving a shallow, saucer-like cup, with distinct radial pleats on the outside, roughened on the inside. **Capillitium** very elastic, barely attached, blowing away at the first puff, of pale pink threads, 3–5 μm diam, marked with transverse bars, cogs and half rings arranged in spiral patterns. **Spores** in mass rose, colourless in transmitted light, with a few scattered warts, 7–8 μm diam. **Plasmodium** white, becoming bluish-pink as it develops into sporangia. [Fig. 92]

Illustrations: DM 1: 181,182; E: pl. 35; FMI 2: 178; L3: pl. 177; MA: fig. 86; NB: 103.
Habitat: on fallen branches, especially of oak, on the rotting ends of small branches and in damp crevices along the length of larger branches.
Distribution: very common throughout the British Isles [112, H38, C]. Cosmopolitan.

Notes: the very pale pink sporangia with capillitium that blows away at the first puff make this common species easy to identify.

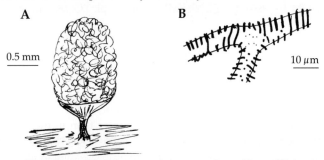

Fig. 92. *Arcyria incarnata*: A: sporangium; B: capillitium.

Arcyria insignis Kalchbr. & Cooke
Grevillea **10**: 143. 1882. South Africa.

Sporocarps scattered, short-stalked sporangia, shortly ovate with an acute apex, pale rose, often with an orange tint, 1–1.5 mm tall. **Hypothallus** common to a group of sporangia, generally inconspicuous. **Stalk** to 0.7 mm high, brownish-orange, the base filled with subglobose cells, 18–30 μm diam. **Peridium** remaining as a shallow, saucer-shaped cup, radially wrinkled, pale yellow, the inner surface warted, sometimes in a network. **Capillitium** of pale yellow to colourless threads, closely attached to the cup, marked with rings and half rings, 3–5 μm diam. **Spores** yellowish pink in mass, colourless in transmitted light, with scattered groups of warts, 8–10 μm diam. **Plasmodium** white. [Fig. 93]

Illustrations: DM 1: 183; E: pl. 31; FMI 2: 180; L3: pl. 181; MA: fig. 87.
Habitat: fallen branches.
Distribution: known from two collections from Norfolk, the last being in 1948 [1]. Recorded from Central Europe, the Mediterranean region, both Old and New World tropics, Australia and New Zealand.

Notes: the small size, fixed capillitium marked with rings, scattered sporangia and rose colour are the features of this species. The Norfolk records are supported by specimens and may represent casual occurrences of a species more familiar in warmer climates. It should be looked for in the light of present climatic change.

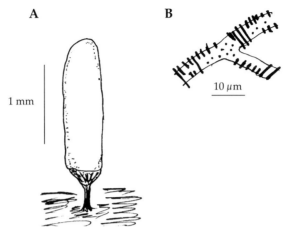

Fig. 93. *Arcyria insignis*: A: sporangium; B: capillitium.

Arcyria major (G. Lister) Ing
Trans. Br. mycol. Soc. **50**: 556. 1967. Luton, Bedfordshire.
Syn. *Arcyria insignis* var. *major* G. Lister

Sporocarps short-stalked sporangia, crowded into large developments, to 5 cm across, bright coral-pink, fading to a dull reddish-brown when old, 2.5–3 mm high. **Hypothallus** silvery, common to the whole group. **Stalk** red-brown, short, to 0.3 mm high, filled in the lower part with round cells 15–30 µm diam. **Peridium** persisting as a shallow, funnel-shaped cup with smooth edges, pleated, covered with large papillae. **Capillitium** very elastic, often forming a plume 5–6 mm long, which falls over, easily blown out of the cup, tubes 2.5–3 µm diam, decorated with half rings arranged spirally. **Spores** in mass rose, almost colourless in transmitted light, densely but very minutely warted with groups of larger warts, 7.5–9.5 µm diam. **Plasmodium** white. [Fig. 94]

Illustrations: DM 1: 185; FMI 2: 183; NB: 114.
Habitat: on fallen branches.
Distribution: rare, scattered from the south Midlands to Shropshire, in Wales only in Breconshire [6]. Scattered across Europe, North and South America and Africa but not common.

Notes: the tightly packed sporangia, bright colours, and the very expanded capillitium which breaks away leaving broken tubes attached to the cup, separate this species. The spore markings are only visible under oil immersion.

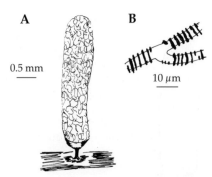

Fig. 94. *Arcyria major*: A: sporangium; B: capillitium.

Arcyria minuta Buchet
Mém. Acad. Malgache **6**: 42. 1927. Madagascar.
Syn. *Arcyria carnea* (G. List.) G. List.; *A. gulielmae* Nann. Bremek.

Sporocarps short-stalked sporangia, crowded, 1–3 mm tall, cylindrical but flat-topped, salmon-pink, fading to beige. **Hypothallus** inconspicuous, shared by the group. **Stalk** 0.2–0.4 mm tall, pink, the base filled with round cells 15–30 μm diam. **Peridium** leaving a shallow cup, almost flat, small, pleated, rose-coloured, the inside with a few irregular papillae. **Capillitium** with a dense net, not very elastic, firmly connected to the cup, tubes 3–5 μm diam, densely warted and with cogs, rarely with spines and half rings. **Spores** in mass pale salmon-pink, colourless in transmitted light, densely and very minutely warted (oil immersion) and with scattered larger warts, 8–10 μm diam. **Plasmodium** white. [Fig. 95]

Illustrations: DM 1: 187; E: pl. 125; FMI 2: 186; MA: fig. 79; NB: 111.
Habitat: on fallen branches, mainly of broad-leaved trees
Distribution: uncommon, scattered in England and Wales, in Scotland only in Mull and Orkney, not in Ireland [24]. Outside the British Isles the distribution is uncertain because of confusion with other pink species, but widespread in Europe, although never common; definite records from Australia and New Zealand.

Notes: the flat-topped, pink sporangia with fixed capillitium and the markings of the threads being more or less limited to cogs make this species easy to identify.

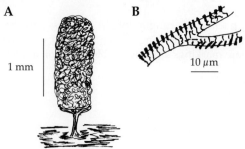

Fig. 95. *Arcyria minuta*: A: sporangium; B: capillitium.

Arcyria obvelata (Oeder) Onsberg
Mycologia **70**: 1286. 1978. France.
Syn. *Arcyria nutans* (Bull.) Grev.

Sporocarps short-stalked sporangia, tightly clustered in large developments, pale yellow, when young upright, short cylindrical, smooth, when mature drooping and loofah-like, to 15 mm tall when fully expanded. **Hypothallus** inconspicuous, common to the whole group. **Stalk** yellow, gradually widening to the cup, the base filled with round cells 25 μm diam. **Peridium** leaving a deep, funnel-shaped cup, covered on the inside with spines connected by a net. **Capillitium** very elastic, becoming procumbent on maturity, easily separated from the cup, tubes 3–5 μm diam, with many club-shaped free ends, striped longitudinally and covered with spines, cogs, half rings, or even with a network of fine ridges, the decoration often appearing to be spirally arranged. **Spores** in mass pale yellow, very pale in transmitted light, 7–8 μm diam, very minutely warted with pale warts, with some scattered, darker warts in small groups. **Plasmodium** white. [Fig. 96]

Illustrations: DM 1: 188; E: pl. 34; FMI 2: 188; L3: pl. 179; MA: fig. 90; NB: 109.
Habitat: on fallen trunks and branches, especially of beech, also on dead branches of oak still attached to the tree, occasionally on conifer logs; from mid-summer to late autumn.
Distribution: very common throughout the British Isles [109, H38, C]. Cosmopolitan.

Notes: when fresh this species is pale yellow and so could be misidentified, but when the capillitium expands there is nothing like it. A few colour variations have been mentioned in the literature but these do not appear to occur in the British Isles.

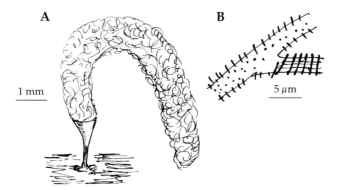

Fig. 96. *Arcyria obvelata*: A: sporangium; B: capillitium.

Arcyria oerstedtii Rostaf.
Mon.: 278. 1875. Denmark.

Sporocarps short-stalked sporangia, tightly packed in large developments, bright red, fading to brownish-red, when young upright, cylindrical to 2 mm tall, when expanded drooping and loofah-like, to 13 mm long. **Hypothallus** shared, inconspicuous. **Stalk** dark, the base filled with round cells 20 µm diam. **Peridium** leaving a few red flakes on the capillitium but otherwise remaining as a shallow, thin cup, pleated on the outside and with the inside covered with papillae joined by a network of fine ridges. **Capillitium** very elastic, becoming procumbent, not strongly attached to the cup and easily blown away, the tubes 3–5 µm diam, ornamented with spines up to 5 µm long. **Spores** in mass red, pale red to ochraceous in transmitted light, 7–9 µm diam, densely and minutely warted (oil) and with a few scattered larger warts. **Plasmodium** white. [Fig. 97]

Illustrations: DM 1: 189,190; E: pl. 32; FMI 2: 191; L3: pl. 180; MA: fig. 92; NB: 110.
Habitat: on stumps and rotten roots at the base of trunks of beech and conifers, less commonly on fallen trunks and branches.
Distribution: uncommon, scattered from Cornwall to Orkney, absent from Ireland [50]. Widespread in North America, Asia, Europe, South Africa, New Zealand and Australia but never common.

Notes: the red loofah-like sporangia with spiny capillitium, even when faded, are distinctive. The other drooping species have more compact, fatter sporangia and do not droop as much, the markings on the capillitium are also more varied.

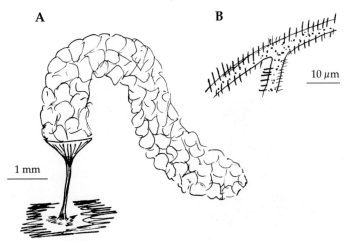

Fig. 97. *Arcyria oerstedtii*: A: sporangium; B: capillitium.

Arcyria pomiformis (Leers) Rostaf.
Mon.: 271. 1875. Germany.

Sporocarps stalked sporangia, scattered, ovate to globose, bright ochraceous, 1 mm tall, the sporangium 0.7 mm diam. **Hypothallus** inconspicuous. **Stalk** white, 0.4 mm long, the base with round cells 30 μm diam. **Peridium** leaving a small cup, smooth or faintly pleated on the outside, well endowed with warts and reticulations on the inside. **Capillitium** elastic, evenly expanded to form a more or less globose, upright mass, tubes 3–6 μm diam, with some free ends covered in spines, either smooth or variously ornamented with spines, cogs and warts. **Spores** in mass ochraceous, almost colourless by transmitted light, very minutely warted with some scattered, larger warts (oil) 7–8 μm diam. **Plasmodium** white, becoming shining pale ochraceous as it matures. [Fig. 98]

Illustrations: DM 1: 192; E: pl. 32; FMI 2: 194; L3: pl. 176; MA: fig. 93; NB: 116.
Habitat: on small fallen branches, especially of oak, hornbeam and pine, and on bark of living trees, especially oak; appears to tolerate some acid deposition.
Distribution: common throughout the British Isles [106, H37, C]. Probably cosmopolitan.

Notes: the scattered, rounded sporangia and the ochraceous colour are usually sufficient to distinguish this common species. However, in moist chamber culture of bark it may be short-cylindrical and resemble *A. cinerea*. The more prominent markings on the inside of the cup are helpful as is the colour of the developing sporangium which emerges as a white structure from the plasmodium and goes through an ochraceous or even honey-coloured phase. The apex of the sporangium is never acute as it is in *A. cinerea*.

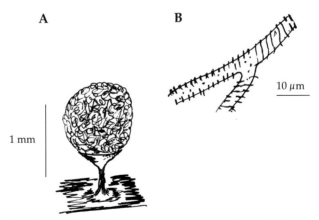

Fig. 98. *Arcyria pomiformis*: A: sporangium; B: capillitium.

Arcyria stipata (Schwein.)Lister
Mycet.: 189. 1894. Pennsylvania.

Sporocarps short-stalked sporangia, densely crowded and appressed in large developments, shining coppery-pink fading to reddish ochraceous, to 3 mm tall. **Hypothallus** shared, membranous, dark brown. **Stalk** very short, often appearing to be absent, red-brown, filled with round cells, *c.* 13 μm diam. **Peridium** persistent, shining, often iridescent, red with copper reflections, eventually breaking away except for the cup. **Capillitium** forming a rather lax net, loosely attached and easily blown away, tubes 2.5–5 μm diam, decorated with spines and ridges connected by a partial reticulation, the whole ornamentation appearing to be spirally arranged. **Spores** in mass coppery-red, pale red to almost colourless in transmitted light, 6–8 μm diam, very minutely warted (oil) with a few groups of larger warts. **Plasmodium** yellow, then white, becoming pink as the sporangia ripen. [Fig. 99]

Illustrations: DM 1: 194 (especially fine); E: pl. 33; L3: pl. 178; MA: fig. 94; NB: 108.
Habitat: on fallen trunks, especially of beech.
Distribution: rare, southern, scattered from Devon to Yorkshire and the Isle of Man [14]. Widespread in Europe, North America, Asia, New Zealand and Oceania, but never common.

Notes: the almost pseudoaethalial habit, the persistent peridium and the copper colour make this a distinctive species.

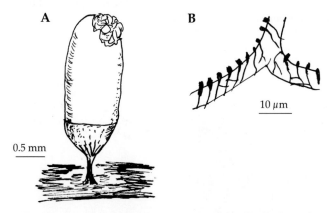

Fig. 99. *Arcyria stipata*: A: sporangium; B: capillitium.

CORNUVIA Rostaf.
Vers. Syst. Mycet.: 15. 1873.

Sporocarps sessile sporangia or short plasmodiocarps. **Capillitium** not elastic, a network of flexible threads marked with coarse rings, with free ends. **Spores** reticulate. A single species, *C. serpula* (Wigand) Rostaf.

Notes: in some works this is retained in the *Trichiaceae* and this may be justified by the nature of the spores, which are more like *Trichia* than *Arcyria*, but the capillitium threads do not have spiral bands. In this respect it is more like *Perichaena* but the capillitium is clearly distinctive.

Cornuvia serpula (Wigand) Rostaf.
in Fuckel, *Jahrb. nass. Ver. Nat.* **27–28**: 76. 1873. Germany.

Sporocarps sessile sporangia, clustered in small groups, occasionally short plasmodiocarps, shining golden-yellow, 0.3 mm diam. **Peridium** membranous. **Capillitium** a soft network of branched, yellow threads, 3–5 μm diam, marked with prominent rings at right angles to the axis, either clustered in small groups or evenly spaced along the thread, the surface otherwise smooth, with a few free ends. **Spores** yellow in mass, pale yellow by transmitted light, 10–12 μm diam, coarsely banded-reticulate, with 8–12 meshes to the hemisphere. **Plasmodium** creamy-white. [Fig. 100]

Illustrations: DM 1: 227; L3: pl. 170; MA: fig. 98.
Habitat: on heaps of spent tan (oak) bark.
Distribution: only known in the British Isles from a tannery at Grampound, Cornwall where it occurred in 1906 [1]. Elsewhere reported from Germany and Denmark, North America, India and Africa, but always rare.

Notes: the distinctive rings on the capillitium are unlike the markings on any other myxomycete. The demise of tan-yards makes it unlikely that we shall again find this species in the British Isles.

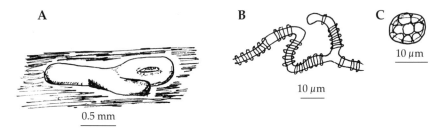

Fig. 100. *Cornuvia serpula*: A: plasmodiocarp; B: capillitium; C: spore.

PERICHAENA Fr.
Symb. Gast.: 11. 1817.

Sporocarps mostly sessile sporangia or plasmodiocarps, in a few cases stalked sporangia. **Peridium** double, the outer layer granular and brittle, often covered with a deposit of calcium oxalate crystals, the inner membranous. **Capillitium** of hollow tubes, branched, ornamented with spines or warts, the capillitium often sparse and, rarely, absent. **Spores** in mass yellow, in some non-British species reddish-brown. Eighteen species recognised of which seven occur in the British Isles; the type is *P. corticalis* (Batsch) Rostaf.

KEY TO SPECIES

1	Sporangia stalked	*pedata*
–	Sporocarps sessile	2
2 (1)	Dehiscence by a clearly preformed lid	3
–	Dehiscence irregular	4
3 (2)	Sporangia hemispherical, the line of dehiscence wavy, hypothallus conspicuous, spores 10–14 µm diam	*corticalis*
–	Sporangia flat, angular from contact with neighbours, line of dehiscence straight, hypothallus inconspicuous, spores 9–12 µm diam	*depressa*
4 (2)	Capillitium scanty, smooth	*liceoides*
–	Capillitium abundant, spiny or warty	5
5 (4)	Capillitium spiny, sporocarps plasmodiocarps or solitary ochraceous sporangia	6
–	Capillitium with warts and ridges, sporangia heaped, bright yellow	*luteola*
6 (5)	Spines on capillitium 2–4 µm long, primarily sporangiate, mostly on bark of living trees	*chrysoperma*
–	Spines on capillitium less than 1 µm long, primarily plasmodiocarpous, mostly in leaf litter	*vermicularis*

Perichaena chrysosperma (Currey) Lister
Mycet.: 196. 1894. Batheaston, Somerset.

Sporocarps sessile sporangia or short plasmodiocarps, which may be branched or ring-shaped but do not form a sinuous network, to 0.5 mm diam or to 3 mm in length, dull ochraceous to dark brown or even black, especially when prematurely dried. **Peridium** double, the outer layer membranous, shining, often, especially in bark, marked by a pattern of dark lines, giving a reticulate effect, usually without crystalline deposits. **Capillitium** of yellow threads 2–4 µm diam, usually very spiny, the spines to 4 µm in length; capillitium usually present but sometimes scanty. **Spores** in mass yellow, 8–10 µm diam, spinulose. **Plasmodium** white, becoming yellow then ochraceous as the sporangia mature. [Fig. 101]

Illustrations: DM 1: 206; E: pl. 27; FMI 2: 252; L3: pl. 184; MA: fig. 67; NB: 95.

Habitat: on fallen branches, occasionally on herbivore dung, but most commonly on the mossy bark of living trees, especially in western areas.
Distribution: common in upland Britain, much rarer in the lowlands [76, H17, C]. Cosmopolitan.

Notes: the short, occasionally branched plasmodiocarps which are relatively wide, the darker colour, spiny capillitium and smaller spores distinguish this from *P. vermicularis*, which occasionally occurs in bark cultures.

Fig. 101. *Perichaena chrysosperma*: A: plasmodiocarp; B: capillitium.

Perichaena corticalis (Batsch) Rostaf.
Mon.: 293. 1875. Germany.

Sporocarps sessile sporangia, sometimes short plasmodiocarps, gregarious, hemispherical or slightly flattened, 0.2–1 mm diam, bright reddish-brown or grey from a deposit of calcium oxalate crystals. **Hypothallus** conspicuous as a horny sheet. **Peridium** double, the outer layer granular, the inner membranous, marked by a distinct wavy, equatorial line of dehiscence, the upper part lifting off as a lid. **Capillitium** rather scanty, of slender yellow threads, occasionally branched, minutely warted or spiny, 1.5–4 µm diam. **Spores** in mass golden-yellow, bright yellow by transmitted light, 11–13 µm diam, minutely warted over most of the surface. **Plasmodium** grey or brown. [Fig. 102]

Illustrations: DM 1: 207; E: pl. 26; FMI 2: 253; L3: pl. 186; MA: fig. 68; NB: 93.
Habitat: regularly on the bark of fallen ash trunks, infrequently on bark of other trees in moist chamber culture.
Distribution: common in the south, thinning out northwards [102, H30, C]. Cosmopolitan.

Notes: the circumscissile dehiscence and the scanty and sparsely ornamented capillitium make this an easy species to identify. It is never angular as in *P. depressa*. The var. *liceoides* on leaf litter and dung is treated as a distinct species below.

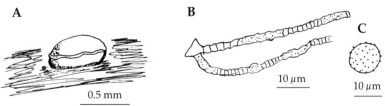

Fig. 102. *Perichaena corticalis*: A: sporangium; B: capillitium; C: spore.

Perichaena depressa Lib.
Pl. Crypt.: 378. 1837. Belgium.

Sporocarps sessile sporangia, flattened, so closely aggregated so that the individual sporangia become angular, 1–1.5 mm across, chestnut-brown to almost black, occasionally grey due to deposits of calcium oxalate. **Hypothallus** inconspicuous. **Peridium** of two layers, the outer slightly leathery, coloured as above, the inner membranous, dehiscing through a straight marginal fissure, forming a flat lid and a shallow cup. **Capillitium** abundant, of thin tubular threads, 1–2.5 μm diam, marked with regular constrictions, giving a beaded effect, smooth or with small spines. **Spores** in mass bright yellow, pale yellow in transmitted light, 9–12 μm diam, covered with small, pale warts. **Plasmodium** white, yellow or pale brown. [Fig. 103]

Illustrations: DM 1: 209; E: pl. 23,24; FMI 2: 258; L3: pl. 189; MA: fig. 69; NB: 94.
Habitat: on bark of fallen trees, especially ash, occasionally in cultures of bark from other trees, rarely on dung.
Distribution: southern, thinning out rapidly northwards, rare in Ireland and uncommon in Wales, rare and only at low altitude in Scotland but reaching Orkney [71, H3, C]. Cosmopolitan.

Notes: the flat, angular, crowded sporangia with chestnut lids opening to the bright yellow spore mass and the beaded appearance of the capillitium make this a very distinctive species.

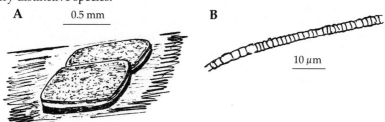

A   0.5 mm   B   10 μm

Fig. 103. *Perichaena depressa*:   A: sporangium;   B: capillitium.

Perichaena liceoides Rostaf.
Mon.: 295. 1875. Germany.
Syn. *Perichaena corticalis* var. *liceoides* (Rostaf.) Lister

Sporocarps minute sessile sporangia, 0.1–0.4 mm diam, dull yellow. **Hypothallus** inconspicuous. **Peridium** double, the outer layer granular, the inner membranous. **Capillitium** scanty, often absent, the threads smooth and little branched. **Spores** in mass yellow, paler by transmitted light, 13–16 μm diam, with prominent spines. **Plasmodium** pale reddish-brown. [Fig. 104]

Illustrations: FMI 2: 255.
Habitat: herbivore dung and leaf litter from shrubs such as privet.
Distribution: very rare, recorded from Somerset, Essex and Co. Wicklow [2, H1].

Known from Germany, Denmark, Austria, Spain, Sweden, France, Morocco, Mongolia, Sri Lanka, Tanzania, Madagascar and North America.

Notes: the minute size, lack of lid, scanty capillitium and larger, spinier spores separate this from *P. corticalis*, although most modern authors prefer to unite them. It shows similarities with *P. luteola* but differs in capillitial characters. When totally devoid of capillitium this species could also be mistaken for *Licea tenera*, which has been reported from dung. It is likely that those records of *L. tenera* on dung may refer to the present species, although the spores of *P. liceoides* are very spiny and there should be no difficulty.

10 μm

Fig. 104. *Perichaena liceoides*: spore.

Perichaena luteola (Kowalski) Gilert
Mycol. Res. **99**: 215. 1995. California.
Syn. *Calonema luteolum* Kowalski; *Arcyodes luteola* (Kowalski) Nann.-Bremek.

Sporocarps heaped, sessile bright yellow, sporangia, 0.1–0.5 mm diam. **Hypothallus** inconspicuous. **Peridium** single, thin, glistening. **Capillitium** of yellow tubular threads, branching and with swollen areas, free ends few, blunt, marked with warts and ridges/furrows, 2–3 μm diam. **Spores** in mass deep yellow, pale greenish-yellow in transmitted light, 12–15 μm diam, spinulose. **Plasmodium** not seen. [Fig. 105]

Illustrations: FMI 2: 262.
Habitat: cow and sheep dung.
Distribution: known only from the islands of Colonsay and Harris in the Hebrides [2]. Reported from North America, France, Croatia and Spain.

Notes: the synonymy shows how difficult it has been to classify this species. It is, however, clearly a *Perichaena* and seems distinct from *P. liceoides* which is, perhaps, its closest relative. The heaped sporangia suggest *Oligonema* but there are no traces of spirals on the capillitium.

A   0.25 mm   B

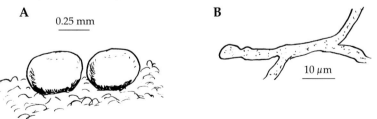

10 μm

Fig. 105. *Perichaena luteola*: A: sporangia; B: capillitium.

Perichaena pedata (Lister & G. Lister) G. Lister
J. Bot., Lond. **75**: 326. 1937. Uplyme, Devon.

Sporocarps stalked sporangia, 0.3–0.7 mm tall, the sporangium 0.3–0.4 mm diam, yellow or pale brown. **Hypothallus** inconspicuous. **Stalk** slender, black, longer than the sporangial diameter. **Peridium** single, membranous, dehiscing into lobes. **Capillitium** abundant, of branching threads 3–4 µm diam, with scattered small spines and (under SEM) small pits, often completely smooth, elastic. **Spores** in mass bright yellow, yellow in transmitted light, 9–10 µm diam, covered in small spines. **Plasmodium** pale reddish-brown. [Fig. 106]

Illustrations: NB: 97.
Habitat: on straw and garden litter.
Distribution: rare, in England from Devon to Stafford, absent from Wales and Ireland, in Scotland only at low altitude in Aberdeenshire [11]. Its distribution outside the British Isles is obscure because of confusion with other species but it has been reported from the Netherlands.

Notes: this is the only stalked Perichaena in our islands. Its relationship with *P. chrysosperma* is close but its major 'look-alike' is *Hemitrichia minor*, which has been classified in *Perichaena* by many authors. The two species are certainly similar but *P. pedata* never has spiral markings on the capillitium and has a more slender stalk, whereas *H. minor* has a shorter, fatter stalk and faint spiral bands on the capillitium. The pits in the capillitial threads are probably diagnostic but can only be seen under SEM.

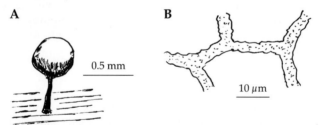

Fig. 106. *Perichaena pedata*: A: sporangium; B: capillitium.

Perichaena vermicularis (Schwein.) Rostaf.
Mon. App.: 34. 1876. North Carolina.

Sporocarps elongated plasmodiocarps, often forming a branching network up to 2 cm long, more often 0.5 x 3 mm, ochraceous or, usually, pale yellow. **Hypothallus** inconspicuous. **Peridium** of two closely appressed layers, often splitting along the line of the plasmodiocarp, releasing the elastic capillitium. **Capillitium** abundant, yellow, of branching tubes 3–4 µm diam, decorated with short spines, less than 1 µm long. **Spores** in mass yellow, paler in transmitted light, 10–14 µm diam, minutely and densely warted. **Plasmodium** usually pale pink but may be pale yellow or even pale blue. [Fig. 107]

Illustrations: DM 1: 211,212; E: pl. 26; FMI 2: 264; L3: pl. 187; MA: fig. 73; NB: 96.
Habitat: in leaf litter, especially of sycamore in winter, often deeply buried in the
leaf pile, occasionally on bark of living trees in moist chamber.
Distribution: scattered and generally uncommon [38, H4, C]. Cosmopolitan.

Notes: the long, sinuous plasmodiocarps often forming a net, the pale colours and
abundant capillitium with short spines make this a distinctive species.
P. chrysosperma does not form such long or convoluted plasmodiocarps, is more
ochraceous and has long spines on the capillitium. They may occur in the same
bark culture.

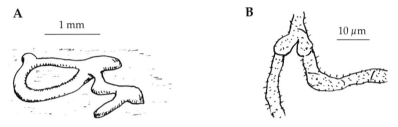

Fig. 107. *Perichaena vermicularis*: A: plasmodiocarp; B: capillitium.

TRICHIACEAE Cheval.
Fl. Gén. Env. Paris **1**: 322. 1826.

Sporocarps sporangia or plasmodiocarps. **Capillitium** of tubular threads, usually with several spiral bands along their length and always with the ornamentation arranged in spirals, the tubes may be short and unbranched (elaters) or branched and united into a network with few free ends. **Spore** mass usually yellow but may have orange to red or brown shades. Seven genera, those below plus *Calonema* Morgan and *Ditrichia* Li.

KEY TO GENERA

1   Capillitium of branched threads forming a network, with few free ends
                                                                    Hemitrichia
–   Capillitium of simple threads, rarely branched and never forming a
         network   2

2 (1)   Capillitium of short, free elaters with prominent spiral bands and sharp,
         pointed ends, spore mass yellow   *Trichia*
–   Capillitium of long elaters or spirals faint, spore mass yellow, orange red
         or brown   3

3 (2)   Capillitium of very long elaters, usually bent in half, with prominent
         spiral bands covered in long spines, spore mass orange or red   *Metatrichia*
–   Capillitium with poorly developed spiral markings   4

4 (3)   Sporangia usually stalked, scattered, iridescent, spore mass brown,
         capillitial threads attached to peridium by plaited junctions   *Prototrichia*
–   Sporangia sessile, tightly grouped, spore mass yellow, elaters with blunt
         ends and faint spirals   *Oligonema*

HEMITRICHIA Rostaf.
Vers. Syst. Mycet.: 14. 1873.

Sporocarps sessile or stalked sporangia or plasmodiocarps. **Capillitium** a network of branched and anastomosing threads with few free ends, marked with spiral bands which may be spiny or smooth. Eighteen species, the type is *H. clavata* (Pers.) Rostaf.

Notes: many species of *Trichia* have aberrant forms with branched capillitium and show a striking similarity to species in *Hemitrichia* – a series of species-pairs could be drawn up. Without cultural studies it is not possible to comment further on relationships; suffice it to say that the two genera are very close.

KEY TO SPECIES

1   Sporocarps sessile sporangia or plasmodiocarps   2
–   Sporocarps stalked sporangia (the stalk may be short)   4

2 (1)	Sporocarps reticulate plasmodiocarps	*serpula*
–	Sporocarps sessile sporangia	3

3 (2)	Spores 9–12 µm diam, not obviously reticulate without oil immersion; on bark of living trees or fallen branches	*abietina*
–	Spores 14–18 µm diam, seen to be clearly banded reticulate without oil; on larch litter, very rare	*chrysospora*

4 (1)	Sporangia grey, resembling *Arcyria cinerea*	*leiocarpa*
–	Sporangia yellow or brown	5

5 (4)	Capillitial spirals well marked	6
–	Capillitial spirals faint, only well seen under SEM	9

6 (5)	Stalks containing round cells, not dark refuse matter	7
–	Stalks without round cells but with dark refuse matter	8

7 (6)	Stalks gradually widening into the deep vase-like cup of the sporangium, capillitium rough, plasmodium white	*clavata*
–	Stalks slender, abruptly widening into shallow cup, capillitium smooth, plasmodium deep pink to claret	*calyculata*

8 (6)	Capillitium with spines and longitudinal stripes; on wood and bark	*intorta*
–	Capillitium smooth; on leaf litter and *Calluna* stems	*leiotricha*

9 (5)	Peridium smooth	*minor*
–	Peridium with large dark pustules	*pardina*

Hemitrichia abietina (Wigand) G. Lister
Mycet. edn 2: 227. 1911. Germany.
Syn. *Arcyria abietina* (Wigand) Nann.-Bremek.

Sporocarps scattered, sessile sporangia, subglobose, 0.3–0.7 mm in height, bright yellow, becoming dull with age. **Hypothallus** membranous, shared, iridescent. **Stalk** usually absent but rarely will be to 0.2 mm long, yellow-brown, filled with round cells, 10–16 µm diam. **Peridium** single, membranous, iridescent, remaining as a deep, basal cup. **Capillitium** elastic, a tangle of branching threads, 5–7 µm diam, not attached to the peridium, decorated with 2–4 warty, spiral bands, with a few blunt, free ends. **Spores** in mass bright yellow, almost colourless in transmitted light, 10–13 µm diam, warted, under oil immersion seen to form a delicate reticulum. **Plasmodium** rose. [Fig. 108]

Illustrations: FMI 2: 216; E: pl. 46; L3: pl. 168; MA: fig. 113.
Habitat: bark of living trees, especially sycamore, and on fallen branches.
Distribution: rare, scattered, north to Perthshire [10, H2]. Widespread but uncommon in Europe, North America, Japan and Samoa.

Notes: the small, sessile sporangia with thin peridium and spores whose faint reticulations can only be seen under oil distinguish this rare species. It is more likely to found in the field than in most chamber cultures.

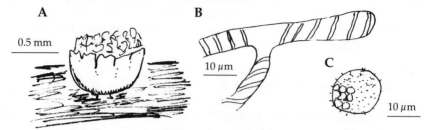

Fig. 108. *Hemitrichia abietina*: A: sporangium; B: capillitium; C: spore.

Hemitrichia chrysospora (Lister) Lister
Mycet.: 178. 1894. Lyme Regis.

Sporocarps sessile sporangia or short, curved plasmodiocarps, globose, 0.2–0.5 mm diam, bright yellow, fading to dull brown. **Hypothallus** inconspicuous. **Peridium** membranous, the outside sometimes with granular deposits. **Capillitium** of yellow branching threads, 3–5 µm diam, marked with 3–5 distinct, close-set, spiral bands, without spines, the spirals connected by short longitudinal striae, there are a few pointed free ends, and connections to the peridium. **Spores** in mass bright yellow, pale yellow in transmitted light, 14–18 µm diam, marked with well-defined bands forming a reticulum with 6–9 meshes to the hemisphere, the spore showing a border in optical section 1.5–2 µm high. **Plasmodium** not seen. [Fig. 109]

Illustrations: DM 1: 232; L3: pl. 169; MA: fig. 367
Habitat: on larch litter.
Distribution: only recorded from Devon and Dorset in the neighbourhood of Lyme Regis; not seen since 1898 [2]. Known elsewhere with certainty only from Germany.

Notes: the spores are remarkably like those of *Trichia verrucosa* and the present species has been likened to a sessile form of it. Many species of *Trichia* have aberrant developments with branching, anastomosing capillitium and, until cultural work is possible – very difficult in *Trichiaceae* – this species is maintained.

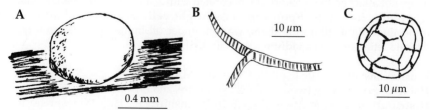

Fig. 109. *Hemitrichia chrysospora*: A: sporangium; B: capillitium; C: spore.

Hemitrichia clavata species group

Two species are included, which were not separated until the work of Martin and Alexopoulos (1969) so older British records cannot be assigned – the aggregate records are [83, H6].

Hemitrichia clavata (Pers.) Rostaf.
in Fuckel, Jahrb. nass. Ver. Nat. **27-28**: 75. 1873. Germany.

Sporocarps stalked sporangia, gregarious, 1–3 mm high, pear-shaped, bright yellow fading to olivaceous yellow. **Hypothallus** brown, inconspicuous. **Stalk** stout, up to 1 mm high, yellowish-brown, filled with round cells 10–15 μm diam, expanding in width from the base and gradually merging with the base of the sporangium. **Peridium** single, membranous, leaving a deep basal cup with an irregular, torn margin. **Capillitium** elastic of yellow tubes 5–7 μm diam, marked with 3–5 spiral bands which are covered in fine warts (oil immersion) with a few, blunt, free ends. **Spores** in mass deep yellow, pale yellow in transmitted light, 8–11 μm diam, very finely warted, the warts forming an incomplete reticulum, with a border to 1 μm high. **Plasmodium** white. [Fig. 110]

Illustrations: DM 1: 233,234; FMI 2: 220; L3: pl. 167a; MA: fig. 114; NB: 142.
Habitat: on fallen trunks and branches of broad-leaved trees,
Distribution: uncommon, scattered [39, H3]. Widespread in cool temperate Europe, Australia, New Zealand and North America, in the tropics and subtropics only on mountains.

Notes: the deep cup which gradually widens from the stout stalk, the rough capillitium, white plasmodium and warty, rather than spiny, reticulation of the spores separate this from *H. calyculata,* which is far more common.

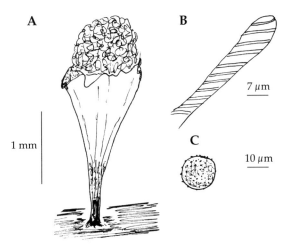

Fig. 110. *Hemitrichia clavata*: A: sporangium; B: capillitium; C: spore.

Hemitrichia calyculata (Speg.) M.L. Farr
Mycologia **66**: 887. 1974. Argentina.
Syn. *Hemitrichia stipitata* (Massee) T. Macbr.

Sporocarps stalked sporangia, in groups, 1–2.5 mm high, 0.5–1 mm diam, yellow
to ochraceous. **Hypothallus** conspicuous, red, often forming a coloured base to
the stalk. **Stalk** slender, dark, to 2 mm high, filled with round cells 7–10 µm diam,
suddenly widening just below the sporangium. **Peridium** thin, shining, leaving a
shallow cup, often with the torn margins folded back like a frill. **Capillitium** an
elastic network of yellow, branching and anastomosing threads, 5–7 µm diam,
decorated with 4–5 thin spirals which appear smooth under high power (but are
minutely spinulose under oil.) **Spores** in mass bright yellow or ochraceous, paler
in transmitted light, 6.5–7 µm diam, ornamented with a delicate reticulum of fine
spines. **Plasmodium** pink, deepening to claret or even deep red. [Fig. 111]

Illustrations: DM 1: 231; E: pl. 45 (as *clavata*); FMI 2: 218; L3: pl. 167f (as *clavata*);
MA: fig. 120; NB: 146.
Habitat: on fallen trunks and large branches, especially of beech.
Distribution: common in the south, thinning out northwards [80, H3].
Cosmopolitan, the only member of the aggregate in tropical lowlands.

Notes: the shallow cup which suddenly widens from the narrow stalk, the
smooth capillitium, red plasmodium and hypothallus and spiny, rather than
warty, reticulation on the spores separate this from the similar *H. clavata*.

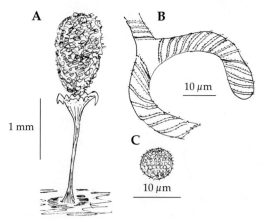

Fig. 111. *Hemitrichia calyculata*: A: sporangium; B: capillitium; C: spore.

Hemitrichia intorta (Lister) Lister
Mycet.: 176. 1894. Hitchin, Hertfordshire.

Sporocarps short-stalked sporangia, sometimes sessile on a constricted, stalk-like base, 0.3–0.7 mm high, yellow to cinnamon-brown. **Hypothallus** inconspicuous. **Stalk** stout, dark reddish-brown to black, to 0.5 mm tall. **Peridium** thin, shining, leaving a cup. **Capillitium** sparse, of long, orange-yellow, branched threads, 3–4 μm diam, twisted into a loose network, with 4–5 regular spiral bands covered with small spines connected by prominent longitudinal striae. **Spores** in mass golden-yellow, paler in transmitted light, 8–10 mm diam, finely warted. **Plasmodium** watery white. [Fig. 112]

Illustrations: DM 1: 237; L3: pl. 172; MA: fig. 115; NB: 143.
Habitat: on small fallen branches.
Distribution: rare, recorded from Kent, Hertfordshire, Warwickshire, Staffordshire and Yorkshire [5]. Scattered in Europe and North America and also found in Sri Lanka.

Notes: among the species with short stalks and prominent spirals on the capillitium this is distinguished by the spiny threads and woodier habitat.

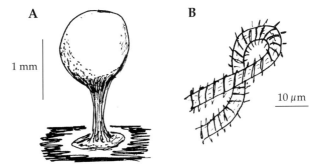

Fig. 112. *Hemitrichia intorta*: A: sporangium; B: capillitium.

Hemitrichia leiocarpa (Cooke) Lister
Mycet.: 177. 1894. Maine.
Syn. *Arcyria leiocarpa* (Cooke) Massee

Sporocarps long-stalked with subglobose to short cylindric sporangia, 0.4–0.7 mm diam and to 1.5 mm tall, grey to pale ochraceous. **Hypothallus** inconspicuous. **Peridium** disappearing above leaving a shallow, fluted cup. **Stalk** slender, filled with round cells, grey. **Capillitium** a loose net of grey branching and anastomosing threads, strongly attached to the cup, 3–5 μm diam, marked with 3–5 spirals, mostly smooth but where the spirals are faint, with a few small spines. **Spores** grey or pale ochraceous in mass, colourless in transmitted light, 7–9 mm diam, faintly warted. **Plasmodium** colourless, becoming white on fruiting. [Fig. 113]

Illustrations: E: pl. 9; FMI 2: L3: pl. 168; MA: fig. 88; NB: 118.
Habitat: on *Sphagnum* compost in a hothouse.
Distribution: known only from a collection from the Royal Botanic Garden, Edinburgh; not seen since 1925 [1]. Not uncommon in the warmer central and southern parts of Europe, common in the tropics of both hemispheres and in Japan and New Zealand.

Notes: this species has a superficial resemblance to *Arcyria cinerea*, especially in colour but is, in shape, more like a long-stalked *A. pomiformis*. However, the spirals on the capillitium should resolve this. Any *A. cinerea*-like sporangia found in hothouses should certainly be checked microscopically.

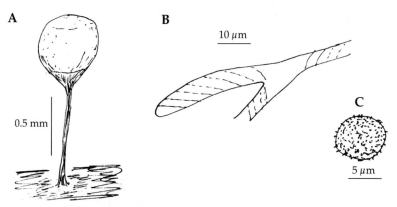

Fig. 113. *Hemitrichia leiocarpa*: A: sporangium; B: capillitium; C: spore.

Hemitrichia leiotricha (Lister) G. Lister
Mycet. edn 2: 224. 1911. Uplyme, Devon.

Sporocarps short-stalked sporangia, usually solitary but occasionally in small groups, to 1.5 mm high, globose, 0.5–0.9 mm diam, ochraceous, shiny. **Hypothallus** inconspicuous. **Stalk** dark brown to black, opaque, stout, usually less than half the sporangial diameter. **Peridium** of two layers, the inner membranous, the outer with inclusions of refuse particles, dehiscing at the apex. **Capillitium** of long, rarely branched tubes, coiled like ropes, 3–4 µm diam, marked with 3–6 delicate, smooth spirals. **Spores** in mass yellow, pale yellow in transmitted light, 9–13 µm diam, covered in fine spines. **Plasmodium** watery white. [Fig. 114]

Illustrations: DM 1: 238; E: pl. 44; FMI 2: 226; L3: pl. 172; NB: 144.
Habitat: in leaf litter, especially in heathy woods and on decaying *Calluna* stems.
Distribution: uncommon, scattered north to Inverness, no records from Ireland [26]. Uncommon in Europe, North America, Japan and Sri Lanka.

Notes: the small size, dark stalk and smooth capillitium, together with the apparent preference for heather stems, help to identify this uncommon species.

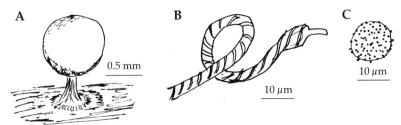

Fig. 114. *Hemitrichia leiotricha*: A: sporangium; B: capillitium; C: spore.

Hemitrichia minor G. Lister
J. Bot., Lond. **49**: 62. 1911. Japan.
Syn. *Perichaena minor* (G. Lister) Hagelst.

Sporocarps short-stalked sporangia, (sessile in Mediterranean forms on decaying cacti,) 0.2–0.4 mm high, usually solitary, 0.15–0.3 mm diam, pale ochraceous yellow. **Hypothallus** inconspicuous. **Stalk** usually short but may be as long as the sporangial diameter, black. **Peridium** smooth, dry. **Capillitium** of long, mostly unbranched yellow tubes, 3 μm diam, marked with 3–4 spirals which are faint (best seen under SEM) and covered with long spines to 4 μm in length. **Spores** in mass yellow, paler in transmitted light, 10–12 μm diam, densely warted. **Plasmodium** white. [Fig. 115]

Illustrations: E: pl. 45; FMI 2: 230; L3: pl. 187; MA: fig. 71.
Habitat: on liverwort-covered fallen branches, occasionally on the bark of living trees, always seemingly associated with liverworts.
Distribution: scattered, commoner in the west [49, H2, C]. Known from North America, Europe, Belize, Australia, New Zealand, Japan and the Philippines, but probably confused with other species.

Notes: the faint spirals and spore markings separate this from *H. leiotricha*, the lack of pustules and gelatinous peridium and long capillitial spines from *H. pardina* and the presence of spirals from *Perichaena pedata*. This last species has been much confused with *H. minor* and only the use of SEM has sorted out the morphological differences, although the spirals can be seen in a good light microscope if the lighting is properly adjusted. The sessile form on old *Opuntia* cladodes is common in the Mediterranean area and the Canary Islands, it may represent a separate species. This group of superficially similar species are of different sizes, have different morphology and occur in different microhabitats; as in other myxomycete groups ecological data *must* be taken into account when making taxonomic decisions.

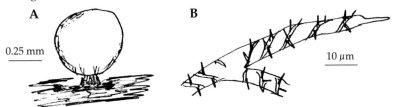

Fig. 115. *Hemitrichia minor*: A: sporangium; B: capillitium.

Hemitrichia pardina (Minakata) Ing **nov. comb.**
Basionym: *Hemitrichia minor* var. *pardina* Minakata, *in* Lister, *Trans. Br. mycol. Soc.*
5: 82. 1915. Japan.

Sporocarps short-stalked sporangia, scattered, to 0.8 mm high, dull olive-yellow
with prominent dark brown to black pustules. **Hypothallus** inconspicuous. **Stalk**
short, to 0.3 mm high, black. **Peridium** of two layers, the inner membranous, the
outer gelatinous, drying smooth with prominent pustules. **Capillitium** of long,
scarcely branched tubes, 2–4 μm diam, with a few faint spirals, covered in short
spines to 1 mm in length. **Spores** in mass olive-yellow, pale greenish-yellow in
transmitted light, 9–11 μm diam, faintly warted. **Plasmodium** white. [Fig. 116]

Illustrations: FMI 2: 230; NB: 141.
Habitat: on the bark of living trees, more rarely in leaf litter.
Distribution: known so far from Devon, Somerset, Dorset, Surrey, Warwickshire,
Staffordshire, Co. Durham and north Wales, but perhaps not separated from
H. minor in the past [8]. Overseas distribution not clear because of confusion with
other species but definitely known from the Netherlands, Spain and Japan.

Notes: the short spines on the capillitium, darker colours, spotted appearance,
slightly larger size and the lack of association with liverworts seem sufficient to
give this specific status distinct from *H. minor.*

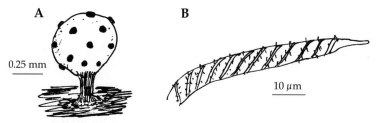

A

B

0.25 mm

10 μm

Fig. 116. *Hemitrichia pardina*: A: sporangium; B: capillitium.

Hemitrichia serpula (Scop.) Rostaf.
in Lister, *Mycet.*: 179. 1894. Austria.

Sporocarps long, intricately branched and netted plasmodiocarps, up to 0.6 mm
wide and to 15 mm long, yellow. **Hypothallus** reddish-brown, following the
pattern of the plasmodiocarp. **Peridium** thin, smooth, splitting lengthwise.
Capillitium elastic, of coiled yellow tubes, 4–8 μm diam, with 3–4 spirals and
long spines, occasionally also with faint longitudinal striae, any free ends pointed
and spiny. **Spores** in mass bright golden-yellow, pale yellow in transmitted light,
11–16 μm diam, clearly banded reticulate with a border 1 μm high. **Plasmodium**
white, then yellow. [Fig. 117]

Illustrations: DM 1: 242; E: pl. 47; FMI 2: 232; L3: pl. 170; MA: fig. 119; NB: 145.
Habitat: on woody litter in hothouses (outside the British Isles on fallen wood
and twiggy litter in forests).

Distribution: known only from hothouses in Carlisle, Edinburgh and Glasgow, last seen in 1881 [3]. Elsewhere widespread in Europe and abundant in the tropics, probably cosmopolitan.

Notes: a very conspicuous species, easy to identify, which makes its absence from British forests difficult to understand as it occurs as close as the Netherlands. Perhaps the current warming of the climate will enable it to establish itself with us.

A   B   C

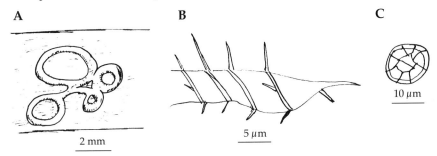

Fig. 117. *Hemitrichia serpula*: A: plasmodiocarp; B: capillitium; C: spore.

METATRICHIA Ing
Trans. Br. mycol. Soc. **47**: 51. 1964.

Sporocarps stalked or sessile sporangia, often tightly packed. **Peridium** thick, dehiscing by a lid or preformed lines. **Capillitium** very elastic, of long elaters folded back on themselves, usually red. **Spores** red. Seven species, the type is the African *M. horrida* Ing.

KEY TO SPECIES

1   Sporangia globose, black, long-stalked, dehiscing into petal-like lobes,
       spore mass orange   *floriformis*
–   Sporangia cylindrical or funnel-shaped, purple-red, short-stalked,
       dehiscing by a cap, spore mass red   *vesparium*

Metatrichia floriformis (Schwein.) Nann.-Bremek.
Proc. K. Ned. Akad. Wet. C **85**: 556. 1982. New York State.
Syn. *Trichia floriformis* (Schwein.) G. Lister

Sporocarps stalked sporangia, often with several stalks united, giving a cluster of sporangia at the top, usually gregarious in large developments, 3–4 mm high, sporangium obovate to globose, dark chestnut-brown, more commonly shining black, sometimes marked with yellow lines. **Hypothallus** shared by whole development, dark red. **Stalk** tubular, hollow, dark red to black, red in transmitted light. **Peridium** tough, the inner layer membranous, the outer cartilaginous, dehiscing into a small number of petaloid lobes, folding back to reveal the spore mass. **Capillitium** of long, orange-red unbranched tubes, coiled and folded back on themselves, 5–6 μm diam, with 4–6 smooth spirals, gradually tapering to long points. **Spores** in mass bright orange, red in transmitted light, 10–12 μm diam, densely and minutely spinulose. **Plasmodium** dark red to black. [Fig. 118]

Illustrations: DM 1: 200,210; E: pl. 43; FMI 2: 237; L3: pl. 163; MA: fig. 105; NB: 150.
Habitat: on fallen trunks and branches, usually when very rotten and damp, rarely on well-rotted horse dung.
Distribution: earlier in the century this was a rare species but it has become one of the commonest and is found in secondary woodland everywhere [111, H39, C]. Probably cosmopolitan, again following a rapid expansion.

Notes: the petaloid dehiscence, black sporangium and translucent red, hollow stalk separate this from *Trichia botrytis*, the shape and orange spore mass from *M. vesparium*.

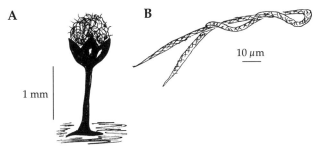

Fig. 118. *Metatrichia floriformis*: A: sporangium; B: capillitium.

Metatrichia vesparium (Batsch) Nann.-Bremek.
Proc. K. Ned. Akad. Wet. C **69**: 348. 1966. Germany
Syn. *Hemitrichia vesparium* (Batsch) T. Macbr.

Sporocarps sessile or stalked sporangia, densely crowded when sessile, in groups of up to 12 sharing united stalks when stipitate, to 2.5 mm high, sporangia subcylindrical, conical to subovate, 0.4–0.7 mm diam, dark red, reddish-purple to nearly black, shiny, iridescent. **Hypothallus** red, running into the stalk. **Peridium** of two (occasionally three) layers, the outer cartilaginous, the inner membranous, usually dehiscing by a preformed lid. **Capillitium** of a few very long coiled tubes, 5–6 µm diam, red, with 3–5 spirals and spines to 4 µm long. **Spores** in mass red, rusty-red or scarlet, pale orange-red in transmitted light, 9–10 µm diam, ornamented with warts which are wider at the top and produce the effect of a border on the spore in optical section. **Plasmodium** dark red or black. [Fig. 119]

Illustrations: DM 1: 203; E: pl. 44; FMI 2: 239; L3: pl. 166; MA: fig. 121; NB: 149.
Habitat: fallen trunks, especially of elm or beech.
Distribution: frequent in the south of England, thinning out northwards, rare in Wales and Ireland, very rare in Scotland, north to Aberdeenshire [63, H4]. Widespread in north temperate regions, less common in the tropics or the southern hemisphere, reported from Australia and New Zealand.

Notes: the distinctive shape, like a wasps' nest, the shining purple-red sporangia and the red spore mass make this an easy species to identify. When the stalks are joined this species can look a bit like *M. floriformis* but the colour of the spore mass is quite sufficient to separate them and if there is any doubt the spiny capillitium of *M. vesparium* is diagnostic.

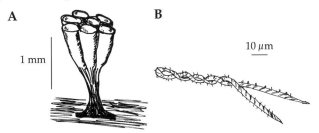

Fig. 119. *Metatrichia vesparium*: A: sporangia; B: capillitium.

OLIGONEMA Rostaf.
Pamietn. Towarz. Nank. Sin. Paryzo 6: 291. 1875.

Sporocarps sessile sporangia, usually tightly massed. Peridium thin, membranous, often shining. **Capillitium** of elaters, sparsely branched, with faint spirals and sometimes spines or warts. **Spores** in mass yellow or orange. Four species, the type is *O. schweinitzii* (Berk.) G.W. Martin.

KEY TO SPECIES

1	Sporangia heaped, globose, spores with incomplete net	*schweinitzii*
–	Sporangia clustered but not heaped, pear-shaped, spores with complete net	*flavidum*

Oligonema flavidum (Peck) Peck
Ann. Rep. N.Y. State Mus. **31**: 423. 1879. New York State.

Sporocarps sessile sporangia, densely clustered in a single layer, pear-shaped, taller than wide, to 0.8 mm high and 0.5 mm wide, bright yellow and shining. **Hypothallus** inconspicuous. **Peridium** thin, the inside marked with papillae forming a fan shape. **Capillitium** of elaters, 3–5 μm diam, sparsely branched, marked with incomplete spirals and covered with warts, some of which are arranged in spiral patterns. **Spores** yellow in mass and in transmitted light, 13–16 μm diam, with a complete reticulation of bands forming large meshes interspersed with a few rows of small meshes. **Plasmodium** yellow. [Fig. 120]

Illustrations: DM 1: 244; FMI 2: 242; L3: pl. 165; MA: fig. 74; NB: 123.
Habitat: on small sticks and branches in marshes and in dried up ponds.
Distribution: rare, known only from Dorset, Sussex, Warwickshire and Shropshire [5]. Scattered in Europe, North America and north Africa.

Notes: the clustered but not heaped, pear-shaped sporangia and completely reticulate spores separate this species from the commoner *O. schweinitzii*.

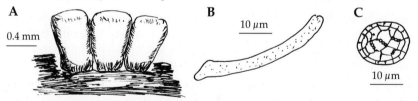

A   0.4 mm   B   10 μm   C   10 μm

Fig. 120. *Oligonema flavidum*: A: sporangia; B: elater.

Oligonema schweinitzii (Berk.) G.W. Martin
Mycologia **39**: 460. 1947. Belgium
Syn. *Oligonema nitens* (Lib.) Rostaf.

Sporocarps sessile sporangia, densely heaped in a pulvinate mass, sporangia globose, shining yellow, 0.1–0.5 mm diam. **Hypothallus** inconspicuous. **Peridium**

thin, the inner surface smooth. **Capillitium** of elaters, few, short, 3–5 μm diam, decorated with faint spirals, or occasional thin rings, otherwise smooth. **Spores** yellow in mass and in transmitted light, 12–16 μm diam, marked with an incomplete reticulation of large and small meshes, with a broad border in optical section. **Plasmodium** white or yellow. [Fig. 121]

Illustrations: DM 1: 246; E: pl. 13; FMI 2: 246; L3: pl. 164; MA: fig. 76; NB: 122.
Habitat: on small sticks and branches in marshes and in dried-up ponds; rarely in wet heaps of sawdust from broad-leaved trees.
Distribution: uncommon, mainly in the south, in Wales only in Flintshire, rare in Scotland but reaching Orkney, in Ireland only in Co. Down [31, H1]. Scattered in Europe, North America, Japan and north Africa.

Notes: the bright yellow heaps of minute sporangia on wet sticks are the hallmarks of this species.

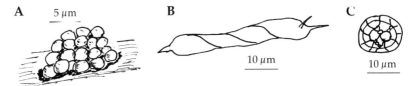

Fig. 121. *Oligonema schweinitzii*: A: sporangia; B: elater; C: spore.

PROTOTRICHIA Rostaf.
Pamietn. Towarz. Nank. Sin. Paryzo **8** (4): 38. 1876.

Sporocarps short-stalked or sessile sporangia, rarely plasmodiocarps. **Peridium** thin, transparent, iridescent. **Capillitium** of unbranched threads which are twisted about each other to form spirals, attached to the base of the sporangium, the ends separating and attached to the peridium. **Spores** in mass pinkish-brown then brown. A single species, *P. metallica* (Berk.) Massee.

Prototrichia metallica (Berk.)Massee
J. R. Microscop. Soc. 1889: 350. 1889. Tasmania.

Sporocarps stalked or sessile sporangia, globose, 0.5–2 mm diam, rarely forming short plasmodiocarps, reddish-brown with strong iridescent reflections of green or blue. **Stalk**, when present, dark, narrowing to the sporangium. **Peridium** thin, membranous, marked on the inside by the points of attachment of the capillitium. **Capillitium** abundant, of yellow-brown threads, spirally banded and twisted about each other, strongly attached at the base and the 'string' unravelling so that the individual tips can attach to the inside of the peridium. **Spores** in mass at first pinkish-brown rapidly fading to orange-brown or dull olive-brown, yellow in transmitted light, spiny, 10–13 diam. **Plasmodium** white. [Fig. 122]

Illustrations: DM 1: 214,215; FMI 2: 268; L3: pl. 195; MA: fig. 66.
Habitat: on woody litter in forests, especially coniferous.
Distribution: scattered, uncommon, rare in Scotland (in spite of the abundance of conifer woodlands) [46, H8]. Widespread in Europe, North America, New Zealand and Australia but never common.

Notes: the neat, stalked, iridescent sporangia and the very characteristic capillitium make this easy to identify. When the sporangia are sessile it can be mistaken for *Calomyxa metallica*, until the spirals on the capillitium are seen.

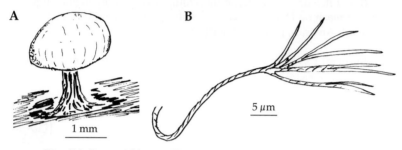

A

B

1 mm

5 µm

Fig. 122. *Prototrichia metallica*: A: sporangium; B: capillitium.

TRICHIA Haller
Hist. Stirp. Helv. **3**: 114. 1768.

Sporocarps sessile or stalked sporangia or short plasmodiocarps. **Capillitium** elastic, of free elaters, sparingly branched, pointed at the tips and marked with 2–5 spiral bands. **Spores** yellow, ochraceous or dull brown in mass, very pale in transmitted light. Thirty species; the type is *T. varia* (Pers.) Pers.

KEY TO SPECIES

1	Sporocarps stalked, sometimes with a few sessile sporangia in the development	2
–	Sporocarps sessile or shortly plasmodiocarpous, occasionally with short stalks	6
2 (1)	Spores prominently banded-reticulate, sporangia clustered on united stalks, elaters short	*verrucosa*
–	Spores with faint, spiny reticulation or warted, elaters tapering to fine points	3
3 (2)	Stalk translucent, filled with round cells, peridium ochraceous, unmarked, spores with faint reticulation (oil immersion)	*decipiens*
–	Stalk opaque, filled with granular matter, peridium dark, mottled with yellow lines, spores warted	4

4 (3)   Spore mass yellow, peridium dark brown to black, sporangium minute; on leaf litter   *flavicoma*

–   Spore mass ochraceous, peridium brown, larger; on wood and bark   5

5 (4)   Sporangia 1.5–2 mm high, elaters with long tapering tips; on wood   *botrytis*

–   Sporangia less than 1.5 mm high, elaters with short tips; on moss on bark   *munda*

6 (1)   Elaters with two spiral bands, often loose and more prominent on one side   7

–   Elaters with 3–4 spiral bands, tighter, more regular   8

7 (6)   Sporocarps sessile sporangia, short plasmodiocarps or short-stalked sporangia, elaters clearly lopsided spirals, spores 11–16 µm diam, on wood   *varia*

–   Sporocarps sessile sporangia, elaters, narrow, regular, spores 7–9.5 µm diam; on dung   *fimicola*

8 (6)   Spores reticulated   9

–   Spores spinulose or warted   12

9 (8)   Spores delicately reticulate, sporangia crowded, spore mass orange-yellow, elaters spiny   *scabra*

–   Spores coarsely reticulate, often incomplete or with varying mesh size   10

10 (9)   Sporangia taller than broad, elaters smooth, spores with an interrupted reticulum   *favoginea*

–   Sporangia globose or pulvinate   11

11 (10)   Spore mass bright lemon yellow, elaters smooth, spore reticulation of large meshes; on moss and very rotten wood   *affinis*

–   Spore mass ochraceous, elaters spiny, spore reticulation a mixture of large and small meshes; on wood which is still solid   *persimilis*

12 (8)   Spores 13–18 µm diam, sporangia black; alpine   *alpina*

–   Spores less than 13 µm diam, sporangia yellow or brown   13

13 (12)   Sporangia yellow brown to reddish-brown   *contorta*

–   Sporangia pale, shining yellow   *lutescens*

Trichia alpina (R.E. Fr.) Meyl.
Bull. Soc. Vaud. Sci. Nat. **53**: 460. 1921. Sweden.

Sporocarps sessile, pulvinate sporangia or short plasmodiocarps, 0.5–0.7 mm wide and to 10 mm long, dark purplish chestnut to black. **Hypothallus** thin, membranous, red. **Peridium** cartilaginous, tough, the outer layer granular, the inner yellow, thin and translucent. **Capillitium** of dull yellow elaters, 6–8 µm wide, marked with 3–6 spirals bands. **Spores** in mass bright yellow, tending to orange-yellow, bright yellow in transmitted light, 14–16 μm diam, minutely spinulose. **Plasmodium** orange-red. [Fig. 123]

Illustrations: DM 1: 251; E: pl. 40; FMI 2: 277; L3: pl. 162; MA: fig. 99.
Habitat: (in Europe) on sticks and dead herbaceous stems at the edge of melting snow, or inside hollow herbaceous stems of mountain plants weeks after the snow has melted) but in Britain known from a stick of *Prunus lusitanica* in a frozen ditch!
Distribution: only recorded from Weybridge, Surrey, in 1922 and not seen since [1]. Common and widespread in the mountains of Europe, America and Japan.

Notes: the traces of red plasmodium on the outside and inside of old, flattened stems of *Cirsium spinosissimum* in the Alps, the black peridium and bright yellow spore mass make this an easy species to identify. The characteristic red plasmodial traces have been seen on old thistle stems near snow in Perthshire but the sporangia were not found. It is likely to occur on those mountain ledges in Scotland with tall-herb vegetation that traps snow for at least three months.

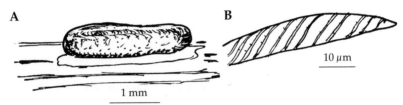

Fig. 123. *Trichia alpina:* A: plasmodiocarp; B: elater.

Trichia botrytis (J.F. Gmel.) Pers.
Neues Mag. Bot. **1**: 89. 1794. Germany.
var. **botrytis**

Sporocarps stalked sporangia, pear-shaped. 0.6–0.8 mm diam, 2–4 mm high, often clustered on united stalks, reddish or purplish-brown to almost black, marked with yellow lines of dehiscence giving a very characteristic, mottled effect. **Hypothallus** inconspicuous. **Stalk** dark yellow or shades of brown, filled with dark refuse material. **Peridium** dehiscing along the yellow lines but not in a petal-like pattern. **Capillitium** of simple elaters, 4–5 μm diam, marked with 3–5 smooth spirals and tapering to long fine points. **Spores** in mass dull ochraceous, pale by transmitted light, 9–11 μm diam, minutely warted. **Plasmodium** brown. [Fig. 124]

Illustrations: DM 1: 251,252; E: pl. 43; FMI 2: 280; L3: pl. 163; MA: fig. 100; NB: 137.
Habitat: on fallen branches and trunks, especially common on oak and conifers.
Distribution: very common throughout the British isles [112, H39, C]. Cosmopolitan within the temperate regions but, as with most members of the genus, only on mountains in the tropics.

var. **cerifera** G. Lister
J. Bot., Lond. **53**: 211. 1915. Lyme Regis, Dorset.

Differs from the type variety in having flakes of greenish-yellow wax on the peridium and stalk, giving the sporangium a distinctive green appearance.

Illustrations: NB: 137.
Habitat: on small sticks and branches, especially of conifers.
Distribution: rare, scattered across England, Wales and Scotland [8]. Recorded from several parts of Europe, and New Zealand but always uncommon.

Notes: the mottled peridium, opaque stalk, ochraceous spore mass and long tapering elaters characterise this common species. The only species with which it could be confused are *T. erecta* Rex which has much broader yellow bands on the peridium, short elaters and larger spores, and *T. subfusca* Rex, which is smaller and also lacks the tapering tips to the elaters; both are rare and neither has been found in the British Isles. Specimens of *Metatrichia floriformis* which are brown rather than black may also be mistaken but that species has an orange-red spore mass, very long elaters and a translucent red stalk. The var. *cerifera* may be a cold weather form but is very different in appearance so is retained here in the absence of any further evidence.

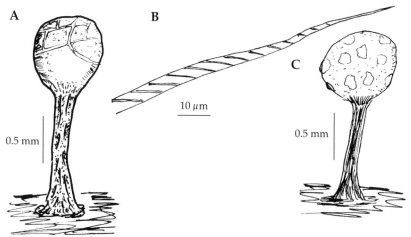

Fig. 124. *Trichia botrytis*: A: sporangium; B: elater; C: var. *cerifera*.

Trichia contorta (Ditmar) Rostaf.
Mon.: 259. 1875. Germany.
var. **contorta**

Sporocarps sessile sporangia or short plasmodiocarps, subglobose on a restricted base or pulvinate, 0.5–0.8 mm wide, or to 4 mm long if plasmodiocarpous, dull yellow-brown to dark reddish-brown. **Hypothallus** white, conspicuous.

Stalk normally absent but may, rarely, be represented by a very short black column. **Peridium** usually cartilaginous, thickened with granular material, occasionally covered in a thin deposit of calcium oxalate. **Capillitium** of simple or sparsely branched elaters, ochraceous in mass, 3–5 µm diam, with 4–5 spirals which may be regular or uneven, smooth or with spines of varying length, often with swollen ends and occasionally with swellings in the middle of the elater, the tips of the elaters usually bearing one or two curved spines. **Spores** in mass bright ochraceous, pale yellow in transmitted light, 10–13 µm diam, spinulose. **Plasmodium** white. [Fig. 125]

Illustrations: DM 1: 254; E: pl. 40; FMI 2: 282; L3: pl. 162; MA: fig. 101; NB: 127.
Habitat: fallen twigs and small branches, rarely on the bark of living trees.
Distribution: frequent and widespread in the British Isles [67, H8, C]. Widespread in temperate Europe, America, Australia and Japan.

Notes: the rather rough elaters, medium-sized, warted spores and dull colours separate this species from others in the genus. The varieties which follow are based on small differences, but they do appear to be fairly constant.

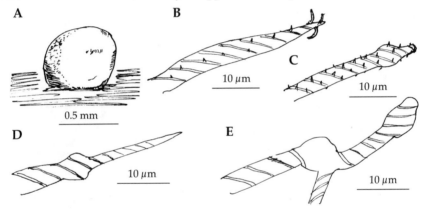

Fig. 125. *Trichia contorta*: A: sporangium; B: elater; C: var. *iowensis* elater;
D: var. *attenuata* elater; E: var. *karstenii* elater.

var. **attenuata** Meyl.
Ann. Cons. Jard. Genève **15–16**: 320. 1913. Switzerland.

Differs from the type variety in having long tapering tips to the elaters, no swellings and the spore mass when fresh is golden-yellow.

Illustrations: FMI 2: 282; NB: 128.
Habitat: on fallen bark and leaf litter.
Distribution: rare, recorded from Kent, Hertfordshire, Herefordshire, Perthshire and Shetland [5]. Scattered in Europe but never common.

var. **inconspicua** (Rostaf.) Lister
Mycet.: 169. 1894. Europe, probably Germany.

Differs from the type in having regular elaters without swellings and in its generally smaller size.

Illustrations: L3: pl. 162.
Habitat: small twigs and leaf litter.
Distribution: scattered but not uncommon [30, H1]. Widespread and not uncommon in Europe and North America.

var. **iowensis** (T. Macbr.) Torrend
Broteria **7**: 55. 1908. Iowa.

Differs from the type variety in the long spines on the elaters and the blunt or swollen tips.

Illustrations: DM 1: 255; FMI 2: 282; NB: 128.
Habitat: on small, fallen branches.
Distribution: rare, only recorded from Kent and Shropshire [2]. Known from various parts of Europe and North America but always seems to be rare.

var. **karstenii** (Rostaf.) Ing
Trans. Br. mycol. Soc. **48**: 647. 1965. Finland.
Syn. *Hemitrichia karstenii* (Rostaf.) Lister

Differs from the type variety in having flattened plasmodiocarps, very long elaters which are sparingly branched and a few free ends, some with rounded swellings.

Illustrations: DM 1: 257; E: pl. 47; FMI 2: 282; L3: pl. 171; MA: fig. 116; NB: 128.
Habitat: bark of living trees and of small, fallen branches.
Distribution: scattered, uncommon [24, H4]. Widespread but nowhere common in Europe, North America, Chile, Japan and Sri Lanka.

Trichia decipiens (Pers.) T. Macbr.
N. Am. Slime-moulds.: 218. 1899. Germany.
var. **decipiens**

Sporocarps stalked sporangia, top-shaped, to 3 mm high, 0.6–0.8 mm diam, shining olive or yellow-brown. **Hypothallus** inconspicuous. **Stalk** to 1 mm long, brown below, yellow above, filled with round cells, broadening imperceptibly into the sporangium. **Peridium** thin but firm, dehiscing at about mid-height, either by a preformed fissure, leaving a cup below and a lid above, or in a more irregular fashion. **Capillitium** olivaceous, of simple elaters, 5–6 μm diam, with 3–5 spirals, smooth, tapering to long, thin points. **Spores** in mass olivaceous yellow, pale yellow in transmitted light, 10–13 μm diam, marked with a delicate reticulation over much of the surface, only seen easily under oil immersion, the rest of the surface minutely warted. **Plasmodium** white, pink or orange. [Fig. 126]

Illustrations: DM 1: 258; E: pl. 42; FMI 2: 286; L3: pl. 158; MA: fig. 108; NB: 135,136.
Habitat: on fallen logs and branches.
Distribution: very common everywhere [111, H39, C]. Cosmopolitan but only at altitude in the tropics.

Notes: the translucent, cell-filled stalks and thin peridium are the obvious distinguishing features. The reticulation of the spores is difficult to see except under oil immersion. The colour of the plasmodium is usually white but the orange form, often very spectacular in large developments, is not associated with different morphology. The pink form is mostly found in var. *olivacea*.

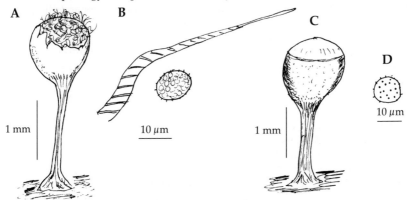

Fig. 126. *Trichia decipiens*:
A: sporangium; B: elater and spore; C: var. *olivacea*; D: spore.

var. **olivacea** Meyl.
Bull. Soc. Vaud. Sci. Nat. **44**: 500. 1908. Switzerland.

Differs from the type variety in having globose sporangia with a distinct circumscissile dehiscence, as if by a preformed lid. The colour is also more olive and less yellow. **Spores** are quite different, being warted, with no trace of reticulum. **Plasmodium** pink.

Illustrations: DM 1: 259; FMI 2: 286; NB: 136.
Distribution: information is unsatisfactory as few workers have separated this variety in their records. The only positive British identification is a recent collection from Herefordshire but it is certainly nearly as common as the type. Herbarium material, including the author's own, has not yet been studied to ascertain its occurrence. It is known to be widespread in Europe.

Notes: the difference in spore markings suggest that this should be treated as a distinct species but most modern authors maintain it as a variety, some reluctantly.

var. **hemitrichioides** Brandza
Ann. Sci. Univ. Jassy **8**: 272. 1914. Romania.

Differs from the type variety in its smaller size, less than 1.5 mm high, scattered developments and bright yellow, rather than ochraceous spore mass. It resembles a small *Hemitrichia calyculata* but does not have the elaters branching into a network. **Spores** as in var. *decipiens*. **Plasmodium** white.

Distribution: data scarce, the variety has only recently been added to the British list and is so far known from Herefordshire and the Isle of Arran [2]. It is not uncommon in Europe.

Trichia favoginea species group

The three species included in this group were recognised as distinct until the work of Farr (1958) who concluded that they constituted a single, variable species. However, most of her material was from North America. In Europe the three species separated here are readily distinguished morphologically and ecologically. Cultural studies would be helpful but the genus is notoriously difficult in this respect.

Trichia favoginea (Batsch) Pers.
Neues Mag. Bot. **1**: 90. 1794. Germany.

Sporocarps sessile sporangia, clustered, taller than wide, mid-yellow, to 2 mm high, 0.6–0.7 mm wide. **Hypothallus** membranous, colourless. **Peridium** membranous, with irregular stripes, under low power, which are thicker in section. **Capillitium** of long elaters, 6–8 μm diam, with 4–5 spiral bands separated by slender stripes parallel to the axis of the elater, normally smooth but sometimes with an odd spine, the tips conical, ending in a smooth point. **Spores** in mass yellow, paler in transmitted light, 13–15 μm diam, with a coarse reticulation of tall bands, 3–5 meshes to the hemisphere, in optical section showing a border to 2 μm tall. **Plasmodium** white. [Fig. 127]

Illustrations: DM 1: 263; E: pl. 37; FMI 2: 289; L3: pl. 159; MA: fig. 104; NB: 132,133.
Habitat: on rotten wood, mostly on large fallen branches.
Distribution: rare, scattered in England north to Leicester, not recorded from Wales, only in Angus in Scotland and Co. Down in Ireland [14, H1]. Widespread in Europe, North America, India, Japan, Australia, New Zealand and Chile; in tropical regions only at high altitude.

Notes: the shape of the sporangia, the wider elaters with longitudinal stripes and the coarsely reticulated spores separate this from the common species of the aggregate.

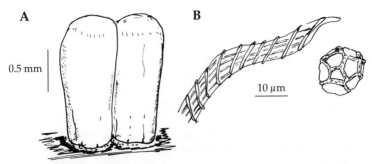

Fig. 127. *Trichia favoginea*: A: sporangia; B: elater and spore.

Trichia affinis de Bary
in Fuckel, *Jahrb. Nass. Ver. Nat.* **23–24**: 336. 1870. Germany.

Sporocarps sessile, subglobose sporangia, 0.8–1 mm diam, shining lemon-yellow to golden-yellow, in large developments on a common, membranous hypothallus. **Peridium** thin, membranous, shining, marked with irregular stripes. **Capillitium** of golden or lemon-yellow elaters, 4–6 μm diam, marked with 4–5 spiral bands, smooth, sometimes with longitudinal striae, with conical, pointed ends. **Spores** in mass lemon-yellow, almost colourless in transmitted light, 13–15 μm diam, marked with a coarse reticulation of bands, 3–5 meshes to the hemisphere, forming a border 1 μm high. **Plasmodium** white. [Fig. 128]

Illustrations: DM 1: 250; E: pl. 38; FMI 2: 274; L3: pl. 160; NB: 133.
Habitat: on moss and wood on very rotten logs and stumps.
Distribution: very common throughout the British Isles [111, H39, C]. Cosmopolitan in temperate regions, only at altitude in the tropics.

Notes: the pale yellow colour, subglobose sporangia, coarsely reticulate spores and the occurrence on very rotten, mossy wood enable this species to be distinguished, even in the field. Under the microscope the narrower elaters and spore border separate it from *T. favoginea* and the smooth capillitium and coarser spores from *T. persimilis*. Like the next species this myxomycete is frequently attacked by the hyphomycete *Polycephalomyces tomentosus*.

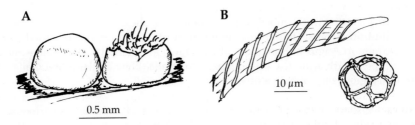

Fig. 128. *Trichia affinis*: A: sporangia; B: elater and spore.

Trichia persimilis P. Karsten
Fauna. Fl. Fennica **9**: 353. 1868. Finland.

Sporocarps sessile, clustered, subglobose sporangia, 0.5–0.8 mm diam, shining ochraceous to yellow-brown, on a common, horny, yellow-brown hypothallus. **Peridium** membranous, opalescent, marked with rows of warts, often as fine lines. **Capillitium** of ochraceous-yellow elaters, 4–6 μm diam, marked with 4–5 closely set spiral bands and studded with short spines, longitudinal striae inconspicuous. **Spores** in mass ochraceous yellow, paler in transmitted light, 11–14 μm diam, marked with a broken reticulation of small meshes, the non-reticulated areas covered with large warts, border of the spore incomplete. **Plasmodium** white. [Fig. 129]

Illustrations: DM 1: 269; E: pl. 38; FMI 2: 299; L3: pl. 160; NB: 133.
Habitat: on fairly new, not very soft, rotten logs, usually without mosses.
Distribution: very common throughout the British Isles [111, H39, C]. Cosmopolitan but only at altitude in the tropics.

Notes: the yellow-brown sporangia, small reticulations on the spores and the habitat on wood which is not very rotten, separate this species from *T. affinis*. The large sheets of sporangia resemble the situation in *T. scabra* but the spore colour of that species is more orange, the hypothallus, looking like honeycomb, is darker brown, and the spore reticulations are very delicate.

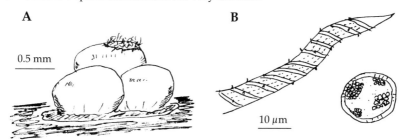

A

0.5 mm

B

10 μm

Fig. 129. *Trichia persimilis*: A: sporangia; B: elater and spore.

Trichia fimicola (Marchal) Ing
Trans. Br. mycol. Soc. **50**: 557. 1967. Belgium.
Syn. *Trichia varia* var. *fimicola* Marchal

Sporocarps scattered, sessile sporangia, subglobose on a constricted base, 0.3–0.5 mm diam. **Hypothallus** inconspicuous. **Peridium** thin, membranous, with granular surface. **Capillitium** of short elaters, 3 μm diam, with two spiral bands, not obviously lopsided, smooth, with blunt endings. **Spores** in mass pale ochraceous, pale yellow in transmitted light, 7–9.5 μm diam, faintly warted. **Plasmodium** pink. [Fig. 130]

Illustrations: none.

Habitat: on hare and rabbit dung in coastal dunes and shingle beaches.
Distribution: Dungeness (Kent), Tentsmuir (Fife) and Bull Island (Co. Dublin) are the only known sites in the British Isles [2, H1]. Otherwise only known from Belgium.

Notes: the small size, habitat and elaters with only two spirals, and above all the small spores (for a *Trichia*) separate this rare species. It does not look much like *T. varia*. It is clearly under-recorded as the habitat is common and more work is needed in culturing dung from coastal ecosystems.

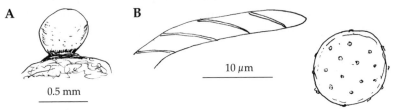

Fig. 130. *Trichia fimicola*: A: sporangium; B elater and spore.

Trichia flavicoma (Lister) Ing
Trans. Br. mycol. Soc. **50**: 558. 1967. Lyme Regis, Dorset.
Syn. *Trichia botrytis* var. *flavicoma* Lister

Sporocarps stalked sporangia, usually scattered, black, with yellow lines of dehiscence, up to a total of 1 mm high, subglobose sporangia up to 0.5 mm diam. **Hypothallus** not continuous between sporocarps, brown. **Stalk** usually black, grooved. **Peridium** membranous, the outer layer with granular matter except in the translucent lines of dehiscence, through which the spore mass shows. **Capillitium** of yellow elaters, 4 µm diam, with 3–4 regular, smooth spirals, tapering to long points. **Spores** in mass bright golden-yellow, pale yellow in transmitted light, 13–14 µm diam, minutely, palely warted, the warts dense. **Plasmodium** white. [Fig. 131]

Illustrations: DM 1: 264,265; FMI 2: 292; L3: pl. 163; NB: 139.
Habitat: in leaf litter and other vegetable compost.
Distribution: rare, scattered north to Orkney [33]. Distribution in Europe or elsewhere not well known as older authors did not separate this in their records, but known from the Netherlands, Germany, Spain, Portugal and Switzerland.

Notes: the small, black sporangia with bright lemon-yellow spore mass and the habitat on leaves easily separate this from *T. botrytis*; the unbranched elaters from the smaller species of *Hemitrichia*.

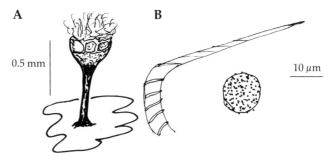

Fig. 131. *Trichia flavicoma*: A: sporangium; B: elater and spore.

Trichia lutescens (Lister) Lister
J. Bot., Lond. **35**: 216. 1897. Norway.

Sporocarps sessile, globose or pulvinate, usually in small groups but sometimes solitary, 0.15–0.7 mm diam, shining bright yellow. **Hypothallus** inconspicuous. **Peridium** thin, pale yellow to almost colourless in transmitted light, clear of granular deposits and bearing the impressions of the spores. **Capillitium** of simple, pale yellow elaters, 3.4–5 μm diam, marked with 5–6 closely set spirals, sometimes not prominent, smooth, usually blunt-ended or with swollen ends. **Spores** in mass bright yellow, pale yellow in transmitted light, 10–14 μm diam, densely warted. **Plasmodium** pale pink. [Fig. 132]

Illustrations: DM 1: 266; E: pl. 41; FMI 2: 294; L3: pl. 161; MA: fig. 106.
Habitat: on the bark of living trees and on recently fallen branches.
Distribution: rare, scattered, north to Aberdeenshire [21, H6]. Rare in North America, New Zealand and Japan and uncommon in Europe.

Notes: the pale thin peridium and the pale, smooth elaters without spiny ends separate this from *T. contorta*, of which it was once regarded as a variety. The pale pink colour of the plasmodium appears to be constant in bark cultures.

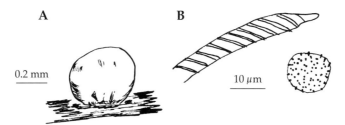

Fig. 132. *Trichia lutescens*: A: sporangium; B: elater and spore.

Trichia munda (Lister) Meyl.
Bull. Soc. Vaud. Sci. Nat. **56**: 327. 1925. Moffat, Dumfries-shire.
Syn. *Trichia botrytis* var. *munda* Lister

Sporocarps stalked sporangia, scattered, pale brown, shining, with paler lines of dehiscence, to 1.5 μm in height. **Hypothallus** discoid, confined to a single sporangium, brown. **Stalk** much longer than the sporangial diameter, black, grooved, in transmitted light, completely opaque. **Peridium** membranous, the outer layer granular except for the lines of dehiscence which are nearly colourless and allow the colour of the spores to show through. **Capillitium** of simple elaters, pale brown, 4 μm diam, marked with very regular spirals, smooth, tapering to long points. **Spores** ochraceous in mass, pale ochraceous in transmitted light, 10–13 μm diam, covered in flat warts, 0.5 μm high, the tops of which are wider than the base, as seen in optical section. **Plasmodium** white. [Fig. 133]

Illustrations: DM 1: 268, 269; FMI 2: 296; L3: pl. 163; NB: 138.
Habitat: on mosses on the bark of living trees, more rarely on mossy, fallen branches.
Distribution: scattered, frequent, especially in the north and west [46, H18]. Not uncommon in Europe and also recorded from Chile and North America.

Notes: the small, neat, pale sporangia whose lines of dehiscence are less of a contrast than in *T. botrytis*, from which the neat elaters and the habitat also distinguish it. The only species likely to be confused are the non-British *T. erecta* Rex and *T. subfusca* Rex, both with short elaters and different habitat.

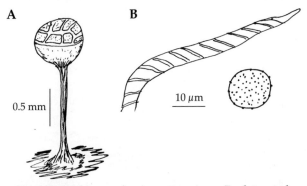

Fig. 133. *Trichia munda*: A: sporangium; B: elater and spore.

Trichia scabra Rostaf.
Mon.: 258. 1875. Germany.

Sporocarps sessile sporangia, globose, 0.5–0.7 mm diam, tightly clustered in large developments several centimetres in extent, bright orange-yellow. **Hypothallus** dark brown, continuous below the whole development and surrounding the bases of the sporangia so that when they have disintegrated it is left like a honeycomb of cups. **Peridium** smooth, shining. **Capillitium** deep orange-yellow, of simple elaters, 5–6 µm diam, marked with 3–4 tight, regular, spiral bands which are densely spinulose, the ends short and pointed. **Spores** in mass deep orange-yellow, yellow in transmitted light, 10–12 µm diam, delicately and completely reticulate. **Plasmodium** white, or occasionally pale yellow. [Fig. 134]

Illustrations: DM 1: 273; E: pl. 39; FMI 2: 301; L3: pl. 159; MA: fig. 109; NB: 131.
Habitat: on rotten logs, especially of elm and beech, characteristic of ancient woodland.
Distribution: common in the south, rare in Scotland but reaches Orkney [85, H9]. Cosmopolitan, occurs at lower altitudes in the tropics than most species of the genus.

Notes: the bright orange-yellow, densely packed sporangia on a brown honeycomb hypothallus, the rough elaters and the delicately reticulate spores all help to identify this species.

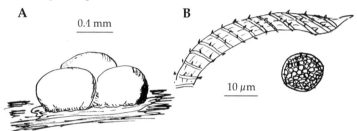

Fig. 134. *Trichia scabra*: A: sporangia; B: elater and spore.

Trichia varia (Pers.) Pers.
Neues Mag. Bot. **1**: 90. 1794. Germany.

Sporocarps mostly clustered, sessile sporangia, short plasmodiocarps or short-stalked sporangia. The stalked **sporangia** are slightly top-shaped, the sessile sporangia are usually pulvinate, 0.5–0.9 mm diam, dull yellow to ochraceous, olivaceous and sometimes shining. **Hypothallus** continuous under the whole development, horny but nearly colourless. **Stalk** when present, stout, black. **Peridium** occasionally encrusted with refuse material but usually smooth. **Capillitium** of long, unbranched elaters, 3–5 µm diam, bearing two narrow, well separated, spiral bands, one side of the elater showing a more prominently angled band than the other, thus giving a somewhat serrated appearance under high power. The tips of the elaters are curved and pointed, about 10 µm long. **Spores** in mass yellow, usually dull, pale yellow in transmitted light, 12–14 µm diam, delicately warted, with the appearance of spots. **Plasmodium** densely milky white, becoming yellow as the sporangia form. [Fig. 135]

Illustrations: DM 1: 273, 274; E: pl. 39; FMI 2: 308; L3: pl. 164; MA: fig. 111; NB: 126.
Habitat: on very rotten, usually soggy, wood, especially of hardwoods, occasionally on herbivore dung.

Distribution: very common throughout the British Isles [111, H39, C]. Cosmopolitan, but only at high altitude in the tropics.

Notes: the prominently lopsided elaters and the characteristic milky white plasmodium changing through very pale yellow to ochraceous on maturity are the features which enable this most common species to be identified.

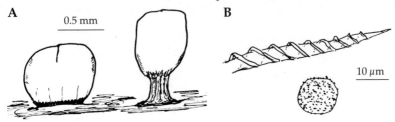

Fig. 135. *Trichia varia*: A: sporangia; B: elater and spore.

Trichia verrucosa Berk.
in Hooker, *Fl. Tasm.* **8**: 269. 1895. Tasmania.

Sporocarps stalked sporangia, with several pear-shaped, bright ochraceous, sporangia in a cluster at the top of united stalks, to 4 mm high. **Hypothallus** membranous, very pale brown. **Stalk** reddish-brown, weak when single and sometimes recumbent, in a group stout and upright. **Peridium** membranous, translucent, papillose. **Capillitium** of long yellow elaters, with 3–5 spirals, smooth, with short, tapering tips. **Spores** in mass bright yellow, yellow in transmitted light, 10–14 μm diam, coarsely reticulate with narrow bands to 1 μm high, the total diameter of the spore reaching 16 μm. **Plasmodium** white. [Fig. 136]

Illustrations: DM 1: 276; E: pl. 37; FMI 2: 311; L3: pl. 161; MA: fig. 112; NB: 134.
Habitat: on small fallen conifer twigs and branches.
Distribution: scattered, especially in the north and west, not common [44, H2]. Widespread in Europe, the Americas, Australasia, Japan and the East Indies, found at lower altitude in the tropics than most species of the genus.

Notes: the clustered habit on shared stalks, the large, narrowly banded-reticulate spores and the papillose peridium are good characters.

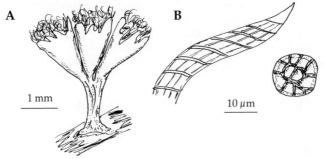

Fig. 136. *Trichia verrucosa*: A: sporangia; B: elater and spore.

STEMONITALES T. Macbr.

Sporocarps sporangia, short plasmodiocarps, aethalia or pseudoaethalia. Peridium persistent or disappearing quickly. **Columella** usually present. **Calcium** salts absent. **Capillitium** of threads, usually branching and forming a network. **Spores** black or purple brown in mass, occasionally with reddish shades, always with lilac or purple shades in transmitted light. **Plasmodium** an aphanoplasmodium, development epihypothallic. Two families: *Schenellacaeae*, with one genus and two species in America, and *Stemonitidaceae*.

Notes: this order is often placed in the sub-class *Stemonitomycetidae* on the basis of the epihypothallic development. However, with so few orders in the class the use of sub-classes is of doubtful value. Several genera have been transferred to *Physarales* because of their subhypothallic development and presence of calcium salts.

STEMONITIDACEAE Fr.
Syst. Mycol. **3**: 75. 1829.

With the characters of the order. Fifteen genera, all represented in the British Isles.

Notes: the division of *Comatricha* and *Stemonitis* into smaller, more narrowly defined, genera has made them more homogeneous (see Nannenga-Bremekamp, 1967.)

KEY TO GENERA

1	Sporocarps aethalia or pseudoaethalia	2
–	Sporocarps sporangiate	4
2 (1)	Capillitium with septate vesicles	*Brefeldia*
–	Capillitium without vesicles	3
3 (2)	Sporocarps with a cortex, capillitium of frayed sheets or a shared network of anastomosing threads, spores more than 12 μm diam	*Amaurochaete*
–	Sporocarps without cortex, capillitium forming a network attached to individual columellae, spores less than 12 μm diam	*Symphytocarpus*
4 (1)	Sporocarps sessile sporangia or short plasmodiocarps	5
–	Sporocarps stalked sporangia	7
5 (4)	Sporangia short cylindrical, peridium persistent, columella present or absent	*Paradiachea*
–	Sporangia globose, pulvinate or shortly plasmodiocarpous, columella absent	6

6 (5)   Peridium iridescent, dry, associated with lichens   *Diacheopsis*
–   Peridium gelatinous when wet, associated with mosses or algae
                                                                       Colloderma

7 (4)   Stalk horny, tubular, translucent   8
–   Stalk fibrous, usually solid but if appearing hollow then obviously fibrous
         and opaque   10

8 (7)   Sporangia globose or ovate, minute; on bark of living trees   *Macbrideola*
–   Sporangia cylindrical, larger; on wood and leaves   9

9 (8)   Outermost branches of capillitium united to form a delicate, complete
         surface net   *Stemonitis*
–   No surface net   *Stemonaria*

10 (7)   Peridium persistent, iridescent   *Lamproderma*
–   Peridium disappearing, at most leaving a collar or a few flakes   11

11 (10) Capillitium not anastomosing, with few branches, sporangia minute; on
         bark of living trees   *Paradiacheopsis*
–   Capillitium anastomosing; sporangia larger; on various substrates   12

12 (11) Tip of columella expanded into a conspicuous black disc from which the
         capillitium descends   *Enerthenema*
–   Tip of columella not expanded   13

13 (12) Surface net present, at least in lower half of cylindrical sporangium
                                                                   Stemonitopsis
–   Surface net usually lacking, sporangia globose, ovate or
         short-cylindrical   14

14 (13) Sporangia globose, peridium leaving a collar at base   *Collaria*
–   Sporangia globose, ovate to short-cylindrical, without a collar *Comatricha*

AMAUROCHAETE Rostaf.
Vers. Syst. Mycet.: 8. 1873.

Sporocarps aethalia or pseudoaethalia, with a common cortex which soon fragments. **Capillitium** of frayed sheets or a network of anastomosing threads attached to the base or to columellae. **Spores** black. Four species; the type is *A. atra* (Alb. & Schwein.) Rostaf.

KEY TO SPECIES

1	Pseudocapillitium of stiff, frayed sheets	*atra*
–	Pseudocapillitium a network of soft, branching threads	*tubulina*

Amaurochaete atra (Alb. & Schwein.) Rostaf.
Mon.: 211. 1874. England.
Syn. *Amaurochaete fuliginosa* (Sow.) T. Macbr.

Sporocarps pulvinate aethalia, to 2 cm high and 8 cm long, black. **Hypothallus** thin, white, becoming brown at maturity. **Cortex** thin and brittle, shining black with a delicate pattern of thin white lines, breaking up into large fragments and falling off. **Pseudocapillitium** arising from the base of the aethalium as a series of black, stiff, frayed fan-like plates, dividing into finer threads. **Spores** in mass black, dark purple-brown in transmitted light, paler on one side, often slightly ovoid, 12–13 µm diam, minutely warted. **Plasmodium** cream then pink, becoming black as the spores develop. [Fig. 137]

Illustrations: E: pl. 125; L3: pl. 136; MA: fig. 127; NB: 312.
Habitat: on newly felled trunks of conifers.
Distribution: scattered across the British Isles, understandably commoner in areas with large conifer plantations [62, H3]. Widespread in Europe, North America, Australia and Japan.

Notes: the black shining aethalia on unrotted conifer trunks and the pseudocapillitium, which is reminiscent of *Enteridium lycoperdon*, make this an easy species to identify.

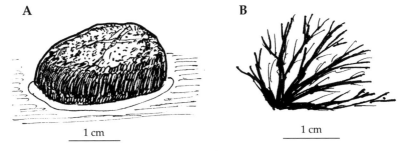

A

B

1 cm

1 cm

Fig. 137. *Amaurochaete atra*: A: aethalium; B: pseudocapillitium.

Amaurochaete tubulina (Alb. & Schwein.) T. Macbr.
N. Am. Slime-Moulds, edn 2: 150. 1922. Germany.
Syn. *Amaurochaete cribrosa* (Fr.) T. Macbr.

Sporocarps pseudoaethalia, to 5 mm high and 10 cm in length, black. **Hypothallus** forming a thin brown margin around the base of the sporocarp. **Cortex** black, fragile, when fresh showing a pimply appearance, from the pressure of the tips of the component sporangia. **Columella** straight, thick, black. **Capillitium** a woolly network of branching threads attached to the columellae but not to any peridial fragments or the cortex. **Spores** black in mass, purple-brown in transmitted light, globose, 15–18 μm diam, finely warted. **Plasmodium** cream, then deep pink, becoming black as the spores develop. [Fig. 138]

Illustrations: E: pl. 48; L3: pl. 217; MA: fig. 129; NB: 313.
Habitat: on newly felled conifer trunks.
Distribution: scattered from Surrey to Inverness, rare [10]. Widespread but never common, in Europe, North America and Japan, especially in mountain forests.

Notes: superficially similar to *A. atra* but easily told by the capillitium.

A   B

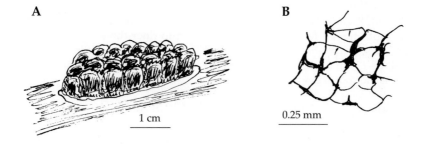

1 cm   0.25 mm

Fig. 138. *Amaurochaete ubulina*: A: pseudoaethalium; B: capillitium.

BREFELDIA Rostaf.
Vers. Syst. Mycet.: 8. 1873.

Sporocarp an aethalium, usually flattened, of large extent. Cortex soon disappearing. Columella present. **Capillitium** of sparsely branched threads attached to the columella, containing septate vesicles. A single species, *B. maxima* (Fr.) Rostaf.

Brefeldia maxima (Fr.) Rostaf.
in Fuckel, *Jahrb. Nass. Ver. Nat.* **27–28**: 70. 1873. Europe.

Sporocarp an extensive, sheet-like aethalium, to 15 mm thick and frequently reaching a metre square, purple-black. **Cortex** thin, showing a pattern of marks associated with the tops of the component sporangia. **Hypothallus** extensive, conspicuous, silvery. **Capillitium** arising from flattened pillar-like columellae, forming a dense network of black threads, the junctions bearing multicellular ellipsoid vesicles. **Spores** sooty-black in mass, yellow-brown in transmitted light, 9–12 μm diam, clearly warted. **Plasmodium** white, becoming violet and finally black as the spores develop. [Fig. 139]

Illustrations: L3: pl. 136; MA: fig. 124; NB: 315.
Habitat: stumps and rotten tree bases, sometimes fruiting on the soil and litter at the base of stumps.
Distribution: widespread and becoming more frequent, north to Inverness [65, H3, C]. Widespread in the Americas and Europe.

Notes: the characteristic vesicles in the capillitium are unlike any other structure in the Myxomycetes. This is the largest species and may give the impression that a stump has been coated with cold, rather lumpy, porridge, but after two days it seems to be covered in soot.

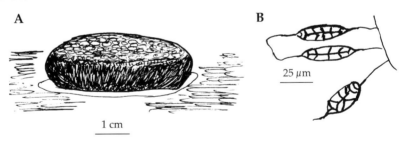

Fig. 139. *Brefeldia maxima*: A: aethalium; B: capillitium

COLLARIA Nann.-Bremek.
Proc. K. Ned. Acad. Wet. C **70**: 208. 1967.

Sporocarps stalked sporangia, globose. **Hypothallus** discoid, small. **Stalk** hollow, of parallel fibres, opaque, at least in the upper portion. **Peridium** disappearing after a while but leaving a distinct collar at the base. **Capillitium** with flexuous branches arising from the columella but not forming a surface net. Six species, the type is *C. rubens* (Lister) Nann.-Bremek.

KEY TO SPECIES

1	Sporocarps on dead wood	2
–	Sporocarps on leaf litter	3

2 (1)   Peridium fairly persistent, iridescent, capillitium of flexuous threads, densely anastomosed, columella not forked   *arcyrionema*
–   Peridium disappearing early, capillitium dichotomously branched from a forked columella   *elegans*

3 (1)   Capillitium attached to the peridial collar as well as the columella, spore mass pinkish-brown   *rubens*
–   Capillitium not attached to the collar, spore mass dull brown   *lurida*

Collaria arcyrionema (Rostaf.) Nann.-Bremek.
in Ing, *Trans. Br. mycol. Soc.* **78**: 444. 1982. Poland.
Syn. *Lamproderma arcyrionema* Rostaf.

Sporocarps stalked sporangia, 1–2.5 mm high, globose, 0.4–0.6 mm diam, silvery or iridescent bronze. **Stalk** black, stiff, up to three-quarters of the total height. **Peridium** membranous, persisting for a few days then fragmenting, leaving a distinct collar at the base. **Columella** cylindrical, slender, reaching the centre of the sporangium, dividing into two or more branches, which further divide to give the dense, curled mass of anastomosing threads which make up the **capillitium**. **Spores** in mass black, violet-grey in transmitted light, 7–9 μm diam, minutely punctate, sometimes with small clusters. **Plasmodium** white. [Fig. 140]

Illustrations: E: pl. 65; L3: pl. 129; MA: fig. 187.
Habitat: mossy stumps, rarely on leaves.
Distribution: scattered across the British Isles, commonest in the extreme south but reaches northern Scotland [31, H3]. Cosmopolitan.

Notes: the silvery peridium, persistent collar and densely anastomosing capillitium are the key characters of this uncommon species.

Collaria elegans (Racib.) Dhillon & Nann.-Bremek.
in Ing, *Trans. Br. mycol. Soc.* **78**: 44. 1982. Poland.
Syn. *Comatricha elegans* (Racib.) G. Lister

Sporocarps stalked sporangia, tending to be in groups but sometimes scattered, to 2 mm tall, but occasionally as short as 0.5 mm, globose, 0.3–0.5 mm diam. **Hypothallus** discoid. **Stalk** constructed of netted fibres, black, up to three-quarters of the total height. **Peridium** disappearing early, leaving a small basal collar. **Columella** reaching the centre of the sporangium, forking into a number of thick branches, but predominantly into just two. **Capillitium** of dichotomous branches, not anastomosing until the outer part of the sporangium is reached, leaving many free ends. **Spores** deep purple-brown or black in mass, pale lilac-brown in transmitted light, 8–10 μm diam, minutely spinulose. **Plasmodium** white. [Fig. 141]

Illustrations: E: pl. 60; L3: pl. 124; MA: fig. 163; NB: 369.
Habitat: on small, fallen branches, especially of conifers.
Distribution: frequent and widespread in Great Britain, rare in Ireland [74, H2]. Not uncommon in Europe, the Americas, Australia, New Zealand and Asia.

Notes: the small dark sporangia, especially when seen on the 'horizon' of a stick, show the characteristic forked columella when the spores are blown away.

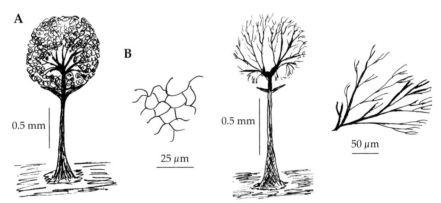

Fig. 140. *Collaria arcyrionema*:
A: sporangium; B: capillitium.

Fig. 141. *Collaria elegans*:
A: sporangium; B: capillitium.

Collaria lurida (Lister) Nann.-Bremek.
Ned. Myx.: 236. 1974. Lyme Regis, Dorset.
Syn. *Comatricha lurida* Lister

Sporocarps stalked sporangia, gregarious, globose, rarely short-ovoid, dull brown, to 1.5 mm high, 0.2–0.5 mm diam. **Hypothallus** inconspicuous. **Stalk** black, to three-quarters of the total height. **Peridium** soon disappearing leaving a conspicuous collar at the base. **Columella** short, cylindrical, not reaching the centre of the sporangium, divided at the tip into several thick branches. **Capillitium** of brown threads, not anastomosing, with many long, colourless free ends. **Spores** purple-brown in mass, pale lilac-grey in transmitted light, 7–10 μm diam, strongly warted. **Plasmodium** white. [Fig. 142]

Illustrations: E: pl. 60; L3: pl. 127; MA: fig. 169.
Habitat: leaf litter, especially of holly and ivy.
Distribution: a rare species of the south of England, in Wales only in Denbighshire, in Scotland only in Inverness and Mull, in Ireland only in Co. Antrim [19, H1]. Scattered in Europe, North America, Japan and India.

Notes: the distinctive basal collar without attachment to the capillitium and the dull colour separate this from *C. rubens* which is reddish, often ovate and has the capillitial attachment to the collar. However, both are rarely seen.

Collaria rubens (Lister) Nann.-Bremek.
Ned. Myx.: 236. 1974. Lyme Regis, Dorset.
Syn. *Comatricha rubens* Lister

Sporocarps stalked sporangia, gregarious, ovate to ellipsoid, rarely globose, to 2 mm high and 0.4 mm wide, pinkish-brown. **Hypothallus** discoid, brown. **Stalk** fine, black. **Peridium** membranous, pinkish-brown, leaving a conspicuous collar-like cup at the base, to which the lower part of the capillitium is attached. **Columella** reaching to two-thirds of the sporangial height, cylindrical. **Capillitium** arising from all parts of the columella, as well as the collar, flexuous, anastomosing. **Spores** in mass pinkish-brown, pale brown in transmitted light, 7–8 μm diam, minutely spinulose. **Plasmodium** white. [Fig. 143]

Illustrations: E: pl. 65; L3: pl. 127; MA: fig. 176; NB: 368.
Habitat: in leaf litter, especially of ivy and holly.
Distribution: commoner than the last but still a rare species, north to Orkney [29]. Scattered and uncommon in Europe and North America.

Notes: the collar, colour and capillitial attachment to the collar separate this species from *C. lurida*, with which it often grows.

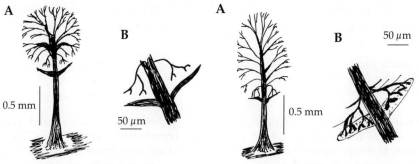

Fig. 142. *Collaria lurida*:
A: sporangium; B: peridial collar.

Fig. 143. *Collaria rubens*:
A: sporangium; B: peridial collar.

COLLODERMA G. Lister
J. Bot., Lond. **48**: 312. 1910.

Sporocarps sessile sporangia or short plasmodiocarps, the outer layer of the peridium is gelatinous and forms a thick jelly-like layer when wet, as it dries it shrinks and the inner, membranous layer shows through. **Columella** absent. **Capillitium** of branched threads with cross-branches forming a lattice. Four species, of which the type is *C. oculatum* (Lippert) G. Lister.

KEY TO SPECIES

| 1 | Sporangia dark, shining, spores pale, 11–12 µm diam | *oculatum* |
| – | Sporangia brown, dull, spores dark, 14–16 µm diam | *robustum* |

Colloderma oculatum (Lippert) G. Lister
J. Bot., Lond. **48**: 312. 1910. Austria.

Sporocarps sessile sporangia or short plasmodiocarps, occasionally with stalk-like structures which are probably portions of hypothallus on the tips of moss leaves, sporangia pulvinate, globose or hemispherical, 0.3–1 mm diam, plasmodiocarps to 3 mm long, olive-brown to black, often iridescent when dry. **Hypothallus** dark brown. **Peridium** with a gelatinous outer layer and a thin, membranous, inner layer, which peeps through the gelatinous cover as it dries, justifying the specific epithet. **Capillitium** threads colourless or dark, thin, sparsely branched but with cross-branches at right angles, sometimes beaded, paler towards the peridium. **Spores** in mass dark brown, purple-grey in transmitted light, 11–12 µm diam, spiny. **Plasmodium** dark brown or black, dense. [Fig. 144]

Illustrations: E: pl. 49; L3: pl. 213; MA: fig. 122; NB: 302.
Habitat: on mosses on the bark of living trees, on mosses on wet rocks in ravines and on algal slimes on fallen trunks, nearly always associated with cyanobacteria.
Distribution: widespread and not uncommon, especially in the west and north [73, H11]. Widespread in Europe, North America, New Zealand and Japan.

Notes: the gelatinous layer of the peridium with the iridescent 'eye' peeping through and the squarely cross-branched capillitium are features to look out for. The capillitium resembles that of *Didymium* species and further confuses the current ordinal classification of the Myxomycetes!

A   B

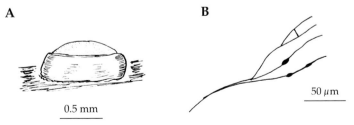

0.5 mm   50 µm

Fig. 144. *Colloderma oculatum*: A: sporangium; B: capillitium.

Colloderma robustum Meyl.
Bull. Soc. Vaud. Sci. Nat. **58**: 83. 1933. Switzerland.

Sporocarps sessile sporangia, pulvinate, usually oval in outline, 1–2 mm broad, brown. **Hypothallus** brown. **Peridium** with gelatinous outer layer and dry, membranous inner layer. **Capillitium** abundant, dark, slender, regularly branching at acute angles. **Spores** black in mass, dark grey in transmitted light, 14–16 μm diam, with long spines. **Plasmodium** dark grey. [Fig. 145]

Illustrations: MA: fig. 123.
Habitat: on mosses on dead wood.
Distribution: rare, known from Devon, Somerset, Kent and Middlesex [4]. Elsewhere only recorded from Switzerland, Hungary and New South Wales.

Notes: easily separated from *C. oculatum* by the lack of iridescence, and the larger and darker spores.

50 μm

Fig. 145. *Colloderma robustum*: capillitium.

COMATRICHA Preuss
Linnae **24**: 140. 1851.

Sporocarps stalked sporangia, globose to cylindrical. **Stalk** solid, fibrous. **Peridium** disappearing early. **Columella** often reaching to the tip of the sporangium. **Capillitium** branching and anastomosing from the whole length of the columella, forming a dense network within the sporangium but rarely with a surface net, and then fragmentary and confined to the base of the sporangium, more often with abundant free ends. **Spores** in mass purple-brown. Over thirty species are now included; the type is *C. nigra* (Pers.) Schröt.

KEY TO SPECIES

1	Sporangia globose	2
–	Sporangia ovate to cylindrical	4
2 (1)	Spores 11–14 µm diam, capillitial tips forming a rigid net	*rigidireta*
–	Spores less than 11 µm diam, if with a net then it is soft and flexuous	3
3 (2)	Sporangia to 9 mm tall, no net	*nigra*
–	Sporangia less than 1 mm tall, with a complete, soft net	*ellae*
4 (1)	Stalk long, much more than half the total height	5
–	Stalk short, much less than half the total height	8
5 (4)	Sporangia pale reddish-brown, pointed at base and apex	*tenerrima*
–	Sporangia dark brown, rounded at base and apex	6
6 (5)	Capillitium permanently attached to the columella	*nigra*
–	Capillitium falling away from the columella	7
7 (6)	Capillitium expanding elastically, spores 8–9 µm diam	*alta*
–	Capillitium not elastic, spores 4–6 µm diam	*fragilis*
8 (4)	Spores reticulate	9
–	Spores warted or spiny	10
9 (8)	Spores banded reticulate, with 20 meshes to the hemisphere, 10–13 µm diam	*mirabilis*
–	Spores warty reticulate, with 15 meshes to the hemisphere, 6–10 µm diam	*reticulospora*
10 (8)	Capillitium branched but not anastomosing, with long free ends pointing outwards, spores 6–7 µm diam	*longipila*
–	Capillitium anastomosing, free ends short or absent, spores more than 7 µm diam	11

11 (10) Major branches of the capillitium thick, parallel, emerging at right angles
         to the columella, the whole network lax and open   *laxa*
–   Major branches of the capillitium thin, if parallel threads sinuous,
         network tight   *pulchella*

Comatricha alta Preuss
Linnaea **24**: 141. 1851. Germany.
Syn. *Comatricha nigra* var. *alta* (Preuss) Lister

Sporocarps stalked sporangia, usually in small groups, occasionally single, long-ovate to short-cylindrical, 3–6 mm high, dark brown. **Hypothallus** reddish-brown, discoid or a common sheet under groups of sporangia. **Stalk** black, 2–3 times taller than the height of the sporangium, opaque, fibrous at the base. **Columella** reaching to the tip of the sporangium, blunt. **Capillitium** abundant, brown, of flexuous threads, branching but scarcely anastomosing, attached mostly at the base, falling away from the columella on maturity as a dark plume, the appearance is of a mat of gossamer-like threads resting on the stalks. **Spores** in mass black, lilac-brown in transmitted light, 7.5–9 μm diam, with a small, pale germination area, densely, palely, minutely warted. **Plasmodium** transparent, white. [Fig. 146]

Illustrations: L3: pl. 123; NB: 358.
Habitat: on newly felled trunks, often on sawn surfaces, especially of elm and beech, typically a summer species.
Distribution: scattered, not uncommon, north to Orkney, in Ireland only recorded in Co. Down [44, H1]. Widespread but uncommon in Europe, distribution elsewhere uncertain; reported from New Zealand.

Notes: the elastic capillitium, behaving a little like an *Arcyria*, leaving a bare columella is very characteristic. This species may not have been separated from *C. nigra* in older records but is quite different.

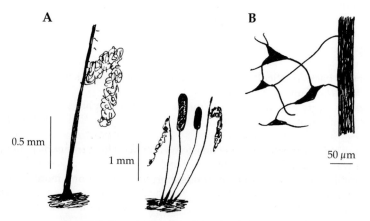

Fig. 146. *Comatricha alta*: A: sporangia; B: capillitium.

Comatricha ellae Härkönen
Ann. Bot. Fenn. **15**: 34. 1978. Norway.

Sporocarps stalked sporangia, scattered, globose, dark brown, 0.6–1 mm high, 0.2–0.4 mm diam. **Stalk** black, of netted fibres, more than half the total height. **Columella** reaching the middle of the sporangium, branching at its apex. **Capillitium** arising along the whole length of the columella but especially at the apex, dark, branching repeatedly and forming an internal network and also a more or less complete net at the surface, with few free ends. **Spores** in mass coppery-brown, darkening on maturity, pale lilac-brown in transmitted light, 7–9 μm diam, almost smooth but with a covering of very pale, fine warts (seen under oil immersion) with a small pale germination pore. **Plasmodium** watery white. [Fig. 147]

Illustrations: original description.
Habitat: bark of living trees.
Distribution: rare, known from Devon, Central London, Cheshire, Yorkshire, Berwickshire, Angus, Inverness, Co. Wicklow and Co. Armagh [7, H2]. Otherwise only reported from Norway, the Netherlands and Switzerland.

Notes: this is like a small *C. nigra* with paler spores and a complete surface net.

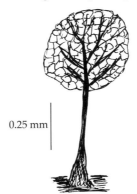

0.25 mm

Fig. 147. *Comatricha ellae*: sporangium.

Comatricha fragilis Meyl.
Bull. Soc. Vaud. Sci. Nat. **56**: 70. 1925. Switzerland

Sporocarps stalked sporangia, in small groups, dark brown, often with a purplish tinge, 2–4 mm high. **Hypothallus** thin, brown, continuous under a group of sporangia. **Stalk** thin, shining, black, opaque, more than half the total height. **Columella** reaching almost to the tip of the sporangium. **Capillitium** thin, reddish-brown, flexuous, branched, attached along the whole length of the columella, but falling away on maturity, the branching closed with no free ends. **Spores** dark purplish-brown in mass, violet-brown in transmitted light, 6–7 μm diam, finely but not closely, warted, with a very small germination pore. **Plasmodium** white. [Fig. 148]

Illustrations: NB: 360.
Habitat: on the bark of living elder.
Distribution: only known in the British Isles from Orkney, last seen in 1966 [1]. It is also recorded from the Netherlands and Switzerland, where there are a few records from the Jura in the early part of the century and a recent gathering from Zermatt, on bark of Arolla pine in moist chamber. The other records are from fallen branches.

Notes: easily separated from cylindrical forms of *C. nigra* by the deciduous capillitium and the smaller spores.

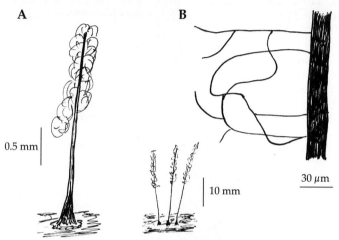

Fig. 148. *Comatricha fragilis*: A: sporangia; B: capillitium.

Comatricha laxa Rostaf.
Mon.: 201. 1874. Germany.

Sporocarps stalked sporangia, usually in small groups, 1–3.5 mm tall, ovoid to short-cylindrical, rarely globose, rounded at base and apex, reddish-brown. **Hypothallus** discoid, small. **Stalk** up to twice as long as the height of the sporangium, black, the base often with a network of fibres and a translucent sheath. **Columella** reaching almost to the tip of the sporangium. **Capillitium** forming a rather open network of thick, black threads, the primary branches parallel and leaving the columella at right angles, thinning out towards the periphery, not forming a surface net and with many pointed free ends. **Spores** in mass reddish-brown, pale lilac-brown in transmitted light, 7–9 µm diam, finely warted. **Plasmodium** white. [Fig. 149]

Illustrations: E: pl. 59; L3: pl. 124; MA: fig. 166; NB: 352.
Habitat: on fallen branches and, less commonly, on the bark of living trees.
Distribution: common in southern Britain, less common in Scotland but reaches Orkney, appears to be commoner in parts of Ireland than *C. nigra* [60, H14, C]. Probably cosmopolitan.

Notes: the ovoid to short cylindrical sporangia, reddish-brown colour and parallel main branches of the capillitium separate this common species from *C. nigra*. Small forms, especially on bark in moist chamber culture, are sometimes difficult to separate from species of *Paradiacheopsis*; careful attention to spore ornamentation and measurement will usually solve any problem.

A   B

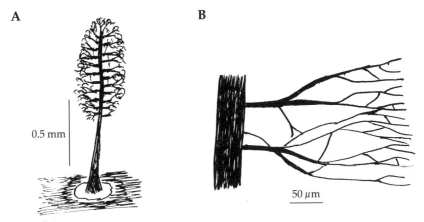

0.5 mm

50 μm

Fig. 149. *Comatricha laxa*: A: sporangium; B: capillitium.

Comatricha longipila Nann.-Bremek.
Acta Bot. Neerl. **11**: 31. 1962. Netherlands.

Sporocarps stalked sporangia, short-cylindrical to ovate, clustered or scattered, to 2 mm high and 0.6 mm diam, brown. **Hypothallus** brown, inconspicuous, single or shared. **Stalk** up to a third of the total height, with a base of netted fibres, opaque above. **Peridium** usually disappearing completely but occasionally leaving a small collar at the base. **Columella** reaching the apex of the sporangium where it merges with the capillitium. **Capillitium** brown, with primary branches at right angles to the columella, dichotomously branching, scarcely anastomosing, produced into long, straight free ends. **Spores** in mass brown, pale red-brown in transmitted light, 6–7 μm diam, finely warted. **Plasmodium** white. [Fig. 150]

Illustrations: MA: fig. 168; NB: 353.
Habitat: on the bark of living trees.
Distribution: rare, recorded from Kent, Northants, Warwickshire, Shropshire, Aberdeenshire and Inverness [6]. Apparently only otherwise known from the Netherlands.

Notes: the small spores, lack of outer capillitial network and the long free ends separate this species from small specimens of *C. laxa*.

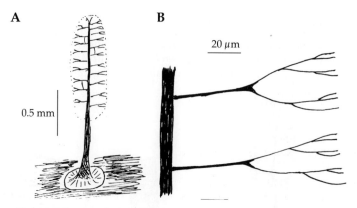

Fig. 150. *Comatricha longipila*:   A: sporangia;   B: capillitium.

Comatricha mirabilis R.K. Benjamin & Poitras
Mycologia **42**: 515. 1950. Illinois.

Sporocarps stalked sporangia, clustered, short-cylindrical, brown, to 1.5 mm high and 0.25–0.35 mm diam. **Hypothallus** conspicuous, brown, common to a cluster. **Stalk** black, about half the total height. **Peridium** soon disappearing except at the base where it may leave a small collar. **Columella** reaching almost to the apex of the sporangium. **Capillitium** of simple, mostly unbranched, purple-brown threads arising from the whole length of the columella, the tips branched into thick, rigid, diverging branchlets which protrude from the surface of the sporangium. **Spores** in mass smoky brown, yellow-brown in transmitted light, 10–13 μm diam, conspicuously and strongly reticulate with a system of raised bands, to 2 μm high, giving 20 meshes to the hemisphere. **Plasmodium** unknown. [Fig. 151]

Illustrations: MA: fig. 171.
Habitat: on rotting straw bales (described from goat dung).

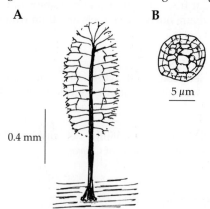

Fig. 151. *Comatricha mirabilis*: A: sporangium; B: spore.

Distribution: recorded on a heap of straw bales at Nutley, East Sussex, for a few years from 1969, disappearing when the bales finally rotted away [1]. Found in a few sites in North America.

Notes: the beautifully banded spores are quite sufficient to identify this species, although the protruding capillitial tips are also distinctive.

Comatricha nigra (Pers.) Schröt.
Krypt.-Fl. Schles. **3**: 118. 1865. Germany.

Sporocarps long-stalked sporangia, globose to short-cylindrical, total height up to 9 mm, dark brown, in groups, often in lines, rarely singly. **Hypothallus** red, scanty. **Stalk** black, hair-like, as much as eight times the height of the sporangium. **Peridium** disappearing completely. **Columella** reaching the centre of the sporangium. **Capillitium** much branched, of slender, flexuous threads, reddish-brown, forming a dense net. **Spores** in mass black, violaceous brown by transmitted light, 9–10 µm, faintly warted or nearly smooth. **Plasmodium** transparent, then white. [Fig. 152]

Illustrations: E: pl. 59; L3: pl. 123; MA: fig. 172; NB: 347.
Habitat: on rotten wood of all kinds, occasionally on bark of living trees in moist chamber cultures, especially of conifers.
Distribution: abundant throughout the British Isles, one of the commonest species [112, H39, C]. Cosmopolitan.

Notes: the long-stalked sporangia, like groups of black pins, are most easily seen by turning a stick and looking along the 'horizon'. The globose form is by far the most likely to be met, the ovoid form is not uncommon but the short-cylindrical forms are rarely met. Most have been re-allocated to other species on characters other than shape.

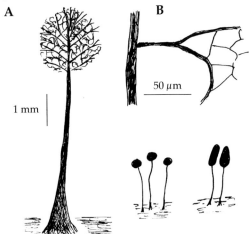

Fig. 152. *Comatricha nigra*: A: sporangia; B: capillitium.

Comatricha pulchella (C. Bab.) Rostaf.
Mon. App.: 27. 1876. Germany.
var. **pulchella**

Sporocarps short-stalked sporangia, in small groups, pinkish-brown, ovoid, with rounded base and apex, 0.7–1.5 mm high. **Hypothallus** discoid, small, rarely shared in a group. **Stalk** up to a half of the total height, black. **Peridium** disappearing. **Columella** tapering, reaching the apex of the sporangium where it merges with the capillitium. **Capillitium** reddish-brown, primary branches at right angles to the columella, branched, flexuous, forming an internal net, looped at the surface but not forming a surface net, of thin threads throughout, without free ends. **Spores** in mass pinkish-brown, rosy-brown in transmitted light, 6.5–8 μm diam, with scattered, small, colourless warts. **Plasmodium** white. [Fig. 153]

Illustrations: E: pl. 63; L3: pl. 126; MA: fig. 173; NB: 355.
Habitat: on leaf litter, especially of holly and ivy.
Distribution: common and widespread in the British Isles [94, H21]. Probably cosmopolitan.

Notes: the shape, colour and habitat are usually sufficient to distinguish this common species.

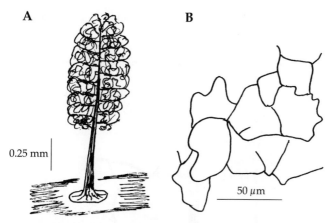

A

B

0.25 mm

50 μm

Fig. 153. *Comatricha pulchella*: A: sporangium; B: capillitium.

var. **fusca** Lister
J. Bot., Lond. **35**: 215. 1897. Wanstead, Essex.

Differs from the type in its brown colour, especially the darker capillitium, slightly larger size and marginally shorter stalks, and the spores being grey-brown rather than rose-brown under transmitted light.

Illustrations: L3: pl. 126; NB: 356.
Distribution: less common, or less commonly separated [15, H1].

Comatricha reticulospora Ing & P.C. Holland
Trans. Br. mycol. Soc. **50**: 685. 1968. Pett Level, Sussex.

Sporocarps short-stalked sporangia, clustered, cylindrical, dark brown, 2–2.5 mm high, 0.4–0.5 mm diam. **Hypothallus** continuous under cluster, shining brown, horny. **Stalk** to 0.7 mm long, striate, dark brown to black, opaque. **Peridium** disappearing quickly. **Columella** thick and irregular, reaching high into the sporangium. **Capillitium** arising along the whole length of the columella, a tangle of brown threads, branching and anastomosing, reaching the surface as long, straight, finely pointed free ends. **Spores** purple-brown in mass, greyish violet in transmitted light, 6–10 μm diam, mostly about 8 μm, delicately reticulated with rows of minute warts, giving 15 meshes to the hemisphere. **Plasmodium** not seen. [Fig. 154]

Illustrations: original description.
Habitat: on rotten wood.
Distribution: known only from Devon, Sussex and Worcestershire [3]. Possibly endemic.

Notes: the only British species with warted-reticulate spores, it otherwise resembles *C. longipila*, but is larger and may look like a *Stemonitopsis*, but lacks a surface net.

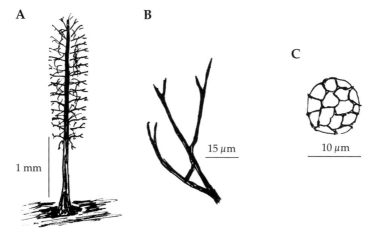

A

B

C

15 μm

10 μm

1 mm

Fig. 154. *Comatricha reticulospora*: A: sporangium; B: capillitium; C: spore.

Comatricha rigidireta Nann.-Bremek.
Proc. K. Ned. Akad. Wet. C **69**: 352. 1966. Netherlands.

Sporocarps stalked sporangia, often in groups of three or four, globose or, more usually, slightly taller than broad, rounded, 0.6–1.1 mm high, 0.2–0.6 mm diam, black. **Hypothallus** discoid, brown. **Stalk** up to twice as long as the diameter of the sporangium, black, the base a network of fibres which may be brown. **Peridium** membranous, shining black, quickly disappearing. **Columella** reaching almost to the tip of the sporangium. **Capillitium** forming a uniform, small-meshed net of strong threads, at the surface forming an angular net of meshes 15–50 µm diam, with few free ends. **Spores** in mass dark brown, pale lilac in transmitted light, 11–14 µm diam, finely warted, with a small, oval germination pore. **Plasmodium** white. [Fig. 155]

Illustrations: NB: 349.
Habitat: bark of living trees.
Distribution: rare, except in Central London, where it is surprisingly widespread on London Plane and other trees in the parks, northwards to Berwickshire [8, H3]. Elsewhere reported from Switzerland, Kenya as well as the Netherlands.

Notes: the small height, but quite large sporangia, with the characteristic outer net make this a distinctive species. Its abundance in Central London is probably due to the large amount of moist chamber culture recently undertaken, but may be due to its preference for the bark of introduced trees, such as plane. Elsewhere in Britain it has been found mostly on oak, poplar or lime.

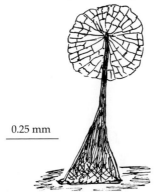

0.25 mm

Fig. 155. *Comatricha rigidireta*: sporangium.

Comatricha tenerrima (M.A. Curtis) G. Lister
Guide Br. Mycet. edn 4: 39. 1919. South Carolina.

Sporocarps stalked sporangia, spindle-shaped, pointed at base and apex, bright pinkish-brown, in small groups or solitary, 1.5–2 mm tall. **Hypothallus** discoid or forming a small sheet under a group, reddish-brown. **Stalk** up to twice the length of the sporangium, reddish-brown and netted at the base, black, shining, opaque at the top. **Columella** continuous to the tip of the sporangium and sometimes projecting beyond the spore mass, not tapering much, black. **Capillitium** abundant, pale brown, attached to the whole length of the columella, very flexuous, branching, forming loops at the periphery, without free ends. **Spores** pinkish-brown in mass, very pale reddish-brown under transmitted light, 7–8 µm diam, almost smooth, under oil immersion seen to be covered with very fine, pale spinules. **Plasmodium** white. [Fig. 156]

Illustrations: E: pl. 53; L3: pl. 126; MA: fig. 180; NB: 357.

Habitat: dead stems of herbaceous perennials, such as hogweed, marsh plants, such as reedmace and reeds, and straw, usually in damp places.

Distribution: not uncommon, scattered north to Shetland, in Ireland only in Co. Offaly [58, H1]. Widespread in Europe, North America, Belize, Brazil, the West Indies and Japan.

Notes: the shape and colour of the sporangia are sufficient to identify this species. It is probably far commoner than the records suggest but occurs in poorly studied habitats.

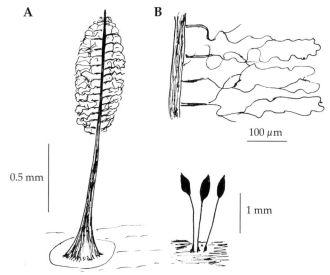

Fig. 156. *Comatricha tenerrima*: A: sporangium; B: capillitium.

DIACHEOPSIS Meyl.
Bull. Soc. Vaud. Sci. Nat. **57**: 149. 1930.

Sporocarps sessile sporangia, iridescent. **Columella** absent; capillitium arising from the base of the sporangium, forming a loose net. Nine species, several of them snowline; the type is *D. metallica* Meylan.

KEY TO SPECIES

1	On lichens on the bark of living trees, spores 18–19 μm diam	*insessa*
–	On lichens on shingle beaches, spores 20–21 μm diam	*mitchellii*

Diacheopsis insessa (G. Lister) Ing
Trans. Br. mycol. Soc. **48**: 648. 1965. Elgin, Morayshire.
Syn. *Lamproderma insessum* G. Lister

Sporocarps sessile sporangia, clustered, subglobose, iridescent purple, 0.8–1 mm diam, rarely short plasmodiocarps to 3 mm long. **Hypothallus** usually inconspicuous, pale brown, but occasionally forming a very short, broad pseudo-stalk. **Peridium** membranous, pale purple in transmitted light. **Columella** absent. **Capillitium** a loose network of broad, purple threads arising from the base, at junctions expanded in flat plates and bearing dark, bead-like thickenings. **Spores** black in mass, pale purple-brown in transmitted light, 18–19 μm diam, closely spinulose. **Plasmodium** shining grey-brown. [Fig. 157]

Illustrations: L3: pl. 215.
Habitat: on foliose lichens on the bark of living trees.
Distribution: in Atlantic woodlands from Devon and Cornwall, Snowdonia, the Lake District to the Scottish Highlands; recorded in Co. Wicklow [12, H1]. Possibly endemic.

Notes: the iridescent peridium and large, spiny spores are different from any other bark species. The related *D. mitchellii* is on terrestrial lichens and has larger spores with unusual spines which are frayed at the tip.

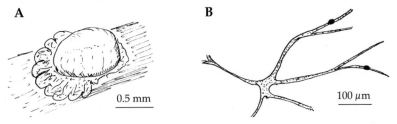

A
0.5 mm

B
100 μm

Fig. 157. *Diacheopsis insessa*: A: sporangium on lichen; B: capillitium.

Diacheopsis mitchellii Nann.-Bremek. & Y. Yamam.
Proc. K. Ned. Akad. Wet. C **86**: 224. 1983. Japan.

Sporocarps sessile sporangia, in small groups, pulvinate, shining, iridescent blue, green or purple, 0.25–0.5 mm diam. **Hypothallus** absent. **Peridium** membranous, persistent, pale yellow or colourless in transmitted light. **Columella** absent. **Capillitium** sparse, of simple or little-branched threads, some with small dark swellings, not forming a network. **Spores** black in mass, dark purplish-grey in transmitted light, 20–21 μm diam, covered with long spines, about 1 μm length, whose tips appear frayed under SEM. **Plasmodium** not seen. [Fig. 158]

Illustrations: original description.
Habitat: on *Cladonia* lichens on a shingle beach (the type is from the bark of living *Cryptomeria*).
Distribution: known only from the Crumbles, East Sussex [1]. Elsewhere known from Japan.

Notes: the habitat, spore size and peculiar ornamentation separate this species. The fact that the Sussex collection is on terrestrial lichens whereas the type and *D. insessa* are on tree lichens is perhaps less important than the special nature of the frayed spines, which are unlike those in any other British myxomycete.

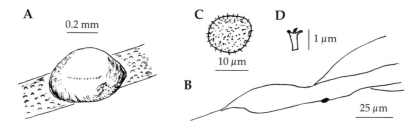

Fig. 158. *Diacheopsis mitchellii*:
A: sporangium on *Cladonia*; B: capillitium; C: spore; D: spore spine.

ENERTHENEMA Bowman
Trans. Linn. Soc. Lond. **16**: 152. 1830.

Sporocarps short-stalked sporangia. **Columella** expanded at the apex into a shiny black disc or shallow funnel from which the capillitium hangs down. Four species; the type is *E. papillatum* (Pers.) Rostaf.

Enerthenema papillatum (Pers.) Rostaf.
Mon. App.: 28. 1876. Germany.

Sporocarps short-stalked sporangia, often in large clusters, 0.6–1.5 mm tall, globose or slightly oblate, with a flattened top and slightly flattened base, 0.4–0.7 mm diam, black when fresh, fading to dark brown on maturity. **Hypothallus** discoid or continuous under a group, rather fragile. **Stalk** grooved, shiny black, netted at the broad base, tapering to the top then suddenly narrowing into the sporangium. **Peridium** soon disappearing, leaving the conspicuous apical plate. **Columella** black, connecting the top of the stalk with the apical plate. **Capillitium** of long, dark, flexuous threads connected to the apical plate, dichotomously branched a few times. **Spores** dark brown to black in mass, grey-brown in transmitted light, 10–12 μm diam, finely warted. **Plasmodium** white. [Fig. 159]

Illustrations: E: pl. 53; L3: pl. 126; MA: fig. 142; NB: 361.
Habitat: recently fallen branches of oak and pine and bark of living trees, especially oak.
Distribution: very common throughout the British Isles [111, H40, C]. Probably cosmopolitan.

Notes: when developed normally this is one of the easiest species to identify. However, it sometimes occurs in bark cultures without an apical disc and then is quite difficult to separate from forms of *Paradiacheopsis solitaria*, with which it often grows. Usually, the fact that the present species has a columella which reaches to the apex of the sporangium is sufficient, as in *Paradiacheopsis* it rarely reaches more than halfway. This is a common species in bark cultures, and is one of the typical species of lowland oak forest. It occurs on the bark of branches as well as trunks and survives to fruit on the fallen branch on the ground.

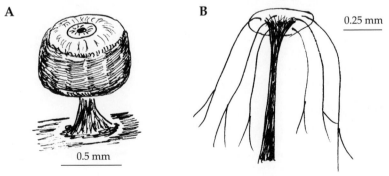

Fig. 159. *Enerthenema papillatum*: A: sporangium; B: capillitium.

LAMPRODERMA Rostaf.
Vers. Syst. Mycet.: 7. 1873.

Sporocarps stalked sporangia, rarely sessile. **Peridium** persistent, iridescent or, at least, shining. **Columella** well developed. **Capillitium** mostly attached to the tip of the columella, forming a network, often attached to the inside of the peridium. About 40 species, many of them snowline; the type is *L. columbinum* (Pers.) Rostaf.

Notes: this is one of the most critical of all myxomycete genera, with important characters in spores and capillitium, but the extent to which environmental factors affect development is unknown. Great care must be taken to obtain material in which the whole capillitium can be seen as the colour of base, middle and apex of threads is often diagnostic. Spore measurements and ornamentation are also of major importance.

KEY TO SPECIES

1	Sporangia clearly stalked, however shortly	2
–	Sporangia with no trace of a stalk; rare	*debile*
2 (1)	Spores strongly banded-reticulate; alpine	*cribrarioides*
–	Spores spiny, warted or reticulated without bands	3
3 (2)	Peridium with distinct, sunken spots	*gulielmae*
–	Peridium uniform	4
4 (3)	Stalk long, more than half total height	5
–	Stalk short, less than half total height	6
5 (4)	Spores dark, 11–14 µm diam; on wood and mosses	*columbinum*
–	Spores pale, 7–9 µm diam; on herbaceous litter	*scintillans*
6 (4)	Spores warted-reticulate	7
–	Spores without reticulations	8
7 (6)	Capillitium with funnel-shaped expansions at tips; alpine, rare	*atrosporum*
–	Capillitium without funnels; lowland, rare	*anglicum*
8 (6)	Spores 15–20 µm diam, with long spines; on wood	*echinulatum*
–	Spores less than 15 µm diam, with short spines; on litter	9
9 (8)	Spores 13–15 µm diam	*sauteri*
–	Spores less than 13 µm diam	10
10 (9)	Spores 8–11 µm diam, pale; lowland	*arcyrioides*
–	Spores 10–12 µm diam, dark; alpine	*carestiae*

Lamproderma anglicum (G. Lister & H.J. Howard) Ing
Trans. Br. mycol. Soc. **78**: 444. 1982. Norwich, Norfolk.
Syn. *Lamproderma atrosporum* var. *anglicum* G. Lister & H.J. Howard

Sporocarps short-stalked to almost sessile sporangia, up to 1 mm tall, 0.5–0.6 mm diam, ovoid to subglobose, dark purple-brown, with blue iridescence. **Stalk** slender 0.1–0.3 mm high. **Columella** long, slender, broadening towards the tip. **Capillitium** joined to the columella with membranous expansions, dark to the tips which are attached to the peridium. **Spores** in mass black, purplish-grey in transmitted light, 11–14 µm diam, reticulated with rows of minute warts. **Plasmodium** not seen. [Fig. 160]

Illustrations: L3: pl. 216.
Habitat: beech litter.
Distribution: known only from Norfolk and Worcestershire; last seen in 1924 [2]. Possibly endemic and may be extinct.

Notes: this poorly known species is dark, like *L. atrosporum*, but that is its only similarity with the common alpine species. The weak stalks and faintly reticulate spores and lack of funnel-like expansions at the junction of the capillitial tips and the peridium are also diagnostic.

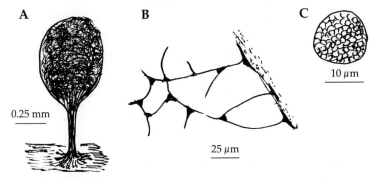

A

B

C

0.25 mm

25 µm

10 µm

Fig. 160. *Lamproderma anglicum*: A: sporangium; B: outer capillitium; C: spore.

Lamproderma arcyrioides (Sommerf.) Rostaf.
Mon.: 206. 1874. Norway.
Syn. *Lamproderma violaceum* (Fr.) Rostaf.

Sporocarps short-stalked sporangia, subglobose with a flattened or umbilicate base, up to 1.5 mm tall, 0.4–0.9 mm diam, shining, iridescent blue, often with violet or bronze reflections. **Hypothallus** membranous, reddish-brown. **Stalk** black, to 1.5 times the diameter of the sporangium. **Columella** reaching to two-thirds of the sporangial height, cylindrical, obtuse. **Capillitium** of pale threads, rarely darker than pale brown and then only in the middle, arising from the upper part of the columella and branching to form a dense network, very slender towards the tips. **Spores** in mass black, purplish-grey in transmitted light, 8–11 μm in diam, minutely spinulose. **Plasmodium** white. [Fig. 161]

Illustrations: E: pl. 67; L3: pl. 132; MA: fig. 186; NB: 371.
Habitat: leaf litter, especially of ivy.
Distribution: widespread but not common, north to Inverness; not recorded from Ireland [62]. Widely recorded in North America, the West Indies, Europe, Japan and Australia.

Notes: the small spores, umbilicate sporangia and pale capillitium separate this fairly common species. Some authors regard it as an alpine species but the British material, all lowland, is typical.

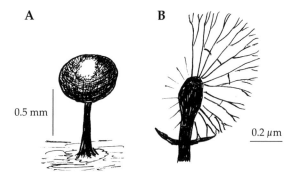

Fig. 161. *Lamproderma arcyrioides*: A: sporangium; B: columella and capillitium.

Lamproderma atrosporum Meyl.
Bull. Soc. Vaud. Sci. Nat. **46**: 51. 1910. Switzerland.

Sporocarps short-stalked sporangia, in groups or scattered, black, shining with silvery reflections, rarely iridescent, subglobose, 1–2.5 mm high, 0.6–1.2 mm diam. **Hypothallus** black, membranous. **Stalk** black, rarely longer than the diameter of the sporangium. **Columella** cylindrical or club-shaped, reaching to the centre of the sporangium. **Capillitium** dark, usually black throughout, the tips expanded into funnel-shaped expansions at the junction with the peridium, these expansions often being yellowish-brown, small peridial fragments often adhere to these funnels. **Spores** black in mass, purplish-brown in transmitted light, 12–15 μm diam, covered with a coarse reticulation of spines, the meshes not always distinct. **Plasmodium** black. [Fig. 162]

Illustrations: L3: pl. 133; MA: fig. 196.
Habitat: on vegetation at the edge of melting snow patches in spring.
Distribution: known from Aberdeen (on forest litter) and in the Cairngorms [2]. Widely found in the mountains of Europe, North America and New Zealand.

Notes: this is one of the commonest alpine species and is very variable. The dark colours of the peridium, capillitium and spores and the spiny reticulations are good characters, especially when the diagnostic funnel-tips of the capillitium are poorly developed or absent, as happens in some specimens. As with all alpine species, sudden cold spells in Spring can affect morphology.

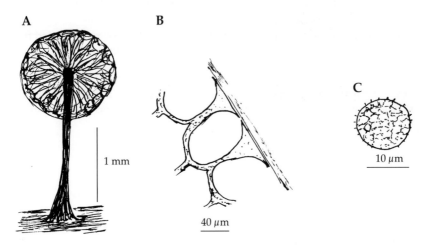

Fig. 162. *Lamproderma atrosporum*: A: sporangium; B: outer capillitium; C: spore.

Lamproderma carestiae (Ces. & De Not.) Meyl.
Bull. Soc. Vaud. Sci. Nat. **57**: 368. 1932. Italy.
Syn. *Lamproderma violaceum* var. *carestiae* (Ces. & De Not.) Lister

Sporocarps short-stalked sporangia, subglobose, to 2 mm high, 0.7–1.4 mm diam, violet-blue or bronze, iridescent. **Hypothallus** black, membranous. **Stalk** short, to 0.8 mm high. **Columella** cylindrical, reaching to the centre of the sporangium. **Capillitium** of dark purple-brown to black threads, stiff at the base, then forming curved branches, colourless at the tips. **Spores** in mass black, violet-brown in transmitted light, 10–12 μm diam, warted. **Plasmodium** not seen. [Fig. 163]

Illustrations: L3: p. 132; MA: fig. 188.
Habitat: vegetation at the edge of melting snow in spring.
Distribution: known from the Cairngorms, Ben Lawers and Aonach Mhòr in the Scottish Highlands [4]. Widespread in the mountains of Europe, North America and New Zealand.

Notes: this is one of the commoner alpine species in Europe and is easily separated from the superficially similar *L. arcyroides* by the dark capillitium, which is only pale at the tips whereas in *L. arcyrioides* it is pale at the base, only slightly darkening in the middle section; it is also much shorter-stalked than *L. arcyrioides*. From *L. sauteri* it differs in the darker, less reddish tints in the capillitium and in the smaller, less prominently warted spores.

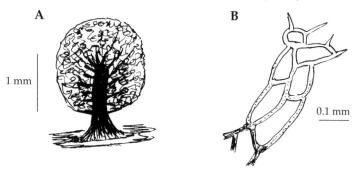

Fig. 163. *Lamproderma carestiae*: A: sporangium; B: outer capillitium.

Lamproderma columbinum (Pers.) Rostaf.
in Fuckel, *Jahrb. Nass. Ver. Nat.* **27–28**: 69. 1873. Europe.

Sporocarps long-stalked sporangia, globose or ellipsoid, to 5 mm tall, 0.5–1 mm diam, scattered or, more usually, in groups, iridescent blue with violet and purple reflections. **Hypothallus** dark purple. **Stalk** long, occupying three-quarters of the total height, black. **Columella** cylindrical with a blunt apex, reaching the centre of the sporangium. **Capillitium** brownish-purple, arising from the whole length of the columella, stiff, forking, then anastomosing to form an open net. **Spores** black in mass, grey-brown in transmitted light, 10–13 μm diam, minutely warted. **Plasmodium** white. [Fig. 164]

Illustrations: E: pl. 66; L3: pl. 131; MA: fig. 189.
Habitat: on moss-covered trunks and stumps and on mosses on wet rocks in Atlantic woods and ravines, and near waterfalls.
Distribution: the commonest of the characteristic species on moss-covered rocks in ravines and, as such, more abundant in the west and north; further east it is more likely to be found on rotten logs covered in wet mosses, often with a thick mat of cyanobacteria as well [80, H19]. Widespread in Europe, temperate North America, Australia and Japan.

Notes: the long stalks and the habitat are usually enough to identify this beautiful species.

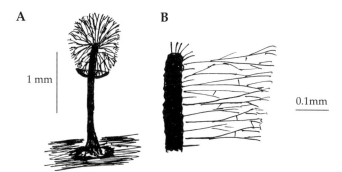

Fig. 164. *Lamproderma columbinum*: A: sporangium; B: capillitium.

Lamproderma cribrarioides (Fr.) R.E. Fr.
Svensk Bot. Tidskr. **4**: 259. 1911. Germany.

Sporocarps short-stalked sporangia, scattered or in small clusters, globose, 0.8–1.1 mm diam, purple-bronze, iridescent. **Stalk** weak, black, often flattened, to 0.6 mm high. **Columella** cylindrical, reaching the centre of the sporangium. **Capillitium** forming a network of flexuous threads, pale purplish-brown, stout at the base, slender and pale at the tip. **Spores** black in mass, dark purplish-brown in transmitted light, 11–16 µm diam, banded-reticulate, the bands 0.5–1.5 µm high, giving between 8 and 24 meshes to the hemisphere. **Plasmodium** dark brown. [Fig. 165]

Illustrations: E: pl. 67; L3: pl. 133 (not *a*); MA: fig. 190.
Habitat: on the tips of shrubs and clubmosses at the edge of melting snow in spring.
Distribution: only known from the Cairngorm mountains, where it is quite common [2]. One of the rarer alpine species of the genus but known from several parts of Europe, North America and Japan.

Notes: the large, bronzy, short-stalked sporangia and the highly distinctive spores make this an easy species to identify. The tips of crowberry and alpine clubmoss are often blackened with the dehiscing sporangia of this species immediately under the chairlift on the upper parts of Cairngorm.

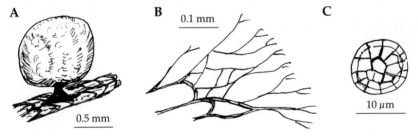

Fig. 165. *Lamproderma cribrarioides*:
A: sporangium on clubmoss; B: capillitium; C: spore.

Lamproderma debile (G. Lister & H.J. Howard) Ing
Trans. Br. mycol. Soc. **78**: 444. 1982. Norwich, Norfolk.
Syn. *Lamproderma violaceum* var. *debile* G. Lister & H.J. Howard

Sporocarps sessile sporangia, in small groups, subglobose on a membranous base, 0.5–0.6 mm diam. **Hypothallus** brown. **Columella** black, short-cylindrical, often absent. **Capillitium** a dense network of colourless or pale purple threads with membranous expansions at the angles. **Spores** black in mass, pale purplish-grey in transmitted light, 9–12 µm diam, minutely spinulose with a few clusters of small warts. **Plasmodium** not seen. [Fig. 166]

Illustrations: L3: pl. 216.
Habitat: beech litter.

Distribution: known only from Norfolk and Worcestershire; last seen in 1974 [2]. Possibly endemic.

Notes: this species had always been found with *L. anglicum*, with which it had been connected as part of *L. atrosporum* by Gulielma Lister, until the 1974 gathering in Worcestershire. The sessile sporangia, pale spores and characteristic membranous expansions at the junctions in the capillitium do not suggest any other species and when a columella is absent, it could easily be included in *Diacheopsis*.

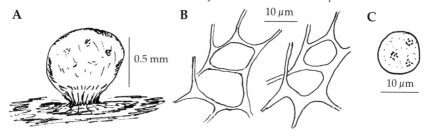

Fig. 166. *Lamproderma debile*: A: sporangium; B: capillitium; C: spore.

Lamproderma echinulatum (Berk.) Rostaf.
Mon. App.: 25. 1876. Tasmania.

Sporocarps stalked sporangia, in small groups, to 4 mm high, globose, 0.5–1 mm in diam, steely blue, iridescent. **Hypothallus** conspicuous, dark brown. **Stalk** black, 1–3 mm high. **Columella** cylindrical, blunt, reaching the centre of the sporangium. **Capillitium** arising mostly from the apex of the columella, stout, forking and anastomosing but not forming a very intricate net, purplish-brown, the tips slender and colourless. **Spores** black in mass, dark grey in transmitted light, 15–20 μm diam, with long black spines. **Plasmodium** white. [Fig. 167]

Illustrations: E: pl. 66; L3: pl. 134; MA: fig. 192.
Habitat: on stumps and logs, especially of conifers.
Distribution: rare, scattered, with no obvious pattern [18, H4]. Recorded from many parts of Europe and North America, also India, Japan, Australia and New Zealand.

Notes: the large, spiny spores are unlike any other species in the British Isles, only the European alpine *L. echinosporum* Meyl. being remotely like it.

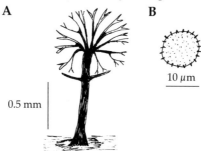

Fig. 167. *Lamproderma echinulatum*: A: sporangium; B: spore.

Lamproderma gulielmae Meyl.
Bull. Soc. Vaud. Sci. Nat. **52**: 449. 1919. Switzerland.

Sporocarps stalked sporangia, scattered, 1–2 mm high, globose, 0.3–0.5 mm diam, silvery blue with black, depressed spots. **Peridium** showing a netted effect in transmitted light. **Stalk** slender, black, 1–1.2 mm high. **Columella** reaching the centre of the sporangium. **Capillitium** arising from the top of the columella, colourless or very pale, branching. **Spores** in mass black, dark purple in transmitted light, 12–15 μm diam, with strong spines. **Plasmodium** yellow. [Fig. 168]

Illustrations: L3: pl. 215; MA: fig. 193; NB: 373.
Habitat: on forest litter, normally at the edge of melting snow in spring.
Distribution: known only from Norfolk and Aberdeen, last seen 1918 [2]. A rare species of alpine forests in Europe and North America.

Notes: the spotted peridium separates this from our other species, although there are several other spotted species in the mountains of Europe and North America. The spines on the spores are shorter than those on *L. echinulatum*.

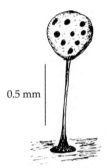

0.5 mm

Fig. 168. *Lamproderma gulielmae*: sporangium.

Lamproderma sauteri Rostaf.
Mon.: 205. 1874. Austria.
Syn. *Lamproderma violaceum* var. *sauteri* (Rostaf.) Lister

Sporocarps stalked sporangia, to 4 mm high, 1–2 mm diam, globose, slightly flattened at the base, dark blue with a metallic sheen, not shining. **Hypothallus** well developed, dark grey. **Stalk** black. **Columella** reaching the centre of the sporangium, slightly broadened at the top. **Capillitium** of coarse, stiff, reddish-purple threads, suddenly pale at the tips so that after the spores are shed the capillitium looks frosted. **Spores** black in mass, purple-brown by transmitted light, 12–14 μm diam, warted, the warts often tall enough to be mistaken for blunt spines. **Plasmodium** colourless. [Fig. 169]

Illustrations: L3: pl. 132; MA: fig. 197.
Habitat: on vegetation at the edge of melting snow patches in spring.

Distribution: known from scattered localities in the Scottish Highlands, only recently seen in the Cairngorms [4]. One of the commoner snowline species in Europe and North America, also known from New Zealand and the Chilean Andes.

Notes: the distinctly reddish capillitium with white tips, the larger, distinctly warted spores and the lack of a shiny iridescence make this large and, outside Britain, common alpine species easy to identify.

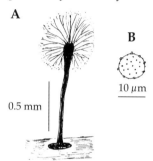

Fig. 169. *Lamproderma sauteri*: A: sporangium; B: spore.

Lamproderma scintillans (Berk. & Broome) Morgan
J. Cinc. Soc. Nat. Hist. **16**: 131. 1894. Sri Lanka.

Sporocarps long-stalked sporangia, 1–2 mm high, globose, 0.3–0.4 mm diam, metallic silvery blue or bronze, iridescent. **Hypothallus** discoid, black. **Stalk** slender, long, occasionally nodding, black. **Columella** cylindrical, blunt, just reaching the centre of the sporangium. **Capillitium** of stiff, straight, sparingly branched brown threads, pale at the base. **Spores** in mass black, violet-brown in transmitted light, 7–9 μm diam, evenly warted. **Plasmodium** white. [Fig. 170]

Illustrations: E: pl. 65; L3: pl. 130; MA: fig. 198; NB: 372.
Habitat: herbaceous litter, especially under holly, and decaying ferns.
Distribution: widespread and generally common in the British Isles, although distinctly lowland [90, H13]. Probably cosmopolitan.

Notes: the small sporangia, small spores, long stalks and the habitat make this common and beautiful species easy to identify.

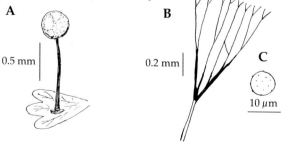

Fig. 170. *Lamproderma scintillans*: A: sporangium; B: capillitium; C: spore.

MACBRIDEOLA H.C. Gilbert
Stud. Nat. Hist. Iowa Univ. **16**: 155. 1934.

Sporocarps minute, stalked sporangia, usually on the bark of living trees. Stalk tubular, horny, hollow, translucent. **Peridium** often leaving a small collar at the base. **Columella** dividing in the mid or upper sporangium. **Capillitium** of a few branches, not anastomosing, sometimes absent. There are about 15 species; the type is *M. scintillans* H.C. Gilbert.

KEY TO SPECIES

1	Spores clustered	*synsporos*
–	Spores free	2
2 (1)	Peridium persistent, shining	*scintillans*
–	Peridium disappearing, at most leaving a collar	3
3 (2)	Spores 12–14 μm diam	*macrospora*
–	Spores less than 10 μm diam	4
4 (3)	Capillitium well developed, of uniformly stout threads	*cornea*
–	Capillitium sparse (or absent), of thin, tapering threads	*decapillata*

Macbrideola cornea (G. Lister & Cran) Alexop.
Mycologia **59**: 112. 1967. Skene, Aberdeenshire.
Syn. *Comatricha cornea* G. Lister & Cran

Sporocarps usually solitary, stalked sporangia, mostly 1 mm high but exceptionally reaching 2 mm, globose, 0.1–0.3 mm in diam, brown. **Hypothallus** discoid, yellow. **Stalk** tubular, translucent, horny, clear reddish-yellow below, darker above. **Columella** brown, cylindrical, just reaching the centre of the sporangium, with a small collar where it joins the stalk, forking into two or three main branches. **Capillitium** of dichotomous branches, ending in short, stiff, diverging branchlets. **Spores** reddish-brown in mass, yellowish-grey in transmitted light, 8.5–9 μm diam, minutely warted, the wall thinner and paler on one side. **Protoplasmodium** colourless. [Fig. 171]

Illustrations: E: pl. 125; L3: pl. 210; NB: 335.
Habitat: on mosses on the bark of living trees.
Distribution: common on trees in the west and north, rare or absent in the east [66, H34, C]. Common in Europe, especially in mountain forests, rare in North America, reported from Australia and Japan.

Notes: the habit of sitting on the tips of epiphytic moss leaves is not shared by other members of the genus. The well-developed capillitium, basal collar and small, free spores separate it readily from the other species. The clearly hollow stalk makes it obviously different from species of *Paradiacheopsis*, which also occur on bark and have a similarly reduced capillitial branching.

Macbrideola decapillata H.C. Gilbert
Stud. Nat. Hist. Iowa Univ. **16**: 158. 1934. Iowa.

Sporocarps stalked sporangia, scattered, globose, dark brown, total height 175–350 μm, diam 50–100 μm. **Stalk** slender, translucent, yellow at the base, brown above, 125–250 μm long. **Peridium** leaving a small collar. **Columella** reaching to three-quarters of the sporangial diameter, rounded at the tip or bearing a few short branches. **Capillitium** often absent but never more than a few filaments arising from the columella, tapering towards the outside. **Spores** in mass dark brown, violet brown in transmitted light, 7–9 μm diam, unevenly warted. **Protoplasmodium** colourless. [Fig. 172]

Illustrations: MA: fig. 161, 182.
Habitat: bark of living trees.
Distribution: known from two sites in West Sutherland, and from Co. Waterford, Co. Galway and Co. Westmeath [1, H3]. Apart from North and Central America, also recorded from Spain and Turkey.

Notes: easily separated from *M. cornea* when the capillitium is absent; when present it can be told from long-stalked specimens of *M. cornea* by the thin and tapering, rather than stout and uniformly thick threads.

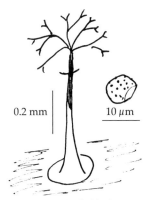
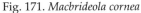
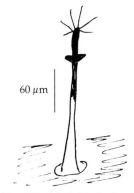

Fig. 171. *Macbrideola cornea*   Fig. 172. *Macbrideola decapillata*

Macbrideola macrospora (Nann.-Bremek.) Ing
Trans. Br. mycol. Soc. **78**: 444. 1982. France.
Syn. *Macbrideola cornea* var. *macrospora* Nann.-Bremek.

Sporocarps usually solitary, stalked sporangia, 1.5–2 mm high, globose, 0.2–0.5 mm diam, reddish-brown. **Hypothallus** discoid, pale brown. **Stalk** tubular, horny, dark brown. **Columella** brown, cylindrical, just reaching the centre of the sporangium, with a small collar where it joins the stalk, forking into two or three main branches. **Capillitium** of dichotomous branches, ending in short, stiff, diverging branchlets. **Spores** reddish-brown in mass, yellowish-grey in transmitted light, 12–14 μm diam, spinulose. **Protoplasmodium** colourless. [Fig. 173]

Illustrations: original description.
Habitat: bark of living trees.
Distribution: rare, down the west side of the country from Devon to Sutherland, Co. Donegal [7, H1]. Known in Europe from France, Spain and Switzerland.

Notes: the larger size, bigger spores, spinulose rather than warted, and the occurrence on bare bark rather than mosses help to separate this rare species from *M. cornea*.

Macbrideola scintillans H.C. Gilbert
Stud. Nat. Hist. Iowa Univ. **16**: 156. 1934. Iowa.

Sporocarps stalked sporangia, globose, total height 125–225 μm, 75–125 μm diam, dark brown, bronze or silver, iridescent. **Stalk** translucent, yellow at the base, brown above, 50–100 μm high. **Peridium** long persistent. **Columella** tapering, often forking at the apex, where it is attached to the peridium by the tip or the forks. **Capillitium** scanty, often consisting only of the branches from the columella, otherwise some simple lateral branches may occur. **Spores** in mass dull brown, light brown in transmitted light, 8–9 μm diam, with large, scattered warts. **Protoplasmodium** shining brown. [Fig. 174]

Illustrations: MA: fig. 183.
Habitat: bark of living trees.
Distribution: known from a single, recent, collection from Co. Antrim [H1]. Elsewhere known from North America, Belize and Sikkim.

Notes: the persistent, silvery peridium gives this rare species the look of a minute *Lamproderma* but the habitat and the tubular stalk rule out that genus.

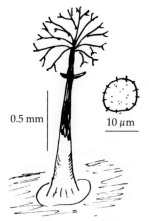

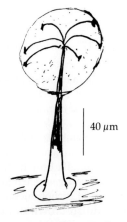

Fig. 173. *Macbrideola macrospora*   Fig. 174. *Macbrideola scintillans*

Macbrideola synsporos (Alexop.) Alexop.
Mycologia **59**: 115. 1967. Rhodes, Greece.

Sporocarps stalked sporangia, globose, dark brown, to 0.5 mm high, 0.25 mm diam. **Peridium** completely disappearing, not even leaving a collar. **Stalk** brown, tapering upwards from the pale, broad base. **Columella** reaching mid-sporangium. **Capillitium** open, arising from tip and sides of columella, branching and forming a net with few free ends. **Spores** brown in mass, pale brown in transmitted light, in tight clusters of 7–15 spores, pear-shaped, warted on the outside, smooth on the inside of clusters, 9.5–10.5 µm diam. **Protoplasmodium** colourless. [Fig. 175]

Illustrations: MA: fig. 179.
Habitat: bark of living trees.
Distribution: known from a single collection on alder bark from Bala, Merioneth, in 1978 [1]. Known from a few places in the Mediterranean, Switzerland and North America.

Notes: the spore clusters can be spotted under a x40 stereomicroscope and are the diagnostic feature. The capillitium forms a net, which is uncommon in the genus. Clearly the species is rare as it is easily identified.

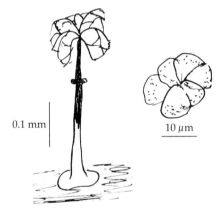

0.1 mm

10 µm

Fig. 175. *Macbrideola synsporos*

PARADIACHEA Hertel
Dusemia **7**: 349. 1956.

Sporocarps sessile sporangia, usually clustered. **Hypothallus** present, sometimes thin, sometimes thick and spongy. Peridium persistent, iridescent. **Columella** present or absent. **Capillitum** a network of branching threads, attached to the columella when present. Five species, the type is *P. cylindrica* (Bilgram) Hertel.

KEY TO SPECIES

1	Columella present, hypothallus absent	*howardii*
–	Columella absent, hypothallus present	*anglica*

Paradiachea anglica Ing & P.C. Holland
Trans. Br. mycol. Soc. **50**: 686. 1968. Chilworth, Surrey.

Sporocarps sessile sporangia, scattered or in small groups, short cylindrical with rounded apex, 0.5–0.7 mm high, 0.4 mm diam. **Hypothallus** a thick, wrinkled, white cushion on which the sporangia sit. **Stalk** and columella absent. **Peridium** single, membranous, minutely wrinkled, silvery iridescent, persistent, pale ochraceous and smooth in transmitted light. **Capillitium** a tangle of pale greyish violet threads which branch freely, with membranous expansions at the larger junctions and numerous free ends. **Spores** blackish-brown in mass, pale greyish-violet in transmitted light, 9–10 μm diam, minutely warted. **Plasmodium** not seen. [Fig. 176]

Illustrations: original description.
Habitat: fallen pine twigs.
Distribution: only known from the type collection, which was from Blackheath, Chilworth, near Guildford, Surrey (not Blackheath, Greenwich, Greater London, as in the protologue) [1]. Possibly endemic.

Notes: the hypothallus forms a cup round the base of the sporangium when the capillitium weathers away. The only confusion could be with species of *Diachea*, but they have a columella.

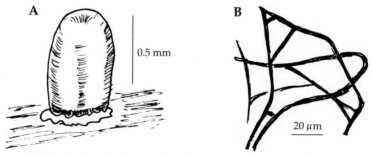

Fig. 176. *Paradiachea anglica*: A: sporangium; B: capillitium.

Paradiachea howardii Ing
Trans. Br. mycol. Soc. **78**: 441. 1982. Norwich, Norfolk.

Sporocarps sessile sporangia, scattered, cylindrical with blunt apex, 0.9–1.2 mm high, 0.4–0.5 mm diam. **Hypothallus** absent. **Peridium** single, membranous, smooth, silvery iridescent, persistent, pale ochraceous in transmitted light, eventually leaving a basal cup. **Columella** spike-like, tapering, half the height of the sporangium, ochraceous in transmitted light. **Capillitium** a tangle of colourless threads, radiating at right angles from the columella and attached to the peridium. **Spores** dark purple-brown in mass, pale purple-brown in transmitted light, 7–10 μm diam, minutely and closely warted. **Plasmodium** not seen. [Fig. 177]

Illustrations: original description.
Habitat: bracken litter.
Distribution: only known from the type collection, made in 1962 [1]. Possibly endemic.

Notes: the differences between these two species are obvious and easy to detect. In both species there are cross-branches in the capillitium which are reminiscent of *Didymium*, the persistent peridium is similar to *Diachea* and the relationships with *Comatricha* were pointed out by Hertel in his original account of the genus.

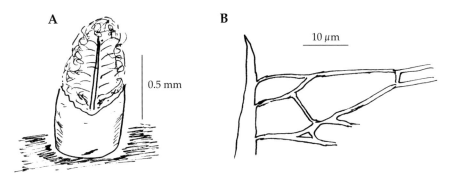

A

B

10 μm

0.5 mm

Fig. 177. *Paradiachea howardii*: A: sporangium; B: columella and capillitium.

PARADIACHEOPSIS Hertel
Dusemia **5**: 191. 1954.

Sporocarps minute, stalked sporangia, mainly on the bark of living trees. **Stalk** solid, fibrous. **Peridium** disappearing quickly. **Columella** dividing in the sporangium to give a branching but not anastomosing capillitium without a surface net. Ten species; the type is *P. curitibana* Hertel.

KEY TO SPECIES

1	Spores with long spines, to 1 μm long	2
–	Spores warted or smooth	3
2	Capillitium branches forming a network, their tips short	*cribrata*
–	Capillitium branches not forming a network, their tips long and tapering	*acanthodes*
3	Capillitium of fine threads with flattened, expanded tips, stalk slender, hair-like	*fimbriata*
–	Capillitium threads without expanded tips, stalk stout at base, narrowing upwards	4
4	Spores 9–10 μm diam, primary branches thick and stiff	*rigida*
–	Spores more than 11 μm diam, capillitium less robust	5
5	Primary branches of the capillitium at right angles to the columella, tips of branches with short spines, spores 11–13 μm diam	*microcarpa*
–	Primary branches of the capillitium not at right angles to the columella, tips blunt, not spine-like, spores 14–16 μm diam	*solitaria*

Paradiacheopsis acanthodes (Alexop.) Nann.-Bremek.
Proc. K. Ned. Akad. Wet. C **89**: 236. 1985. Greece.
Syn. *Comatricha acanthodes* Alexop.

Sporocarps stalked sporangia, 0.4–0.5 mm high, globose, dark brown, 0.2 mm diam. **Hypothallus** discoid, thin, reddish-brown. **Stalk** with a broad, fibrous, yellowish base, tapering upwards, dark and slender above. **Columella** reaching the centre of the sporangium. **Capillitium** of two or three slender, black branches arising from the top of the columella and forking three or four times without anastomosing. **Spores** brown in mass, grey in transmitted light, 12–13 μm diam, with prominent spines up to 1 μm long. **Protoplasmodium** white. [Fig. 178]

Illustrations: MA: fig. 157.
Habitat: bark of living trees.
Distribution: only known from two recent collections from north Wales, from Merioneth and Denbighshire [2]. Elsewhere known from Greece and North America.

Notes: the spiny spores and capillitium not forming a net are the distinctive features of this rare species. The base of the stalk is also far less netted than in *P. cribrata*.

Paradiacheopsis cribrata Nann.-Bremek.
Proc. K. Ned. Akad. Wet. C **71**: 47. 1968. France.

Sporocarps stalked sporangia, 0.2–0.6 mm high, globose, 0.2 mm diam, dark brown. **Hypothallus** discoid, pale yellow or colourless. **Stalk** with a distinctly netted base, like a basket, reddish-brown below, black above. **Peridium** leaving a small collar at the base. **Columella** reaching the centre of the sporangium where it divides into the branches of the capillitium. **Capillitium** branching two or three times, forming a stiff, incomplete globose net at the surface, with many free ends. **Spores** brown in mass, lilac-grey in transmitted light, 12–13 μm diam, with spines to 1 mm long. **Protoplasmodium** colourless. [Fig. 179]

Illustrations: NB: 367.
Habitat: bark of living trees.
Distribution: scattered across the British Isles, not uncommon [46, H3]. Distribution elsewhere is less clear, because of confusion with other species, but known to be widespread in Europe.

Notes: the spiny spores, netted capillitium and basket-like base of the stalk are good characters. This is close to *P. acanthodes* but the capillitial ends forming a spherical basket are sufficient to separate the two.

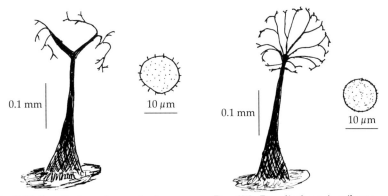

Fig. 178. *Paradiacheopsis acanthodes*   Fig. 179. *Paradiacheopsis cribrata*

Paradiacheopsis fimbriata (G. Lister & Cran) Hertel
Dusenia **7**: 348. 1956. Wanstead Park, Essex.
Syn. *Comatricha fimbriata* G. Lister & Cran

Sporocarps stalked sporangia, often in groups but also commonly scattered, 0.5–1.5 mm high, globose, 0.1–0.4 mm diam, black when fresh, becoming brown when the peridium falls away. **Hypothallus** discoid, brown. **Stalk** long, to three times the length of the sporangium, tapering, hair-like, black. **Peridium** shiny black for a few hours, then disappears completely. **Columella** slender, reaching to the centre of the sporangium, ending suddenly. **Capillitium** of slender threads, once-branched, widening to the tips where they are flattened or club-shaped. **Spores** dark reddish-brown, sometimes with a metallic glint, in mass, dark lilac-grey in transmitted light, 12–13 μm diam, densely and finely warted. **Plasmodium** colourless. [Fig. 180]

Illustrations: E: pl. 61; L3: pl. 214; MA: fig. 164; NB: 364.

Habitat: bark of living trees, often associated with green algae, such as *Desmococcus olivaceus*, with lichens such as *Hypogymnia physodes* or *Lecanora conizaeoides*; characteristic of the bark of conifers but also very common on bark of broad-leaved trees, such as oaks, in areas of acid deposition; even found in the centre of large cities. There are a few records on other substrates, such as *Rubus* stems.

Distribution: common throughout the British Isles, especially in secondary woodland and built-up areas [106, H7, C]. Probably cosmopolitan but under-recorded outside Europe.

Notes: the small, pin-like sporangia are abundant on acid bark, often developing after only one day in moist chamber culture. The flattened ends of the fine capillitium threads are distinctive.

Paradiacheopsis microcarpa (Meyl.) D.W. Mitchell ex Ing **comb. nov.**
Bull. Br. mycol. Soc. **12**: 95. 1978. Switzerland.
Basionym: *Comatricha laxa* var. *microcarpa* Meyl.
Bull. Soc. Vaud. Sci. Nat. **52**: 456. 1919.

Sporocarps stalked sporangia, solitary, 0.5–1 mm high, globose, 0.2–0.5 mm in diam, purple-brown. **Hypothallus** discoid, colourless. **Stalk** broad at the base tapering regularly to the top, black. **Columella** reddish-brown, reaching the centre of the sporangium. **Capillitium** reddish-brown, with major branches at right angles to the columella, forking once or twice, ending in short, spine-like tips. **Spores** in mass dark brown, dark grey in transmitted light, 11–13 μm in diam, finely warted. **Protoplasmodium** colourless to watery white. [Fig. 181]

Illustrations: original description.
Habitat: bark of living trees, especially conifers, but also oak.
Distribution: rare, known from Central London, Snowdonia, Cheshire, Berwickshire and Angus [6]. Not generally recognised elsewhere, except Switzerland where it has been found in several locations recently.

Notes: Mitchell's combination, as originally published, is invalid as the basionym and place of publication were omitted. It is hereby validated. The parallel branches of the capillitium and spiny tips of the branches are sufficient to separate this species from the other species of the genus.

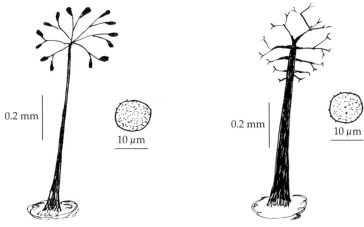

Fig. 180. *Paradiacheopsis fimbriata*   Fig. 181. *Paradiacheopsis microcarpa*

Paradiacheopsis rigida (Brandza) Nann.-Bremek.
in Martin & Alexop. *Myxom.*: 231. 1969. Romania.
Syn. *Comatricha laxa* var. *rigida* Brandza

Sporocarps stalked sporangia, 0.4–0.7 mm high, globose, 0.3–0.4 mm diam, dark brown. **Hypothallus** discoid, brown. **Stalk** with a netted base which is reddish-brown, tapering, black above. **Columella** reaching the centre of the sporangium, tapering. **Capillitium** dividing dichotomously, stiff, forming an open fan with pairs of short, blunt branchlets at the tips. **Spores** in mass dark brown, greyish-brown in transmitted light, 9–10 μm diam, minutely warted. **Protoplasmodium** white. [Fig. 182]

Illustrations: NB: 366.
Habitat: bark of living trees.
Distribution: rare, scattered [11, H5]. Widespread but uncommon in Europe; also recorded from Belize.

Notes: this is a much misunderstood species, with different opinions about the significance of spore size and rigidity of capillitium. As described here the thick, stiff capillitial branches, and the relatively small spores for the genus, are the distinctive features.

Paradiacheopsis solitaria (Nann.-Bremek.) Nann.-Bremek.
Ned. Myxom.: 232. 1974. Netherlands.
Syn. *Comatricha solitaria* Nann.-Bremek.

Sporocarps stalked sporangia, 0.3–0.8 mm high, globose, 0.2–0.4 mm diam, black when fresh, becoming dark brown when the peridium falls away. **Hypothallus** discoid, small, colourless. **Stalk** stout, with a fibrous, netted, not noticeably paler base, black. **Columella** dividing at the centre of the sporangium into a number of branches. **Capillitium** dark purple-brown, branched two or three times, the ends thick but not swollen. **Spores** dark brown in mass, grey-brown in transmitted light, 14–16 µm diam, finely warted. **Protoplasmodium** watery white. [Fig. 183]

Illustrations: NB: 365.
Habitat: bark of living trees, especially in ancient woodland, but also found in urban parks on older trees.
Distribution: common throughout the British Isles [96, H33, C]. Common throughout Europe and known from Chile and New Zealand.

Notes: the large sporangia with stout stalks and the large spores are enough to identify this common species.

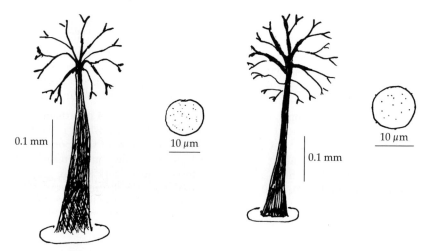

Fig. 182. *Paradiacheopsis rigida*   Fig. 183. *Paradiacheopsis solitaria*

STEMONARIA Nann.-Bremek., R. Sharma & Y. Yamam.

Sporocarps stalked, cylindrical sporangia. **Stalk** hollow, horny. Columella reaching the apex of the sporangium. **Capillitium** without a surface net. Fifteen species; the type is *S. fuscoides* Nann.-Bremek., R. Sharma & Y. Yamam.

Notes: this genus has the appearance and stalk structure of *Stemonitis* but is without a surface net. It also includes some species once placed in *Comatricha*.

Stemonaria longa (Peck) Nann.-Bremek., R. Sharma & Y. Yamam.
Proc. K. Ned. Akad. Wet. C **87**: 453. 1984. New York State.
Syn. *Comatricha longa* Peck

Sporocarps stalked sporangia, densely clustered, cylindrical, feathery, to 10–50 mm high, drooping, dark brown to nearly black. **Hypothallus** shining, black. **Stalk** black or dark red, shining. **Columella** dark, slender, reaching almost to the apex of the sporangium. **Capillitium** sparse, open, forking dichotomously, all the end branches free. **Spores** blue-black in mass, dark brown by transmitted light, 8–10 µm diam, reticulated with a pattern of fine warts. **Plasmodium** yellow. [Fig. 184]

Illustrations: E: pl. 61, photo 2; L3: pl. 122; MA: fig. 167; NB: 311.
Habitat: on rotten wood in hothouse in Britain, on stumps and rotten wood, including standing trunks and worked wood in the tropics and elsewhere.
Distribution: only known in the British Isles from a collection from an orchid house at the Royal Botanic Gardens Kew, made in 1938 [1]. Widespread in the tropics and known from the Americas, Asia, Africa and parts of Europe, but rare in the temperate zone.

Notes: the long, drooping clusters of feathery sporangia are unlike those of any other species.

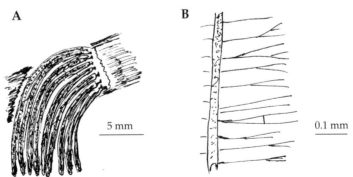

Fig. 184. *Stemonaria longa*: A: sporangia; B: capillitium.

STEMONITIS Gled.
Meth. Fung.: 140. 1753.

Sporocarps stalked, cylindrical sporangia, usually tufted. **Stalk** hollow, horny. **Columella** usually reaching the apex of the sporangium. **Capillitium** forming a dense network between the columella and the periphery, the ends forming a delicate, more or less complete, surface net. About 20 species; the type is *S. fusca* Roth.

KEY TO SPECIES

1	Spores reticulate	2
–	Spores spinulose or warted	6

2 (1) On leaf litter 3
– On wood or bark 4

3 (2) Sporangia 1.5–3 mm tall, spores banded-reticulate, surface net open *inconspicua*
– Sporangia 3 mm tall, spores spiny-reticulate, surface net tight *foliicola*

4 (2) Sporangia 6–20 mm tall, stalk more than a third of the total height, densely tufted, dark brown *fusca*
– Sporangia less than 6 mm tall, stalk less than a third of the total height, in smaller groups, lilac-brown or black 5

5 (4) Sporangia black, spores dark, 8–9 μm diam with 9 or more meshes to the diameter; on bark of living trees *nigrescens*
– Sporangia lilac-brown, spores pale, 6–7 μm diam, with 5 meshes to the diameter; on wood *virginiensis*

6 (1) Spores less than 7 μm diam, smooth 7
– Spores more than 7 μm diam, spinulose or warted 8

7 (6) Spores 5–7 μm diam, sporangia 7–15 mm tall, rusty brown *axifera*
– Spores 4–6 μm diam, sporangia 2–5 mm tall, cinnamon *smithii*

8 (6) Meshes of the surface net large, 20–100 μm diam, sporangia up to 20 mm tall, spore mass chestnut, capillitium with metallic glints *splendens*
– Meshes of the net small, less than 20 μm diam, sporangia rarely more than 10 mm tall, spore mass dull or pale brown, capillitium not metallic 9

9 (8) Columella ending with a distinct zigzag bend or a membranous plate just below the apex of the sporangium, sporangia pale reddish-brown *flavogenita*
– Columella without bend or plate, sporangia dull brown 10

10 (9) Sporangia on wood, 9–13 mm tall, spores almost smooth *lignicola*
– Sporangia on grass or litter, 4–7 mm tall, spores minutely warted *herbatica*

Stemonitis axifera (Bull.) T. Macbr.
N. Am. Slime-Moulds: 120. 1889. France.
Syn. *Stemonitis ferruginea* Ehrenb.

Sporocarps stalked sporangia, cylindrical with pointed apices, closely tufted, bright rusty brown, becoming paler as the spores disperse, 7–15 mm tall. **Hypothallus** common to a cluster, membranous. **Stalk** black, shining, to 7 mm high. **Columella** ending before the apex. **Capillitium** pale reddish-brown, branching regularly to produce a dense and even network, surface net delicate and persistent. **Spores** bright reddish-brown in mass, pale in transmitted light, 5–7 µm diam, nearly smooth. **Plasmodium** usually white, but occasionally pale yellow. [Fig. 185]

Illustrations: E: pl. 56; L3: pl. 119; MA: fig. 143; NB: 323.
Habitat: on rotten wood, rarely on bark of living trees.
Distribution: common throughout the British Isles [105, H34, C]. Cosmopolitan.

Notes: the small pale rust-red sporangia and the small, smooth spores make this common species easy to spot. It is usually smaller than *S. flavogenita* and lacks the characteristic columella structure of that species. It is larger, as are its spores, than the rare *S. smithii*.

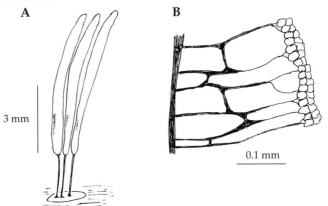

Fig. 185. *Stemonitis axifera*: A: sporangia; B: capillitium.

Stemonitis flavogenita E. Jahn
Verh. Bot. Prov. Ver. Brandenb. **45**: 165. 1904. Germany.

Sporocarps stalked sporangia, cylindrical, blunt, in close tufts, reddish-brown becoming paler as the spores disperse, 4–10 mm tall. **Hypothallus** membranous, from pale grey through red to black. **Stalk** black, up to a third of the total height. **Columella** ending suddenly just below the apex, usually with a zigzag bend or a membranous plate at the tip. **Capillitium** a loose network of threads with many membranous expansions, the surface net delicate but uneven and often short-lived. **Spores** in mass reddish-brown, lilac-brown in transmitted light, 7–9 µm diam, warted. **Plasmodium** usually pale yellow but occasionally white. [Fig. 186]

Illustrations: E: pl. 58; L3: pl. 119; MA: fig. 145; NB: 330.
Habitat: on rotten wood, rarely on bark of living trees.
Distribution: common and widespread in the British Isles, though less so than *S. axifera* [99, H16, C]. Probably cosmopolitan, but less common than *S. axifera*.

Notes: the pale rusty sporangia are larger than those of *S. axifera* and the columella plate or zigzag is highly distinctive, as are the membranous expansions at the capillitial branches.

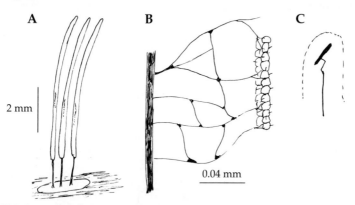

Fig. 186. *Stemonitis flavogenita*: A: sporangia; B: capillitium; C: tip of columella.

Stemonitis foliicola Ing
Trans. Br. mycol. Soc. **50**: 555. 1967. Ruislip, Middlesex

Sporocarps stalked sporangia, tufted, cylindrical, blunt, 3 mm high, dark brown. **Hypothallus** common to a cluster, membranous, dark brown. **Stalk** slender, black, up to a third of the total height. **Columella** black, reaching almost to the apex of the sporangium. **Capillitium** regularly branching, dark brown, with membranous expansions at junctions, forming a tight surface net with some outward pointed spines and a few free ends. **Spores** in mass dark brown, violet-grey in transmitted light, 8–9 µm diam, with a small meshed reticulum of spines. **Plasmodium** white. [Fig. 187]

Illustrations: NB: 333.
Habitat: in leaf litter.
Distribution: known from Sussex, Hertfordshire, Middlesex, Gloucestershire, Flintshire and Aberdeenshire [6]. Elsewhere recorded from the Netherlands and Austria.

Notes: the neat surface net and spiny-reticulate spores separate this from *S. inconspicua*, the habitat from all other species.

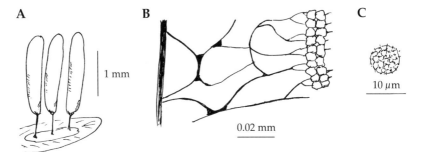

Fig. 187. *Stemonitis foliicola*: A: sporangia; B: capillitium; C: spore.

Stemonitis fusca Roth
Bot. Mag. **1**: 26. 1787. Europe.

Sporocarps stalked sporangia, tufted, cylindrical, blunt, slender, 6–20 mm tall, dark brown. **Hypothallus** common to a tuft of sporangia, membranous, shiny brown. **Stalk** up to half the total height, black, shining. **Columella** reaching the apex of the sporangium. **Capillitium** brown, branching to form a close network with 2–3 meshes between the columella and the periphery, with brown, membranous expansions, forming a surface net with meshes 3–20 μm diam, with spine-like free ends on the meshes. **Spores** dark brown in mass, lilac-brown in transmitted light, 8–9 μm diam, finely reticulated with rows of spines and ridges, 9 meshes across the diameter, in optical section showing a narrow border. **Plasmodium** white. [Fig. 188]

Illustrations: E: pl. 54; L3: pl. 118; MA: fig. 146; NB: 318–320.
Habitat: on fallen trunks, large branches and stumps.
Distribution: very common throughout the British Isles [111, H39, C]. Cosmopolitan.

Notes: the large, dark brown tufted sporangia with conspicuously reticulated spores make this common species easy to identify.

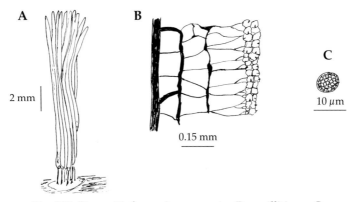

Fig. 188. *Stemonitis fusca*: A: sporangia; B: capillitium; C: spore.

Stemonitis herbatica Peck
Ann. Rep. N.Y. State Mus. **26**: 75. 1874. New York State.

Sporocarps stalked sporangia, tufted, the tufts in groups, cylindrical, blunt, dark brown, 5–7 mm high. **Hypothallus** inconspicuous, shared. **Stalk** short, to a fifth of the total height, black. **Columella** narrowing towards the apex and flexuous. **Capillitium** brown, with 3–4 meshes between columella and periphery, with membranous expansions, surface net without free ends, persistent, meshes 3–20 μm diam. **Spores** dark brown in mass, lilac-brown in transmitted light, 7–9 μm diam, evenly and finely warted. **Plasmodium** white. [Fig. 189]

Illustrations: E: pl. 57; L3: pl. 120; MA: fig. 147; NB: 330.
Habitat: on living grass and leaf litter.
Distribution: frequent and widespread in the British Isles [54, H6]. Probably cosmopolitan.

Notes: the dark colour, non-reticulate spores and the habitat separate this species from small forms of *S. fusca* or the pale species; the habitat, small size and the slightly warted spores separate it from *S. lignicola*.

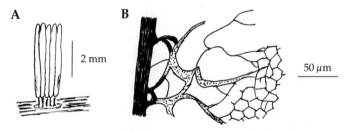

Fig. 189. *Stemonitis herbatica*: A: sporangia; B: capillitium.

Stemonitis inconspicua Nann.-Bremek.
Proc. K. Ned. Akad. Wet. C **69**: 350. 1966. Netherlands.

Sporocarps stalked sporangia, cylindrical, rounded at the apex, in small tufts, 1.5–3 mm tall, dark brown. **Hypothallus** shared in the tuft, membranous. **Stalk** short, to 0.5 mm long. **Columella** tapering upwards, not reaching the apex of the sporangium. **Capillitium** with an open network, surface net thin, fragile, meshes variable in size, angular, with long spines, the net sometimes missing from the apical region. **Spores** in mass dark reddish-brown, paler in transmitted light, 8.5–9.5 μm diam, with a distinct reticulation of bands and a border 0.5 μm high. **Plasmodium** white. [Fig. 190]

Illustrations: NB: 322.
Habitat: leaf litter.
Distribution: Known from Kent, Warwickshire, Merioneth, Caernarvon and Co. Louth [4, H1]. Elsewhere recorded only from the Netherlands and Florida.

Notes: the small size and banded-reticulate spores separate this species from *S. foliicola*.

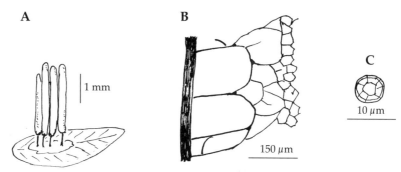

Fig. 190. *Stemonitis inconspicua*: A: sporangia; B: capillitium; C: spore.

Stemonitis lignicola Nann.-Bremek.
Proc. K. Ned. Akad. Wet. C **76**: 478. 1973. Netherlands

Sporocarps stalked sporangia, cylindrical, tufted, 9–13 mm high, 0.25–0.5 mm diam, dark brown. **Hypothallus** silvery, shared. **Stalk** no more than a quarter of the total height, dark, red-brown in transmitted light. **Columella** tapering, wavy, almost reaching the apex of the sporangium. **Capillitium** pale brown, forming a network with 3–5 meshes between the columella and the periphery, with membranous expansions at junctions, surface net with angular meshes 8–25 μm diam, with projecting spine-like extensions at the nodes of the net. **Spores** in mass mid-brown, pale reddish or yellowish-brown in transmitted light, 7–8 μm diam, almost smooth but with minute warts (oil immersion.) **Plasmodium** translucent yellow or white. [Fig. 191]

Illustrations: NB: 327.
Habitat: on rotten wood.
Distribution: scattered, north to Skye [17, H3]. Distribution abroad not clear because of confusion with *S. herbatica* Peck.

Notes: the slender, tapering sporangia in small tufts could be mistaken for *S. fusca*, but the spores are smooth, not reticulated. The spiny surface net is distinctive. It was originally included in *S. herbatica* but is larger, and occurs on wood, rather than leaf litter.

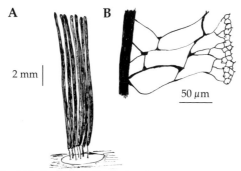

Fig. 191. *Stemonitis lignicola*: A: sporangia; B: capillitium.

Stemonitis nigrescens Rex
Proc. Acad. Sci. Philad. **43**: 392. 1891. Philadelphia.
Syn. *Stemonitis fusca* var. *nigrescens* (Rex) Torrend

Sporocarps stalked sporangia, cylindrical, rounded at base and apex, tufted, 2–5 mm high, blackish-brown to black. **Hypothallus** common to a tuft. **Stalk** black, 0.1–0.5 mm long. **Columella** almost reaching the apex of the sporangium. **Capillitium** of thin threads forming a network with a few expansions at the junctions, with 3 meshes between the columella and the periphery, forming a delicate surface net, with angular meshes 5–30 μm diam, with short spines. **Spores** black in mass, lilac-brown in transmitted light, 9–11 μm diam, with a fine reticulum of spines and ridges, showing as a narrow border in optical section. **Plasmodium** white or greenish-yellow, the latter colour particularly on bark. [Fig. 192]

Illustrations: MA: fig. 150; NB: 320.
Habitat: bark of living trees.
Distribution: scattered, north to Shetland [17, H10, C]. Widespread, but not common, in North America, Europe and Australia.

Notes: the small, dark sporangia, in small tufts, and the dark reticulate spores separate it from all except *S. fusca*. It is darker than *S. fusca*, smaller, and the spores are slightly larger. Several authors prefer to unite this species with *S. fusca* but all have ignored the ecological differences – this is primarily corticolous, whereas *S. fusca* is lignicolous. Until cultural studies have been made *S. nigrescens* is maintained as a species.

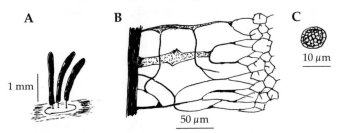

Fig. 192. *Stemonitis nigrescens*: A: sporangia; B: capillitium; C: spore.

Stemonitis smithii T. Macbr.
Bull. Nat. Hist. Univ. Iowa **2**: 381. 1893. Nicaragua.
Syn. *Stemonitis ferruginea* var. *smithii* (T. Macbr.) G. Lister and var. *violacea* Meyl.

Sporocarps stalked sporangia, cylindrical, rounded at base and apex, in tufts, 2–5 mm high, cinnamon. **Hypothallus** shared. **Stalk** about one-fifth of total height, black. **Columella** tapering and flexuous, almost reaching the apex of the sporangium. **Capillitium** pale brown, small-meshed, with 5–8 meshes between the columella and the periphery, forming a surface net with angular meshes, 8–35 μm diam, with minute, spiny, free ends. **Spores** pale cinnamon in mass, almost colourless in transmitted light, 4–6 μm diam, almost smooth but covered with minute, pale warts (oil immersion). **Plasmodium** white. [Fig. 193]

Illustrations: MA: fig 152; NB: 324.

Habitat: small branches and twigs in damp woodland.
Distribution: rare, scattered from Somerset to Aberdeenshire, in Wales only in Denbighshire and in Ireland in Co. Wicklow [19, H1]. Recorded from Europe, North America, Asia and New Zealand, but nowhere common.

Notes: the small size, very small spores and distinctive cinnamon colour are sufficient to identify this uncommon species.

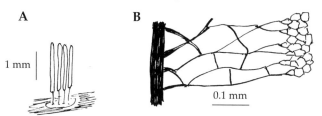

Fig. 193. *Stemonitis smithii*: A: sporangia; B: capillitium.

Stemonitis splendens Rostaf.
Mon.: 195. 1874. Europe.
var. **splendens**

Sporocarps stalked sporangia, cylindrical, blunt, tufted, 10–15 mm tall, dark brown with a reddish tinge. **Hypothallus** silvery, shining, common to a tuft. **Stalk** 1–4 mm long, shining black. **Columella** black, almost reaching the apex of the sporangium, tapering and flexuous towards the tip. **Capillitium** brown, with a metallic glint, the major branches at right angles to the columella, hardly forming a network, but giving rise to a surface net of thick threads, with large, round meshes, 18–50 μm diam, expanded at the junctions within the net. **Spores** in mass dark reddish-brown, lilac-brown in transmitted light, 7–9 μm diam, almost smooth with fine, pale warts (oil immersion). **Plasmodium** white. [Fig. 194]

Illustrations: E: pl. 54; L3: pl. 121; MA: fig. 153; NB: 325.
Habitat: on fallen trunks and on stumps.
Distribution: rare and distinctly Atlantic, New Forest and the western seaboard, north to Wester Ross [8, H3, C]. Cosmopolitan.

Notes: the reddish colour of the spore mass, the metallic glints on the capillitium and the large, graceful sporangia with enormous meshes to the surface net separate this from all other species. It is commonest in the tropics and thins out rapidly northwards, only occurring in the milder parts of the British Isles.

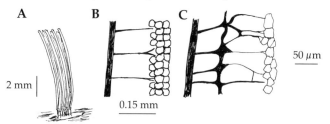

Fig. 194. *Stemonitis splendens*: A: sporangia; B: capillitium; C: capillitium of var. *webberi*.

var. **webberi** (Rex) Lister
Mycet.: 112. 1894. Kansas.

Differs from the type in the smaller size, 5–10 mm high, a better developed internal net, and the surface net being composed of thinner threads and less regular meshes.

Distribution: rare and less Atlantic in pattern, occurring inland [9, H6]. Cosmopolitan, but not always recorded separately from var. *splendens*.

Stemonitis virginiensis Rex
Proc. Acad. Sci. Philad. **43**: 391. 1891. Virginia.

Sporocarps stalked sporangia, tufted, cylindrical rounded at the apex, 2–6 mm tall, pale lilac-brown, fading to dull brown. **Hypothallus** shared, membranous, reddish-brown. **Stalk** less than a third of the total height, black and shining. **Columella** tapering, almost reaching the apex of the sporangium. **Capillitium** of pale brown threads forming a network with small expansions at the junctions, 3–5 meshes between columella and the periphery, surface net delicate and fragile, of angular meshes less than 10 μm diam, with a few outward pointing spines. **Spores** in mass lilac-brown, pale reddish or rose-brown in transmitted light, 6–7 μm diam, reticulate with rows of spines and ridges, the ridges perforated laterally (SEM) forming a large-meshed net with six meshes to the diameter. **Plasmodium** white. [Fig. 195]

Illustrations: E: pl. 55; L3: pl. 125; MA: fig. 156; NB: 321.
Habitat: on rotten wood.
Distribution: uncommon, scattered north to Orkney [21, H8]. Widespread in Europe, North America and New Zealand, but nowhere common.

Notes: the lilac-brown colour of the neat sporangia and the delicate spore reticulation are usually sufficient to identify this species. Under SEM the laterally perforated bands of the reticulum, forming bridges, appear to be rare, if not unique, in the Myxomycetes.

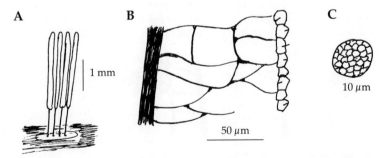

Fig. 195. *Stemonitis virginiensis*: A: sporangia; B: capillitium; C: spore.

STEMONITOPSIS (Nann.-Bremek.) Nann.-Bremek.
Ned. Myxom.: 203. 1974.

Sporocarps stalked, cylindrical sporangia, usually with rounded apices, gregarious but not tufted. **Stalk** fibrous (as in *Comatricha*) not hollow (as in *Stemonitis*). **Columella** reaching to apex of the sporangium. **Capillitium** forming a much branched network of threads ending as a surface net over at least the lower half of the sporangium. Twelve species. The type is *S. hyperopta* (Meyl.) Nann.-Bremek.

KEY TO SPECIES

1	Spores reticulated		2
–	Spores spinulose or warted		5
2 (1)	Spores less than 5 µm diam; on leaf litter, rare		*microspora*
–	Spores more than 5 µm diam; on wood or bark		3
3 (2)	Spore reticulated with rows of spines		*amoena*
–	Spore reticulated with bands or ridges		4
4 (3)	Sporangia lilac-brown, spores 5–6 µm diam; common		*hyperopta*
–	Sporangia dark brown, spores 7–9 µm diam; rare		*reticulata*

5 (1) Peridium silvery, semi-persistent, leaving flakes on the surface, stalks with a silvery-white sheath; common *typhina*

– Peridium disappearing completely, no 'silk stockings' on stalk; rare 6

6 (5) Spores 5.5–7 µm diam *gracilis*

– Spores 8–9 µm diam 7

7 (6) Sporangia slender, stalk up to half total height, capillitium dense *aequalis*

– Sporangia stout, stalk less than a quarter of total height, capillitium lax *subcaespitosa*

Stemonitopsis aequalis (Peck) Y. Yamam.
Myxom. Japan: 625. 1998. New York State.
Syn. *Comatricha nigra* var. *aequalis* (Peck) Sturgis; *C. aequalis* Peck; *Stemonitis aequalis* (Peck) Massee

Sporocarps stalked sporangia, gregarious, cylindrical, nodding, 0.4–0.6 mm diam, 2–6 mm high, dark brown. **Hypothallus** continuous under a colony, membranous, dark brown. **Stalk** black, up to half the total height. **Columella** black, almost reaching the apex of the sporangium. **Capillitium** dense, anastomosing freely, dark, with numerous short free ends, surface net confined to the lower part of the sporangium. **Spores** in mass dark purplish-brown, dark violet-brown in transmitted light, 8–9 µm diam, evenly warted. **Plasmodium** white. [Fig. 196]

Illustrations: L3: pl. 123; MA: fig. 158.
Habitat: on rotten wood.
Distribution: known from a single collection made in Aberdeenshire in 1914 [1]. Known from various parts of North and Central America and Europe, including France and Austria.

Notes: this species is separated on the basis of the long stalk, large, non-reticulate spores and dense capillitium. The species has had a chequered taxonomic history – it certainly has nothing to do with *Comatricha nigra!*

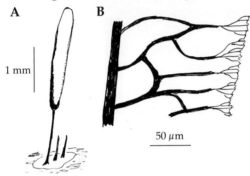

Fig. 196. *Stemonitopsis aequalis*: A: sporangium; B: capillitium.

Stemonitopsis amoena (Nann.-Bremek.) Nann.-Bremek.
Guide Temp. Myxom.: 337. 1991. Netherlands.
Syn. *Comatricha amoena* Nann.-Bremek.

Sporocarps stalked sporangia, in small groups, rarely solitary, cylindrical, 2–3.5 mm tall, rusty brown becoming dark brown with age. **Hypothallus** shining, common to a group or discoid under solitary sporangia. **Stalk** up to a third of the total height, black, netted at the base and merging into the hypothallus. **Columella** tapering and just reaching the apex of the sporangium. **Capillitium** dark, the network having 3–4 meshes between the columella and the periphery, with dark expansions, surface net delicate, of angular meshes which are uneven in size and shape, with a few thread-like, outward pointing, free ends. **Spores** in mass reddish-brown, pale red-brown in transmitted light, 6–7.5 μm diam, with a conspicuous reticulum of spines and ridges giving wide meshes, 3–4 to the diameter. **Plasmodium** white. [Fig. 197]

Illustrations: NB: 337.
Habitat: mostly on bark of living trees, especially of conifers, but occasionally on fallen branches.
Distribution: rare, scattered from Kent to Sutherland, in Wales only in Brecon [13]. Found in several European countries and, recently, in Chile.

Notes: the small size, reddish colours and large-meshed spores mark out this uncommon species.

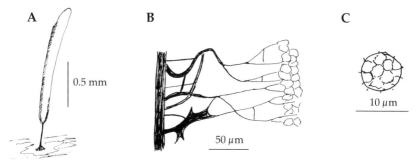

Fig. 197. *Stemonitopsis amoena*: A: sporangium; B: capillitium; C: spore.

Stemonitopsis gracilis (G. Lister) Nann.-Bremek.
Proc. K. Ned. Akad. Wet. C **76**: 486. 1973. Philadelphia.
Syn. *Comatricha pulchella* var. *gracilis* G. Lister

Sporocarps stalked sporangia, gregarious, to 2 mm tall, cylindrical, 0.3 mm diam, rounded at top and bottom, lilac-brown or dark brown. **Hypothallus** shared, brown. **Stalk** about a fifth of the total height, black, shining. **Columella** black, tapering, almost reaching the apex of the sporangium. **Capillitium** of wavy threads, forming a small-meshed network, up to 10 meshes between columella and periphery, without expansions, surface net of angular meshes, 5–25 µm diam, with no spines or free ends. **Spores** in mass brown, lilac-grey or pale brown in transmitted light, 5–7 µm diam, minutely, palely warted. **Plasmodium** not seen. [Fig. 198]

Illustrations: NB: 342.
Habitat: on fallen branches.
Distribution: rare, from Hampshire and Sussex north to Renfrew, not recorded in Wales, in Ireland only in Co. Louth [6, H1]. Not uncommon in the tropics, e.g. Thailand, and also known from France, Australia and North America.

Notes: this species recalls a larger version of *Comatricha pulchella* with darker colours and a partial surface net. It has been much misunderstood and is said to be close to *S. subcaespitosa* but differs in its dense, wavy capillitium and smaller spores. The whole family would benefit from cultural and molecular studies, but they are not easy to cultivate.

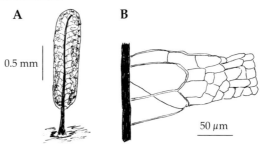

Fig. 198. *Stemonitopsis gracilis*: A: sporangium; B: capillitium.

Stemonitopsis hyperopta (Meyl.) Nann.-Bremek.
Guide Temp. Myxom.: 338. 1991. Switzerland.
Syn. *Stemonitis hyperopta* Meyl.

Sporocarps stalked sporangia, gregarious, 2.5–5 mm high, cylindrical pale lilac
when fresh, fading to brown. **Hypothallus** inconspicuous, red-brown, shared by a
group. **Stalk** 0.2–0.5 mm long, black, netted at the base. **Columella** just reaching
the apex of the sporangium, usually ending abruptly. **Capillitium** red-brown, the
internal net with 5 meshes between the columella and the periphery, threads thin,
with few expansions, surface net fragile, with small angular meshes, 5–15 μm
diam, more or less confined to the lower half of the sporangium. **Spores** in mass
reddish-lilac-brown, pale lilac-grey in transmitted light, 5–7 μm diam, with a fine
reticulum of bands and ridges (oil immersion) the meshes usually being a mixture
and large and small. **Plasmodium** white. [Fig. 199]

Illustrations: E: pl. 55; L3: pl. 125; MA: fig. 148; NB: 339.
Habitat: very rotten conifer wood.
Distribution: widespread in the British Isles, probably increasing with the spread
of coniferous plantations [72, H6]. Widespread in temperate Europe, North and
South America, Japan and New Zealand.

Notes: the pinkish-lilac-brown sporangia, small spores and preference for soggy
conifer branches separate this from the other reticulate species.

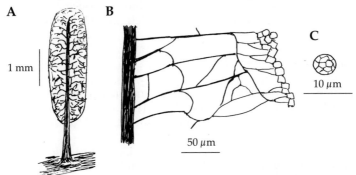

Fig. 199. *Stemonitopsis hyperopta*: A: sporangium; B: capillitium; C: spore.

Stemonitopsis microspora (Lister) Nann.-Bremek.
Guide Temp. Myxom.: 339. 1991. Uplyme, Devon.
Syn. *Stemonitis hyperopta* var. *microspora* (Lister) G. Lister; *S. microsperma* Ing

Sporocarps stalked sporangia, gregarious, subcylindrical to long-conical,
1.7–3.2 mm tall, lilac-grey when fresh, then brown. **Hypothallus** shared,
inconspicuous. **Stalk** 0.5-1.3 mm long, black. **Columella** tapering and reaching
the apex of the sporangium. **Capillitium** red-brown, the internal net with 3–5
meshes between the columella and the periphery, the threads flexuous, without
expansions, surface net fragmentary, with wavy threads and irregular meshes,

without free ends. **Spores** in mass lilac-grey when fresh, almost colourless in transmitted light, 3.5–4.5 μm diam, with a very fine reticulum of low ridges and bands, of large and small meshes. **Plasmodium** white. [Fig. 200]

Illustrations: L3: pl. 125; NB: 340.
Habitat: leaf litter.
Distribution: known only from Devon, Surrey, Essex and Norfolk; not seen for over 70 years [4]. Reported from Europe and North America, but never common.

Notes: the small size, tiny spores and the habitat would enable this species to be identified, should it ever be found again in the British Isles.

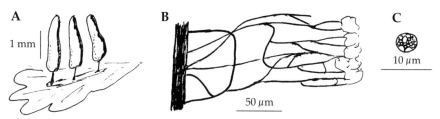

Fig. 200. *Stemonitopsis microspora*: A: sporangia; B: capillitium; C: spore.

Stemonitopsis reticulata (H.C. Gilbert) Nann.-Bremek. & Y. Yamam.
Proc. K. Ned Akad. Wet. C **98**: 325. 1995. North America.
Syn. *Comatricha reticulata* H.C. Gilbert

Sporocarps stalked sporangia, scattered or gregarious, ovate to cylindrical, 1.5–3 mm high, 0.4–0.8 mm wide, dark lilac-brown. **Hypothallus** thin, silvery. **Stalk** black, shining, less than half the total height. **Columella** reaching three-quarters to the apex of the sporangium. **Capillitium** dense, anastomosing, surface net mostly absent, with abundant free ends. **Spores** brown in mass, pale lilac-brown in transmitted light, 7–9 μm diam, faintly banded-reticulate. **Plasmodium** not seen. [Fig. 201]

Illustrations: MA: fig. 174.
Habitat: on rotten conifer wood.
Distribution: only known from a single collection made at Anglezarke, Lancashire, in 1972 [1]. Recorded from several areas of North America as well as Poland; its distribution in the rest of Europe is uncertain.

Notes: this much misunderstood species is the only dark brown banded-reticulate species of the genus occurring on wood. It was previously reported as *Comatricha dictyospora* Celak which is a *nomen dubium*.

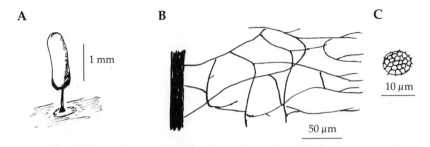

Fig. 201. *Stemonitopsis reticulata*: A: sporangium; B: capillitium; C: spore.

Stemonitopsis subcaespitosa (Peck) Nann.-Bremek.
Guide Temp. Myxom.: 343. 1991. New York State.
Syn. *Comatricha nigra* var. *subcaespitosa* (Peck) G. Lister; *C. subcaespitosa* Peck

Sporocarps stalked sporangia, scattered or gregarious, cylindrical, rounded at top and bottom, 1.5–3 mm tall, dark brown. **Hypothallus** silvery, shining. **Stalk** black, up to a quarter of the total height. **Columella** almost reaching the apex of the sporangium. **Capillitium** lilac-brown, the internal net with large expansions, 3–4 meshes between the columella and the periphery, the surface net almost complete with thin wavy threads forming angular meshes, 6–25 µm diam. **Spores** in mass brown, lilac-brown in transmitted light, 10–11.5 µm diam, finely warted. **Plasmodium** white. [Fig. 202]

Illustrations: MA: fig. 177; NB: 343.
Habitat: fallen branches and, rarely, the bark of living trees.
Distribution: rare, scattered from southern England to Aberdeen, not in Wales or Ireland [10, C]. Known from North America, Chile, France and Morocco but confused with other species.

Notes: some authors equate it to *S. gracilis*, but it differs in the lax capillitium and larger spores. It is similar to *S. brachypus* (Meyl.) Y. Yamam. but differs in its more slender shape, longer stalk and larger spores.

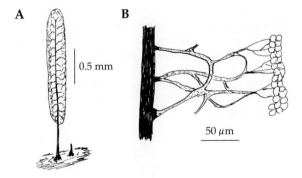

Fig. 202. *Stemonitopsis subcaespitosa*: A: sporangia; B: capillitium.

Stemonitopsis typhina (F.H. Wigg.) Nann.-Bremek.
Guide Temp. Myxom.: 341. 1991. France.
Syn. *Comatricha typhoides* (Bull.) Rostaf.

Sporocarps stalked sporangia, in large groups, cylindrical, 2–5 mm tall, lilac-grey with a silvery reflection when fresh. **Hypothallus** red-brown, shared. **Peridium** long-lasting, silvery lilac-grey, leaving flakes on the capillitium and sometimes a collar at the base. **Stalk** 0.5–2 mm long, black, up to half the total height, covered in a silvery sheath which looks like silk stockings. **Columella** tapering, reaching the apex of the sporangium. **Capillitium** dark brown, the internal net with 3–4 meshes between the columella and the periphery, expanded where it joins the columella, tapering outwards, surface net fragmentary, mostly confined to the lower half of the sporangium, meshes 6–24 µm diam, of thin flexuous threads. **Spores** brown in mass, lilac-brown in transmitted light, 6–8 µm diam, with very fine pale warts (oil immersion) and some large, darker clusters of warts. **Plasmodium** white. [Fig. 203]

Illustrations: E: pl. 62; L3: pl. 125; MA: fig. 181; NB: 341.
Habitat: on very rotten, often soggy, wood, usually of broad-leaved trees.
Distribution: very common throughout the British Isles [112, H40, C]. Cosmopolitan.

Notes: the persistent peridium, the 'silk stockings' on the stalk, and the general resemblance to miniature reedmace, *Typha latifolia*, are the hallmarks of this very common species; the spore markings are also very characteristic.

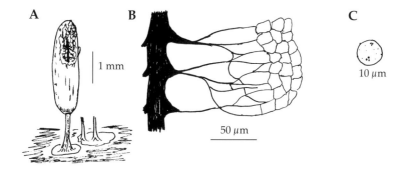

Fig. 203. *Stemonitopsis typhina*: A: sporangium; B: capillitium; C: spore.

SYMPHYTOCARPUS Ing & Nann.-Bremek.
Proc. K. Ned. Akad. Wet. C 70: 218. 1967.

Sporocarps pseudoaethalia, of partly merged sporangia which are sessile or nearly so, cylindrical, with hollow, horny columellae, which may be reduced or absent. **Peridium** disappearing but often leaving flakes on the surface of the capillitium. **Capillitium** dark, branched, forming a net, often with expansions at the junctions, not forming a surface net. Nine species; the type is *S. flaccidus* (Lister) Ing & Nann.-Bremek.

Notes: the genus was set up for those taxa previously included in *Comatricha*, *Stemonitis* or *Amaurochaete* which were regarded as 'flaccid' or 'confluent' forms whose development had been impaired by weather conditions. Examination of a large range of material and field observations suggest that these are not abnormal forms, just different!

KEY TO SPECIES

1	Spores reticulated	2
–	Spores warted or spiny	3
2 (1)	Sporocarps on stumps and fallen trunks	*amaurochaetoides*
–	Sporocarps on *Sphagnum* moss in bogs	*trechisporus*
3 (2)	Spore mass bright chestnut-brown	*flaccidus*
–	Spore mass dark brown	4
4 (3)	Sporocarps on leaf litter, spores warted	*herbaticus*
–	Sporocarps on wood or twigs, spores spiny	*impexus*

Symphytocarpus amaurochaetoides Nann.-Bremek.
Proc. K. Ned. Akad. Wet. C **70**: 220. 1967. Netherlands.
Syn. *Stemonitis fusca* var. *confluens* Lister

Sporocarps pseudoaethalia, pulvinate, 5–50 mm diam and 5 mm high, component sporangia 0.5 mm diam, black. **Hypothallus** thin, forming a raised margin around the sporocarp, silvery. **Peridium** completely disappearing, not leaving flakes on the capillitium. **Columella** absent or irregular and split, different parts of a sporocarp either with or without columellae. **Capillitium** of thick, dark threads, forming a wide-meshed net with a few expanded junctions, and short, stiff free ends. **Spores** in mass black, lilac-brown in transmitted light, 8–10 μm diam, spiny-reticulate. **Plasmodium** white, usually extensive. [Fig. 204]

Illustrations: L3: pl. 118; NB: 308.
Habitat: on stumps and fallen trunks, mostly of broad-leaved trees.
Distribution: uncommon, scattered across the country with no obvious pattern [42, H3]. Recorded from several parts of Europe and New Zealand.

Notes: this looks like an aethalial *Stemonitis fusca* but is darker and the sporangia have lost their identity. The reticulated spores and the habitat are sufficient to separate it in the British Isles although there are other reticulate species elsewhere, e.g. *S. cristatus* Nann.-Bremek. which has prominently crested spores.

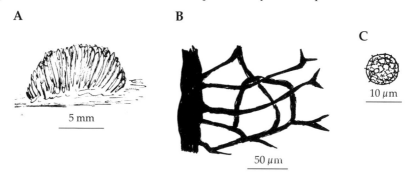

Fig. 204. *Symphytocarpus amaurochaetoides*:
A: pseudoaethalium; B: capillitium; C: spore.

Symphytocarpus flaccidus (Lister) Ing & Nann.-Bremek.
Proc. K. Ned. Akad. Wet. C **70**: 217. 1967. Uplyme, Devon.
Syn. *Stemonitis splendens* var. *flaccida* Lister; *Amaurochaete ferruginea* T. Macbr. & G.W. Martin

Sporocarps pseudoaethalia, pulvinate or flattened pyramids, 4–7 cm diam, rust-coloured, then reddish-brown, the component sporangia cylindrical, 0.5 mm diam. **Hypothallus** often spongy, silvery. **Peridium** leaving flakes which are not connected to the capillitium. **Columella** usually present, irregular, often bent or split, often joined to neighbours, red-brown. **Capillitium** forming a wide-meshed net with expanded nodes and free ends, fragile and breaking away with the spores. **Spores** chestnut-brown in mass, pale reddish-brown in transmitted light, 7–9 μm diam, very palely and minutely warted, often appearing smooth. **Plasmodium** usually white but may be pale yellow. [Fig. 205]

Illustrations: L3: pl. 121; MA: 126; NB: 304.
Habitat: most frequently on dead, standing pine trunks but also on fallen conifer logs, stumps and, occasionally on birch; also on structural softwood in buildings, such as gate and door posts.
Distribution: frequent, especially in mature pinewoods, whether native or plantation [73, H5]. Widespread in temperate North America, Europe, Australia and New Zealand, and also recorded from Pakistan.

Notes: the bright chestnut spore mass is reminiscent of *Stemonitis splendens*, but the round aethalia several metres up a dead pine trunk are very distinctive. The sporocarps are a favourite breeding site for beetles such as *Anisotoma humeralis*.

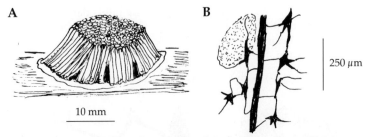

Fig. 205. *Stemonitopsis flaccidus*: A: pseudoaethalium; B: capillitium.

Symphytocarpus herbaticus Ing
Proc. K. Ned. Akad. Wet. C **70**: 229. 1967. Epping Forest, Essex.
Syn. *Stemonitis herbatica* var. *confluens* G. Lister

Sporocarps pseudoaethalia, 8–25 mm diam and 6 mm high, the component sporangia, short-cylindrical, 0.5 mm diam, blunt, grey-brown, the upper surface of the sporocarp areolate with conspicuous ridges. **Hypothallus** thin, inconspicuous. **Peridium** leaving silvery-grey-brown flakes on the upper surface, the base and within the sporocarp, these flakes are pale ochraceous in transmitted light and are marked with areolae with a thickened margin. **Columella** usually absent, if present irregular, dark brown. **Capillitium** pale brown, anastomosing and forming an irregular net of small meshes, 20–50 μm diam, outer branches not forming a surface net nor attached to the peridial flakes. **Spores** house-mouse grey in mass, nearly colourless in transmitted light, 6–8.5 μm diam, minutely spinulose. **Plasmodium** white. [Fig. 206]

Illustrations: original description.
Habitat: forest leaf litter.
Distribution: known only from Kent, Essex, Surrey, Worcestershire, Lincolnshire and Co. Galway [5, H1]. Recorded from North America, Java and Sri Lanka, but not, seemingly from elsewhere in Europe.

Notes: the compact aethalia are paler than *Stemonitis herbatica* and the habitat rules out all species except the next, which is larger, darker and usually on twigs when in the litter. The present species is very different from the usual idea of a 'confluent' *Stemonitis*.

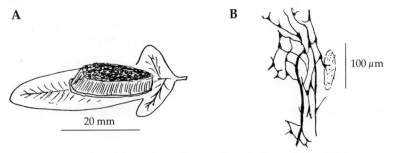

Fig. 206. *Stemonitopsis herbaticus*: A: pseudoaethalium; B: capillitium.

Symphytocarpus impexus Ing & Nann.-Bremek.
Proc. K. Ned. Akad. Wet. C **70**: 227. 1967. Netherlands.

Sporocarps pseudoaethalia, to 3 cm diam and 4–5 mm high, composed of very crowded sporangia whose tips are free, dull black. **Hypothallus** thin, silvery. **Peridium** leaving a few red-brown flakes which are connected to the capillitium. **Columella** red-brown, hollow, darker above and often dividing. **Capillitium** very dark brown, arising from the whole length of the columella, forming an open net, the junctions having pale brown expansions, with thorn-like free ends. **Spores** dull black in mass, violet-brown in transmitted light, 8–9 μm diam, conspicuously spinulose. **Plasmodium** white. [Fig. 207]

Illustrations: NB: 306.
Habitat: on fallen wood, and, frequently in very twiggy litter on the forest floor.
Distribution: uncommon, scattered, mostly in the south [23, H4]. Probably confused with the non-British *Stemonitis confluens* Cooke & Ellis so the data are hard to interpret, but the segregate is recorded from Spain and France as well as the Netherlands.

Notes: the brown spiny, spores and the capillitium forming tangled 'locks' along the lines of the constituent sporangia, separate this species.

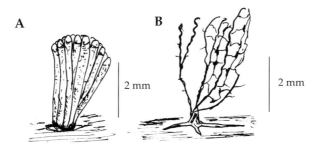

Fig. 207. *Stemonitopsis impexus*: A: pseudoaethalium; B: capillitium.

Symphytocarpus trechisporus (Berk. ex Torrerd) Nann.-Bremek.
Proc. K. Ned. Akad. Wet. C **70**: 219. 1967. Venezuela.
Syn. *Stemonitis fusca* var. *trechispora* Berk. ex Torrerd; *Stemonitis trechispora* (Berk. ex Torrerd) T. Macbr.

Sporocarps pseudoaethalia composed of dense clusters of black sporangia, joined below, free above, 3–7 mm high, black. **Hypothallus** inconspicuous. **Peridium** disappearing completely. **Stalks** of component sporangia very short, black, usually absent. **Columella** black, twisted, disappearing before the apex. **Capillitium** open, irregular, leading to a partial surface net, at least on the upper, free portions of the component sporangia. **Spores** in mass black, purple-brown in transmitted light, 11–13 μm diam, clearly banded-reticulate, with a border 0.5 μm high. **Plasmodium** white. [Fig. 208]

Illustrations: L3: pl. 118; MA: fig. 154.
Habitat: on the surface of *Sphagnum* bogs.
Distribution: rare, only known from Devon and Aberdeenshire [2]. Recorded from North and South America and Japan, but not always separated from other taxa, in spite of the habitat.

Notes: the distinctive habitat should make this species easy to identify and the only other candidate is *Amaurochaete trechispora*, which also occurs on *Sphagnum*, but has larger and darker spores. The capillitium is also said to be different but that may be due to comparing an *Amaurochaete* with a *Stemonitis*. Although kept distinct by most workers the coincidence of the unusual habitat with aethalial/pseudoaethalial forms with only slightly different spores suggests that they are conspecific. However, so little material has been studied that it is not appropriate to synonymise them at this time.

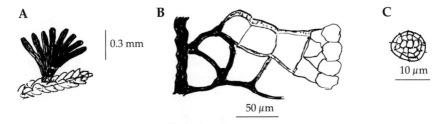

Fig. 208. *Stemonitopsis trechisporus*:
A: pseudoaethalium on *Sphagnum*; B: capillitium; C: spore.

PHYSARALES T. Macbr.
North American Slime-Moulds edn 2: 22. 1922.

Sporocarps stalked or sessile sporangia, plasmodiocarps or aethalia. **Hypothallus**, stalk, columella, peridium and capillitium may all contain deposits of calcium carbonate, crystalline in Didymiaceae. **Spores** dark purple-brown to black in mass, always with a violaceous tint in transmitted light. **Plasmodium** a phaneroplasmodium. Four families recognised, including the non-British Protophysaraceae.

PHYSARACEAE Chevall.
Fl. Gén. Env. Paris 1: 332. 1826.

Sporocarps stalked or sessile sporangia, plasmodiocarps or aethalia. **Hypothallus**, stalk, columella, peridium and capillitium may all contain deposits of calcium carbonate, granular, never crystalline. **Capillitium** of either calcareous tubes, branched or simple, barely connected by limeless tubules (the *badhamioid* type), or a series of swollen calcareous nodes connected by limeless tubules and usually forming a branching network (the *physaroid* type). In *Leocarpus* and *Willkommlangea* the capillitium is said to be duplex and consists of two separate but interwoven systems, rather like a mixture of badhamioid and physaroid elements. Nine genera recognised, of which *Erionema* and *Physarella* are predominantly tropical.

Notes: the limits between the included genera are often poorly defined, *Physarum* grades into *Badhamia, Craterium* and *Fuligo* and several species have been moved between genera on several occasions. The characters used here to separate species and genera are functional rather than absolute.

KEY TO GENERA

1	Capillitium of two distinct types within the same sporangium, of plates and tubules with thickened nodes	2
–	Capillitium of only one type within the same sporocarp	3
2 (1)	Sporangiate, the peridium cartilaginous and brittle, shining chestnut-brown, the fructification resembling a bunch of grapes	*Leocarpus*
–	Plasmodiocarpous, orange, red or yellow, often with parallel rings showing along the length of the plasmodiocarp	*Willkommlangea*
3 (1)	Sporocarps aethalioid	*Fuligo*
–	Sporocarps sporangiate or plasmodiocarpous	4
4 (3)	Capillitium badhamioid, of calcareous tubes and few hyaline tubules	5
–	Capillitium physaroid, a network of calcareous nodes and hyaline tubules	6

5 (4)   Capillitium of tubular columns from base to apex of sporangium
Badhamiopsis
–   Capillitium of branching, calcareous tubes, randomly oriented   *Badhamia*

6 (4)   Sporocarps stalked sporangia, usually with a deep, persistent cup-like base, often with a distinct lid, or if not, with circumscissile dehiscence
Craterium
–   Sporocarps sporangia or plasmodiocarps, dehiscence irregular or by lobes, not circumscissile, peridium rarely leaving a basal cup, if so it is shallow and irregular   *Physarum*

BADHAMIA Berk.
Trans. Linn. Soc. Lond. **21**: 153. 1853.

Sporocarps sessile or stalked sporangia, or short plasmodiocarps. **Hypothallus** well developed, not usually heavily calcareous. **Peridium** with deposits of calcareous granules, rarely lacking, then appearing iridescent. Stalk, when present, often thin and weak. **Columella** absent, but occasionally a pseudocolumella, not attached to the stalk or base of the sporangium, may be present. **Capillitium** typically of calcareous tubes, usually branching to form an open network, with or without limeless tubules. Spores often in clusters, black in mass. About 30 species; the type is *B. capsulifera* (Bull.) Berk.

Notes: the differences between *Badhamia* and *Physarum* are small, but the tubular, non-nodal capillitium with few hyaline tubules – the 'badhamioid' pattern – and the fact that typical members of the genus have clustered spores, make it convenient to keep them separate.

KEY TO SPECIES

1   Spores clustered, capillitium without hyaline tubules   2
–   Spores free, capillitium sometimes with hyaline tubules   7

2 (1)   Spore clusters loose, breaking apart, spores globose, uniformly warted, sporangia large, on membranous stalks; on bracket fungi on logs
utricularis
–   Spore clusters tight, persistent, spores ovoid to ellipsoid, ornamentation only on outer surface of cluster   3

3 (2)   Spore clusters of 10–40 spores, often hollow   *versicolor*
–   Spores in smaller, solid clusters   4

4 (3)   Sporangia orange or yellow with green flecks; on bracket fungi on bark
nitens
–   Sporangia white or grey   5

5 (4)   Sporangia heaped, peridium heavily calcareous, white; on wood *populina*
–   Sporangia not heaped, peridium lightly calcareous, even iridescent   6

6 (5)   Sporangia sessile or short-stalked, spores 13–14 μm diam   *capsulifera*
–   Sporangia sessile, spores 10–11 μm diam   *dubia*

7 (1)   Sporangia stalked, yellowish-green, capillitium badhamioid   *viridescens*
–   Sporangia without green colour   8

8 (7)   Sporocarps sessile sporangia or short plasmodiocarps, bright orange
                                                                      rugulosa
–   Sporocarps without orange colour   9

9 (8)   Spores elliptical with a low, longitudinal ridge, sporangia dull,
        off-white   *apiculospora*
–   Spores globose   10

10 (9) Peridium delicate, more or less iridescent, calcareous material sparse,
        capillitium typically badhamioid   11
–   Peridium thicker, not iridescent, more heavily calcareous, capillitium often
        with hyaline tubules   12

11 (10) Sporangia elongated, stalks long, weak, pale; on bracket fungi *utricularis*
–   Sporangia globose, usually sessile but occasionally on short, weak,
        yellow stalks; on living grass, grass litter, alpine litter and bark
        of living trees   *foliicola*

12 (10) Sporangia long-stalked, spores reticulated   *gracilis*
–   Sporangia short-stalked or sessile, spores not reticulated   13

13 (12) Sporangia small, sessile, heaped, lilac-grey; on vegetation on the surface
        of *Sphagnum* bogs   *lilacina*
–   Sporangia not heaped, white or grey; on other substrates   14

14 (13) Hypothallus, base of sporangium and, when present, short stalks, red,
        spores pale, smooth   *panicea*
–   Without red colouration, spores dark, warted or spiny   15

15 (14) Sporangia globose, stalk, if present, yellow or brown, spores warted
                                                                     macrocarpa
–   Sporangia flattened, stalk, if present, black, spores spiny   *affinis*

Badhamia affinis Rostaf.
Mon.: 143. 1874. Chile.

Sporocarps sessile sporangia, rarely with a short stalk, gregarious, depressed-pulvinate to discoid, 0.3–1 mm diam, pale grey or white, base darker, often black, rarely short plasmodiocarps. **Hypothallus** inconspicuous. **Stalk**, if present, short, black. **Peridium** thin, membranous, usually densely covered with calcareous flakes, giving the sporangium a mottled appearance, sometimes only lightly covered and then dark (especially in moist chamber cultures). **Capillitium** delicate, the tubes narrow and pointed, white, sometimes forming expanded nodes but not forming a branched network and not connected to base or peridium. **Spores** in mass black, dark violet-brown in transmitted light, free, 13–15 µm diam, densely spinulose. **Plasmodium** white. [Fig. 209]

Illustrations: DM 2: 166,167; E: pl. 76; L3: pl. 8; MA: fig. 203; NB: 176.
Habitat: bark of living trees, often on mosses.
Distribution: scattered, commoner in western and upland areas [33, H9]. Widespread in Europe, especially in the mountains, North and South America. Australia and Japan.

Notes: the rather flattened, discoid, sporangia, narrow capillitium tubes and dark, spiny spores are good characters. A taxon with spores 17–18 µm diam, with a pale equatorial band, has been separated as *B. armillata* Nann.-Bremek.; it has not yet been found in the British Isles.

A   B   C

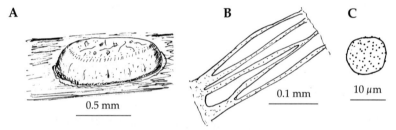

0.5 mm

0.1 mm   10 µm

Fig. 209. *Badhamia affinis*: A: sporangium; B: capillitium; C: spore.

Badhamia apiculospora (Härk.) Eliasson & N. Lundqv.
Bot. Notiser **132**: 560. 1979. Finland
Syn. *Physarum apiculosporum* Härk.; *Badhamia semiannulata* Raub & H.W. Keller

Sporocarps sessile sporangia, crowded, 0.2–0.5 mm diam, mostly globose and flattened but also forming short plasmodiocarps, off-white. **Peridium** double, the outer layer eggshell-like, smooth, the inner membranous. **Capillitium** dense, white, physaroid, often forming a pseudocolumella of massed calcareous nodes in the centre. **Spores** black in mass, pale purple-brown in transmitted light, elliptical with a low longitudinal ridge, 10–13 x 8–10 µm. **Plasmodium** not seen. [Fig. 210]

Illustrations: DM 2: 168; L3: pl. 12; MA: fig. 212.
Habitat: straw heaps.
Distribution: rare, only recorded from the Chilterns, Bedfordshire, Buckinghamshire and Hertfordshire, last seen in 1931 [3]. Scattered in Europe, North America, Egypt and New Zealand.

Notes: the chequered taxonomic history of this rare species is suggested by the, partial, list of synonyms. It is known from barley seeds in moist chamber culture, dung and straw, whereas the true *B. ovispora* Racib., a name misapplied to *B. apiculospora*, is probably associated with decaying bark. This is another of the straw heap species which we have probably lost from the British Isles as a result of changes in the management of cereal crops.

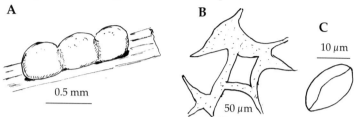

Fig. 210. *Badhamia apiculospora*: A: sporangium; B: capillitium; C: spore.

Badhamia capsulifera (Bull.) Berk.
Trans. Linn. Soc. Lond. **21**: 153. 1853. France.

Sporocarps sessile (very occasionally weakly stalked) sporangia or short plasmodiocarps, 0.5–1.5 mm diam, globose, greyish-white or white. **Stalk,** if present, weak, straw-coloured, a mere continuation of the thin hypothallus. **Peridium** thin, translucent, covered with a network of calcareous deposits, when these are absent or reduced the peridium is often iridescent. **Capillitium** a delicate, fragile network of thin, white, calcareous tubes, of more or less uniform thickness. **Spores** in mass black, purplish-brown in transmitted light, in tight clusters of 6–20, ovoid, warted or with blunt spines (i.e. tall warts) on the outer surfaces of the cluster, smooth elsewhere, 11–14 μm diam. **Plasmodium** bright yellow. [Fig. 211]

Illustrations: DM 2: 169; E: pl. 71; L3: pl. 3; MA: fig. 204; NB: 163.
Habitat: on pleurocarpin moss or foliose lichen-covered branches of living trees, and newly fallen branches; rarely develops in moist chamber culture.
Distribution: frequent, scattered, lowland, but north to Sutherland [46, H2]. Widespread in Europe, North America, India, Japan, Australia and New Zealand.

Notes: var. *repens* G. Lister and var. *arborea* G. Lister represent narrowly plasmodiocarpous and small, corticolous forms, respectively. There are no satisfactory characters to delimit these and they are not adopted here. The thin, iridescent peridium and clustered spores separate the species from all except *B. dubia*, from which it differs in the larger spores.

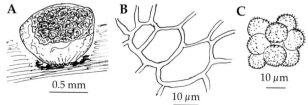

Fig. 211. *Badhamia capsulifera*: A: sporangium; B: capillitium; C: spores.

Badhamia dubia Nann.-Bremek.
Proc. K. Ned. Akad. Wet. C **71**: 49. 1968. Netherlands.

Sporocarps sessile sporangia, in small groups, globose with a narrow base, pale grey, 1–1.5 mm diam. **Hypothallus** inconspicuous. **Peridium** thin, transparent, marked with a delicate network of calcareous veins, often iridescent with purple or green tints. **Capillitium** a coarse net of white calcareous tubes. **Spores** in mass black, purple-brown in transmitted light, in clusters of 7–9, subglobose, 10–11 μm diam, the parts on the surface of the cluster densely and strongly warted, the rest with a few scattered warts, nearly smooth. **Plasmodium** egg-yellow. [Fig. 212]

Illustrations: DM 2: 170; NB: 165.
Habitat: on the bark of branches and trunks of dead standing and newly felled trees.
Distribution: known only from a collection made at Clevelands, near Lyme Regis (on the Devon side of the border) in 1889 [1]. Recorded from Germany, the Netherlands and Spain.

Notes: distinguished from *B. capsulifera* by the smaller spores and complete lack of a stalk.

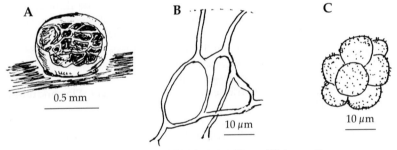

Fig. 212. *Badhamia dubia*: A: sporangium; B: capillitium; C: spores.

Badhamia foliicola Lister
J. Bot., Lond. **35**: 209. 1897. Wanstead, Essex.

Sporocarps sessile or weakly stalked sporangia, gregarious, subglobose to slightly pear-shaped, 0.5–0.6 mm diam, iridescent, grey. **Hypothallus** thin, membranous, pale yellow. **Stalk** weak, thin, yellow. **Peridium** thin, iridescent but often marked with a fine network of calcareous veins. **Capillitium** a delicate network of slender tubes, often nearly limeless. **Spores** in mass black, yellow-brown in transmitted light, free, 11–12 μm diam, minutely warted. **Plasmodium** yellow to pale orange, rarely yellowish-white. [Fig. 213]

Illustrations: DM 2: 171; E: pl. 75; L3: pl. 11: MA: fig. 206; NB: 170.
Habitat: on living grass, grass litter, straw and bark of living trees.
Distribution: frequent, scattered, north to Orkney [52, H8]. Widespread in Europe, North America, Japan, Australia and New Zealand.

Notes: the thin, iridescent peridium, narrow capillitium tubes and short, weak stalks are characteristic. *B. delicatula* D.W. Mitchell & Nann.-Bremek-Bremek., described from France on mossy branches, is very similar, differing mainly in the slightly smaller, paler, but more strongly marked spores, and in the flattened stalks. It may be that the bark records of *B. foliicola* should be placed here but the differences have not been observed in British, or Swiss, material. Until a more detailed study of the correlation between morphological and ecological characters has been carried out it is better to keep one, broad species.

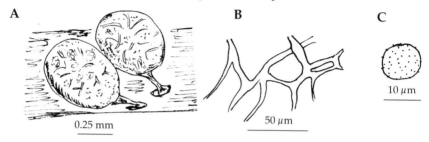

Fig. 213. *Badhamia foliicola*: A: sporangia; B: capillitium; C: spore.

Badhamia gracilis (T. Macbr.) T. Macbr.
in Macbride & Martin, *Myxom*.: 35. 1935. Colorado.
Syn. *Badhamia macrocarpa* var. *gracilis* T. Macbr.

Sporocarps stalked sporangia, rarely sessile, gregarious, globose, umbilicate below, 0.5–0.7 mm diam, to 2 mm tall, white. **Hypothallus** thin, yellow. **Stalk** to 1.3 mm tall, delicate, thin, weak, straw-coloured, twisted, ridged. **Peridium** thin, white, flecked with white calcareous nodules. **Capillitium** of delicate, uniform white tubes, which may be massed at the centre to form a pseudocolumella. **Spores** in mass black, dark brown in transmitted light, free, 12–16 μm diam, closely warted, with clusters of darker warts, and forming a reticulum with 1–6 meshes to the hemisphere. **Plasmodium** white. [Fig. 214]

Illustrations: E: pl. 74 (fig. 7); MA: fig. 207; NB: 174.
Habitat: in Britain on fallen wood and tobacco waste, in the Mediterranean and in deserts characteristic of decaying parts of succulents, especially cacti.
Distribution: known from Morden, Surrey (on wood) and Freshfield, Lancashire (on tobacco waste in dunes; now gone) [2]. Known from the warmer parts of the Americas, Mediterranean Europe, the Middle East, Japan, Africa and China, mostly associated with succulents outside the temperate region.

Notes: the long stalks and reticulate spores separate this from all other British members of the genus; the capillitium should separate it from species of *Physarum*, which it superficially resembles.

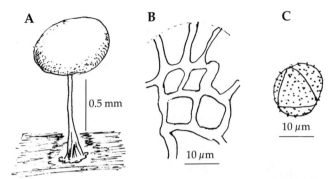

Fig. 214. *Badhamia gracilis*: A: sporangium; B: capillitium; C: spore.

Badhamia lilacina (Fr.) Rostaf.
Mon.: 145. 1874. Sweden.
var. **lilacina**

Sporocarps sessile sporangia, heaped in large clusters, globose, 0.4–0.5 mm diam, lilac-grey. **Hypothallus** thin, transparent, continuous across clusters and with neighbouring clusters. **Peridium** with a membranous inner layer tightly appressed to the outer, very crusty, calcareous layer. **Capillitium** of white tubes with expanded nodes, often clustered at the centre as a pseudocolumella, without hyaline tubules. **Spores** black in mass, dark violet-brown in transmitted light, free, 12–15 μm diam, covered with rough warts and ridges forming a partial reticulum. **Plasmodium** initially white, becoming egg-yellow and often seen below the surface of the water in the bog, attached to *Sphagnum*. [Fig. 215]

Illustrations: DM 2: 175; L3: pl. 13; MA: fig. 208; NB: 178.
Habitat: on vegetation emerging from the surface of *Sphagnum* bogs.
Distribution: as might be expected, western and northern, in areas of high rainfall, where it is quite frequent [47, H7]. Recorded in North America and Europe.

Notes: the bright yellow, aquatic plasmodium is far more conspicuous than the sporangia, which are very difficult to find in the field. However, the plasmodium usually develops well in moist chambers. The colour, heaped sporangia and habitat are enough to identify this species.

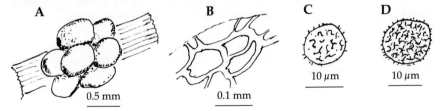

Fig. 215. *Badhamia lilacina*:
A: sporangia; B: capillitium; C: spore; D: var. *megaspora*, spore.

var. **megaspora** Nann.-Bremek.
Med. Bot. Herb Mus. Utrecht **150**: 784. 1958. Netherlands.

Differs from the type variety in the larger, darker spores, 15–20 µm diam, with a more complete reticulum of ridges.

Illustrations: NB: 179.
Distribution: so far known only from Argyll [1] and one swamp in the Netherlands.

Badhamia macrocarpa (Ces.) Rostaf.
Mon.: 143. 1874. Germany.

Sporocarps sessile or stalked sporangia, globose to slightly flattened, 0.5–1 mm diam, white, darker below. **Hypothallus** inconspicuous. **Stalk**, when present, yellow or pale brown, furrowed, upright, or flattened and recumbent. **Peridium** thickly wrinkled, white above, yellow or brown below. **Capillitium** usually physaroid with large calcareous nodes, white. **Spores** black in mass, dark violet-brown in transmitted light, free, 11–15 µm diam, densely warted. **Plasmodium** white or yellow. [Fig. 216]

Illustrations: DM 2: 177; E: pl. 74; L3: pl. 8; MA: fig. 209; NB: 175.
Habitat: on mossy bark of living and fallen trees.
Distribution: uncommon, scattered, north to Aberdeen, in Ireland only in Co. Wicklow [32, H1]. Widespread in Europe, the Americas, Asia and Australia.

Notes: most likely to be confused with *B. affinis* but this has spiny rather than warted spores and a dark stalk, if present. Nannenga-Bremekamp has resurrected *B. melanospora* Speg. which many authors have synonymised with *B. macrocarpa*. It has darker spores with prominent clusters of warts and long stalks and has not been found in the British Isles.

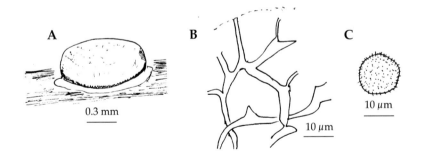

Fig. 216. *Badhamia macrocarpa*: A: sporangium; B: capillitium; C: spore.

Badhamia nitens Berk.
Trans. Linn. Soc. Lond. **21**: 153. 1853. East Bergholt, Suffolk.

Sporocarps sessile sporangia or short plasmodiocarps, gregarious, 0.5–1 mm diam, globose or slightly flattened, yellow, with green and orange flecks, sometimes, when calcareous matter is scant, iridescent. **Peridium** with persistent, membranous inner layer, and flaky, calcareous outer layer. **Capillitium** yellow or dull orange, delicate, with some thickening at the nodes and then appearing physaroid. **Spores** in mass black, violet-brown in transmitted light, in compact clusters of 4–20, mostly 6–12, pyriform, 12–14 x 11–13 μm, coarsely warted on the outer surface, finely warted elsewhere. **Plasmodium** yellow. [Fig. 217]

Illustrations: DM 2: 178; E: pl. 72; L3: pl. 5; MA: fig. 210; NB: 166.
Habitat: on lichens and bracket fungi on the bark of living trees.
Distribution: rare, scattered north to Mull [25, H3]. Scattered across Europe, North America, the West Indies, Canary Islands, Asia, South Africa and New Zealand.

Notes: the orange-yellow colour, tight clusters of spores and the habitat make this beautiful species easy to identify; only *B. versicolor* is similar but this is flesh-coloured and has larger, hollow spore clusters and occurs on mosses.

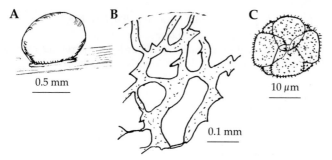

Fig. 217. *Badhamia nitens*: A: sporangium; B: capillitium; C: spores.

Badhamia panicea (Fr.) Rostaf.
in Fuckel, *Jahrb. Nass. Ver. Nat.* **27–28**: 71. 1873. Sweden.

Sporocarps sessile (rarely short-stalked) sporangia or short plasmodiocarps, crowded, often in large developments, depressed-globose, 0.4–2 mm in diam, white. **Hypothallus** thin, membranous, red. **Stalk**, if present, short, red. **Peridium** with a thin inner layer and a thick, white, calcareous outer layer, the base of which is usually red. **Capillitium** white, dense, forming a delicate network of branched tubes, with hyaline tubules connecting them, often aggregated at the centre to form a pseudocolumella. **Spores** in mass black, pale violet-brown in transmitted light, free, 11–14 μm diam, minutely warted. **Plasmodium** white. [Fig. 218]

Illustrations: DM 2: 179; E: pl. 75; L3: pl. 10; MA: fig. 213; NB: 172.
Habitat: on the bark of fallen trunks, especially of beech and elm, rarely in moist chamber culture.
Distribution: common in the south of England, thinning out northwards but reaching Shetland [96, H16, C]. Widespread in Europe, the Americas, Japan and Australia.

Notes: the breadcrumb-like intact capillitium (hand-lens), the calcareous peridium with a red base and the pale, smooth spores make this common species very distinctive. It does occasionally have a more physaroid capillitium and then could be mistaken for *Physarum robustum*, although this does not have a red base, is usually stalked and has darker, warted spores. The occasional sessile forms of *P. pusillum* have a reddish base and a badhamioid capillitium, especially when developed in moist chamber, but they are invariably accompanied by typical, stalked sporangia from the same plasmodium.

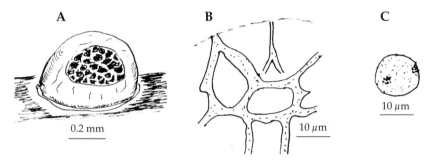

Fig. 218. *Badhamia panicea*: A: sporangium; B: capillitium; C: spore.

Badhamia populina Lister & G. Lister
J. Bot., Lond. **42**: 129. 1904. Epping Forest, Essex.

Sporocarps sessile sporangia, heaped, subglobose, 1.2–1.5 mm diam, white.
Peridium smooth or with a white calcareous net superimposed on the surface.
Capillitium white, a coarse network of tubes, thickened at the junctions and with a few hyaline tubules. **Spores** black in mass, dark brown in transmitted light, clustered, subglobose, 10–13 μm diam, strongly warted on the outer surface, nearly smooth elsewhere. **Plasmodium** white. [Fig. 219]

Illustrations: DM 2: 180; E: pl. 72; L3: pl. 2; MA: fig. 215.
Habitat: on poplar logs.
Distribution: rare, recorded from Surrey, Essex and Yorkshire; last seen in 1938 [4]. Known from Austria, France, Germany and Romania, the Americas and Japan but, apparently, never common.

Notes: the thick, white peridium and very large, heaped sporangia with clustered spores, usually on poplar wood, should allow this species to identified if it occurs again in the British Isles.

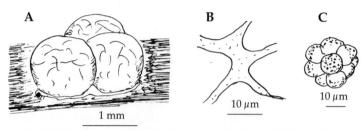

Fig. 219. *Badhamia populina*: A: sporangia; B: capillitium; C: spores.

Badhamia rugulosa T.E. Brooks & H.W. Keller
Mycologia **67**: 1218. 1975. Kentucky.

Sporocarps stalked or sessile sporangia or short plasmodiocarps, gregarious or scattered, 0.3–0.5 mm diam, subglobose, to 1 mm in total height, reddish-orange or yellow, darker below. **Hypothallus** discoid under sporangia, continuous under plasmodiocarps, dark red. Stalk to 0.6 mm tall, black below, red above. **Peridium** double, the inner layer membranous, the outer covered in calcareous flakes. **Capillitium** a dense network of orange tubes, branching and often paler at the ends. **Spores** in mass black, pale violet-brown in transmitted light, free, 10–12 μm diam, distinctly warted. **Plasmodium** yellow-orange. [Fig. 220]

Illustrations: original description.
Habitat: bark of sessile oak.
Distribution: the only record is from Claish Dhearg National Nature Reserve, Argyll [1]. Otherwise known from France and North America.

Notes: the bright orange sporocarps with free spores separate this species easily.

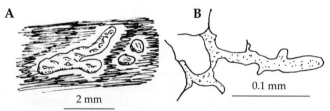

Fig. 220. *Badhamia rugulosa*: A: plasmodiocarps; B: capillitium.

Badhamia utricularis (Bull.) Berk.
Trans. Linn. Soc. Lond. **21**: 153. 1853. France.

Sporocarps stalked sporangia, gregarious in large developments, elongated globose to pear-shaped, 0.5–1 mm diam, blue-grey, iridescent, hanging down. **Hypothallus** thin, dull red. **Stalk** long, thin, weak, yellow or pale brown. **Peridium** thin, white or iridescent, usually marbled with a delicate network of white veins. **Capillitium** white, delicate, of slender, branching tubes. **Spores** blackish-brown in mass, bright violet-brown in transmitted light, in weak clusters which readily disintegrate, leaving spores which appear to be free, globose, strongly warted over whole surface, 10–14 μm diam. **Plasmodium** bright yellow. [Fig. 221]

Illustrations: DM 2: 181; E: pl. 73; L3: pl. 4; MA: fig. 216; NB: 167.
Habitat: on bracket fungi, such as *Stereum hirsutum* and resupinates such as *Phlebia*, on fallen trunks, especially of beech; often hanging down in large clusters.
Distribution: common throughout the British Isles, especially in winter [102, H12, C]. Cosmopolitan.

Notes: the bright yellow plasmodium on fungi is the first sign of this common species; the large clusters of sporangia follow in a day or two. The long, weak stalks, elongate sporangia with marbled peridia are very easily recognised. Only the non-British *B. magna* (Peck) Peck, which has a more delicate capillitium and never has spore clusters, could be mistaken for it; in fact most authors combine them under *B. utricularis*. The sclerotia of this species have been revived after more than 100 years in a dry box.

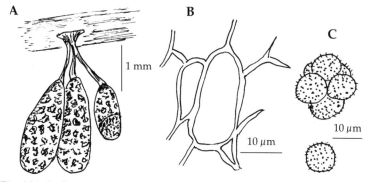

Fig. 221. *Badhamia utricularis*: A: sporangium; B: capillitium; C: spores.

Badhamia versicolor Lister
J. Bot., Lond. **39**: 51, 1901. Rhynie, Aberdeenshire.

Sporocarps sessile sporangia, clustered, globose, 0.2–0.5 mm diam, flesh-coloured or, occasionally, yellowish-grey, fading with age. **Peridium** wrinkled. **Capillitium** of white or apricot tubes in an open network. **Spores** in mass black, dull purple in transmitted light, in hollow clusters of 10–40 elliptical spores, 10–14 x 9–11 μm, warted at the outer end, smooth elsewhere. **Plasmodium** colourless. [Fig. 222]

Illustrations: E: pl. 73; L3: pl. 6; MA: fig. 217.
Habitat: mosses on the bark of living trees.
Distribution: rare, distinctly Atlantic, from Devon, Cornwall, Pembroke, Merioneth and the Scottish Highlands, north to Orkney [13]. Scattered in Europe, especially in the mountains, North America, Hawaii and India.

Notes: the colour of the sporangia and the hollow spore clusters are the distinctive features of this rare species.

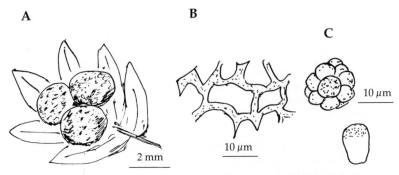

Fig. 222. *Badhamia versicolor*: A: sporangia on moss; B: capillitium; C: spores.

Badhamia viridescens Meyl.
Bull. Soc. Vaud. Sci. Nat. **53**: 452. 1921. Switzerland.

Sporocarps stalked sporangia, scattered, subglobose or pear-shaped, 0.4–0.8 mm in diam, to 1.5 mm in total height, yellowish-green, fading to greenish-grey. **Stalk** yellow-brown, furrowed, to 0.7 mm high. **Peridium** thicker below, leaving a poorly defined cup-like base, spotted and veined with calcareous granules. **Capillitium** badhamioid, yellow, with no hyaline tubules. **Spores** in mass dark brown, pale violet-brown in transmitted light, free, 9–13 μm diam, minutely warted. **Plasmodium** yellow. [Fig. 223]

Illustrations: MA: fig. 218.
Habitat: on lichens, on fallen wood or on the ground.
Distribution: found twice, in Morayshire in 1912 and Somerset in 1983, the former on unidentified lichens on a rotten log, the latter on *Cladonia rangiformis* on a wall [2]. Elsewhere recorded from Germany, Italy, Switzerland and India.

Notes: this rare species could be mistaken for *Craterium aureum*, but for the green colour and the badhamioid capillitium. It is possibly more common and may have been overlooked.

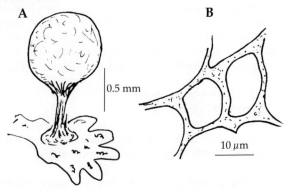

Fig. 223. *Badhamia viridescens*: A: sporangium; B: capillitium.

BADHAMIOPSIS T.E. Brooks & H.W. Keller
Mycologia **68**: 835. 1976.

Differs from *Badhamia* in the columnar arrangement of the capillitial tubes. Two species, the type is *B. ainoae* (Yamash) T.E. Brooks & H.W. Keller.

Badhamiopsis ainoae (Yamash.) T.E. Brooks & H.W. Keller
Mycologia **68**: 1976. Japan
Syn. *Badhamia ainoae* Yamash.

Sporocarps sessile sporangia or short plasmodiocarps, flattened, pulvinate or lentil-shaped, with a narrow base, 0.4–1 mm diam, to 1.5 mm long (plasmodiocarps), white or dark brown (limeless forms). **Peridium** membranous, colourless, shining, with clusters of calcareous granules, especially near the base, often free of granules on the top. **Columella** absent. **Capillitium** of vertical calcareous tubular columns, occasionally forked, rising from base to apex. **Spores** dark brown in mass, violet-brown in transmitted light, 9–11 μm diam, minutely warted. **Plasmodium** pale brown. [Fig. 224]

Illustrations: E: pl. 71; MA: fig. 366.
Habitat: bark of living sycamore trees.
Distribution: rare, only known from north-west Sutherland, where it was found in 1991 [1]. Elsewhere known from France, Spain, Switzerland, Turkey, Japan and North America.

Notes: superficially resembles *Badhamia affinis* but is easily known by the smaller, non-spiny spores and the characteristic arrangement of the capillitium. This columnar structure is reminiscent of the situation in *Didymium sturgisii*.

A   B

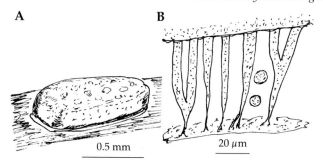

0.5 mm   20 μm

Fig. 224. *Badhamiopsis ainoae*: A: sporangium; B: capillitium.

CRATERIUM Trentep.
in Roth, *Cat. Bot.* **1**: 224. 1797.

Sporocarps stalked sporangia, cup-shaped or subglobose. **Peridium** cartilaginous, with or without a heavy calcareous crust, lower portion persisting as a deep cup, dehiscence circumscissile or by a preformed lid. **Columella** present in some species but more often replaced by a pseudocolumella derived from aggregations of capillitial nodes. **Capillitium** of hyaline tubules connecting calcareous nodes, which may be aggregated to form a central pseudocolumella. Fifteen species; the type is now called *C. minutum* (Leers) Fr.

KEY TO SPECIES

1	Sporangia with preformed lid, dehiscence regular	2
–	Sporangia without an obvious lid, dehiscence irregular	5
2 (1)	Lid distinct, rim of cup smooth	3
–	Lid indistinct, rim of cup irregular	4
3 (2)	Sporangia shining, dark brown, lid brown	*brunneum*
–	Sporangia pale brown or yellow, lid white	*minutum*
4 (2)	Stalk very short, sometimes absent, sporangia subglobose, capillitial nodes small	*aureonucleatum*
–	Stalk long, sporangia short-cylindrical, capillitial nodes large	*leucocephalum*
5 (1)	Sporangia bright yellow	*aureum*
–	Sporangia reddish- or greyish-brown	6
6 (5)	Sporangia globose, stalk black, spores coarsely reticulate; on mosses on wet rocks	*muscorum*
–	Sporangia ovate, stalk reddish, spores with a broken reticulum of warts and wavy lines; on bracken litter	*dictyosporum*

Craterium aureonucleatum Nann.-Bremek.
Acta Bot. Neerl. **10**: 62. 1961. Netherlands.

Sporocarps short-stalked or sessile sporangia, in small groups, subglobose or top-shaped, 0.3–0.5 mm diam, to 0.5 mm tall, orange-brown, dull. **Hypothallus** a large, membranous, white disc. **Stalk** to 0.2 mm long, grooved, dark, orange and clear in transmitted light. **Peridium** of two layers, the inner membranous, the outer thicker, pale orange below, yellow above, the upper part at least clothed with white calcareous granules, often with yellow crystalline discs inside, the apex forming a convex lid, the inside of which is covered in small papillae, the rim of the cup torn and irregular. **Capillitium** a net with small meshes and numerous, small, angular, often branched white or yellow nodes which mass together in the centre to form an orange-yellow pseudocolumella, the nodes may contain yellow crystalline discs. **Spores** in mass dark brown, dark lilac-brown in transmitted light, 9–10 μm diam, finely warted. **Plasmodium** not seen. [Fig. 225]

Illustrations: DM 2: 190; NB: 231.
Habitat: leaf litter.
Distribution: known only from a collection from Glen Tilt, Perthshire, in 1968 [1].
Elsewhere reported from Germany and the Netherlands.

Notes: differs from *C. leucocephalum* in the conical shape and smaller nodes.

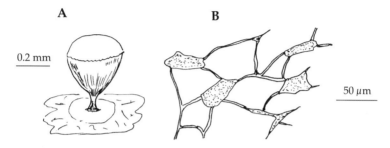

Fig. 225. *Craterium aureonucleatum*: A: sporangium; B: capillitium.

Craterium aureum (Schumach.) Rostaf.
Mon.: 124. 1874. Denmark.

Sporocarps stalked sporangia, ovate or subglobose, 0.4–0.6 mm diam and 0.7–1 mm tall, bright yellow. **Hypothallus** small, discoid, yellow. **Stalk** to 0.5 mm high, grooved, reddish-orange. **Peridium** single, covered in yellow calcareous scales, dehiscence circumscissile, not by a preformed lid, leaving a cup with a ragged rim. **Capillitium** with large, irregular yellow or white nodes, often forming an irregular pseudocolumella in the centre of the sporangium. **Spores** in mass dark brown, pale lilac-grey in transmitted light, 8–9 μm diam, delicately warted. **Plasmodium** yellow. [Fig. 226]

Illustrations: DM 2: 191; E: pl. 102: L3: pl. 67; MA: fig. 225; NB: 230.
Habitat: leaf litter, especially beech.
Distribution: common in the south, thinning northwards to the Scottish Highlands, rare in Ireland [56, H2]. Cosmopolitan.

Notes: the colour separates it from other members of the genus but it is close to *Physarum* and resembles *P. galbeum*, which has a longer stalk and small, round nodes.

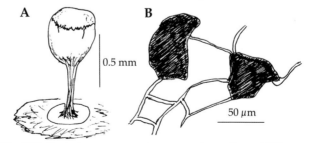

Fig. 226. *Craterium aureum*: A: sporangium; B: capillitium.

Craterium brunneum Nann.-Bremek.
Proc. K. Ned. Akad. Wet. C **76**: 481. 1973. Netherlands.

Sporocarps stalked sporangia, urn-shaped with a well-marked lid, 0.3 mm diam and 0.5 mm tall, total height 1 mm, shining chestnut-brown. **Hypothallus** discoid, orange. **Stalk** to 0.5 mm tall, brown, orange-brown in transmitted light, grooved. **Peridium** without calcareous deposits, smooth, shining, the lid concolorous, supported by a ridge below the smooth rim of the cup. **Capillitium** a fine network of tubules and numerous small, angular white or beige nodes. **Spores** in mass dark brown, lilac-brown in transmitted light, 10–11 μm diam, densely, finely warted. **Plasmodium** not seen. [Fig. 227]

Illustrations: NB: 236.
Habitat: oak leaf litter.
Distribution: rare, known only from Epping Forest, Essex and Ruislip, Middlesex [2]. In Europe is it found in France, Finland, Germany and the Netherlands.

Notes: the shining brown sporangia, with brown, not white, lid separate it from *C. minutum*. It was originally recorded in England as *C. concinnum* but this species is more or less confined to rotting burrs of *Castanea*; it occurs in the Balkans and North America.

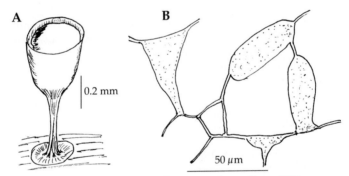

Fig. 227. *Craterium brunneum*: A: sporangium; B: capillitium.

Craterium dictyosporum (Rostaf.) Neubert, Nowotny & Baumann
Die Myxomyceten **2**: 194. 1995. Poland.
Syn. *Badhamia rubiginosa* var. *dictyospora* (Rostaf.) Lister; *Craterium obovatum* var. *dictyosporum* (Rostaf.) Moreno & Illana

Sporocarps stalked sporangia, gregarious, to 1 mm tall, subglobose, ovoid or pear-shaped, 0.5–0.7 mm diam, purple-brown to dull, dark red. **Hypothallus** membranous or discoid, pale red, with or without included calcareous material. **Stalk** thick, cylindrical, filled with calcareous crystalline deposits, white below, reddish above. **Peridium** pale brown, darker below, with scanty calcareous deposits, leaving a deep basal cup. **Columella** cylindrical, red-brown, reaching the centre of the sporangium. **Capillitium** a dense network of tubes, filled with pink or white calcareous granules. **Spores** in mass black, purple-brown in transmitted light, paler on one side, 14–17 µm diam, marked with an incomplete reticulum of low ridges and warts. **Plasmodium** yellow. [Fig. 228]

Illustrations: DM 2: 195; E: pl. 76: L3: pl. 14; MA: fig. 211; NB: 180.
Habitat: bracken and tree leaf litter on acid soils.
Distribution: rare, in southern England in a triangle from Surrey to Norfolk to Worcestershire [9]. In Europe recorded from France, Germany, Italy, Spain, Portugal and the Netherlands, also from Israel, North and South America, South Africa and Japan.

Notes: the only species with which this could be confused is *C. muscorum*, which has more globose sporangia, shorter, black, stalks, more completely reticulate spores and a totally different habitat. The true *C. obovatum* has warted, not reticulate, spores but is otherwise similar.

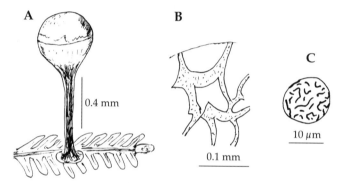

Fig. 228. *Craterium dictyosporum*: A: sporangium on fern; B: capillitium; C: spore.

Craterium leucocephalum (Pers.) Ditmar
in Sturm, *Deutsch. Fl., Pilze* **1**: 21. 1813. Europe.

Sporocarps stalked sporangia, gregarious, globose to top-shaped or cylindrical, 0.3–0.7 mm diam, to 1 mm tall, orange or brown below, white above. **Hypothallus** discoid, usually colourless. **Stalk** cylindrical. grooved, up to half the total height, red-brown, translucent. **Peridium** thick, the inner layer membranous, the outer cartilaginous, red-brown, the upper part encrusted with white calcareous granules and containing yellow crystalline discs or spheres, dehiscing via a cap which leaves a deep cup with a jagged rim. **Capillitium** an open network with large, rounded white or yellow nodes, often with yellow crystalline spheres enclosed, aggregated to form a large, dense, white or yellow pseudocolumella. **Spores** in mass dark brown, lilac-brown in transmitted light, 8–9 µm diam, covered in small, pale warts. **Plasmodium** white. [Fig. 229]

Illustrations: DM 2: 197,200; E: pl. 102; L3: pl. 81; MA: fig. 227; NB: 232, 234.
Habitat: leaf litter.

Distribution: common in the south, thinning out northwards to Sutherland [76, H5]. Cosmopolitan.

Notes: a number of varieties, including var. *scyphoides* (Cooke & Balf.) G. Lister and var. *cylindricum* (Massee) G. Lister have been described, differing largely in the shape of the sporangium. The boundaries between them are small and do not appear to be constant so they are not used here. The yellow discs in the peridium are also found in other species, and in some species of *Physarum*, so are not used as diagnostic characters. The mealy white peridium with an obvious cap and the reddish stalks are quite distinctive. The larger nodes, longer stalks and shape of the sporangium separate this from the rare *C. aureonucleatum*.

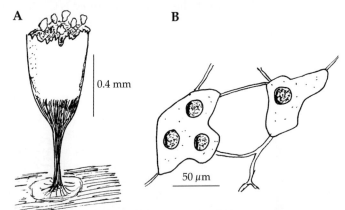

Fig. 229. *Craterium leucocephalum*: A: sporangium; B: capillitium.

Craterium minutum (Leers) Fr.
Syst. Mycol. **3**: 151. 1829. Germany.

Sporocarps stalked sporangia, gregarious, cup-shaped with a distinct, flat lid, 0.2–0.8 mm diam, 0.4–1.2 mm in height, yellow-ochraceous to orange to olive-brown, lid pale, usually white. **Hypothallus** discoid, translucent, orange-brown. **Stalk** to 0.4 mm tall, orange-brown, translucent. **Peridium** of two layers, the outer cartilaginous, smooth, without calcareous deposits, the lid heavily impregnated with calcareous material, the rim of the cup smooth. **Capillitium** of large, white or yellow angular nodes, usually clustered into a pseudocolumella. **Spores** in mass dark brown, lilac-brown in transmitted light, 8–10 μm diam, almost smooth, very finely spinulose (oil). **Plasmodium** orange-yellow to orange-red. [Fig. 230]

Illustrations: DM 2: 202; E: pl. 103; L3: pl. 78; MA: fig. 228; NB: 235.
Habitat: leaf litter, especially of holly and oak, and on living stems of herbaceous plants and grasses in the ground layer of woods; also on dead stems of herbaceous perennials and brambles.
Distribution: common throughout the British Isles [111, H38, C]. Probably cosmopolitan.

Notes: the neat orange-brown goblets with a white lid are easily separated from all other species.

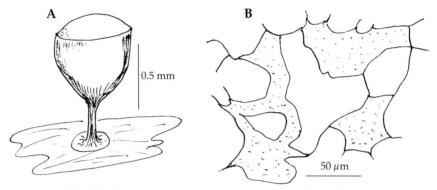

Fig. 230. *Craterium minutum*: A: sporangium; B: capillitium.

Craterium muscorum Ing
Trans. Br. mycol. Soc. **78**: 443. 1982. Llanymawddwy, Merioneth.
Syn. *Badhamia rubiginosa* var. *globosa* Lister & G. Lister; *Badhamia globosa* (Lister & G. Lister) L. Kriegelst.

Sporocarps stalked sporangia, gregarious, globose, 0.7 mm diam, height 1.5 mm, pinkish-brown. **Hypothallus** dark red, discoid. **Stalk** short, 0.5 mm high, dark brown to black, the lower part with a network of strands on the surface. **Peridium** pale brown covered with a thin deposits of pink calcareous granules. **Columella** club-shaped, reaching the centre of the sporangium, dark brown. **Capillitium** a dense network of branching tubes with pink calcareous deposits. **Spores** in mass black, dark purple-brown in transmitted light, 13–16 μm diam, marked with a coarse, but complete reticulation of dark, tall ridges. **Plasmodium** yellow. [Fig. 231]

Illustrations: DM 2: 203; L3: pl. 14: MA: fig. 211 c and g.
Habitat: on mossy rocks in Atlantic oakwoods, ravines and by waterfalls.
Distribution: rare but widespread in western and northern regions of high rainfall [25, H3]. The distribution elsewhere is confused because of misidentification of closely allied species and neglect of the importance of the habitat. It is, however, known from Germany.

Notes: the globose sporangia, dark stalks, reticulate spores and the habitat are sufficient to identify this uncommon member of the ravine association. The photograph on DM 2: 204 shows unusually reddish stalks and also suggests a different habitat; the specimen is more likely to be *C. dictyosporum*.

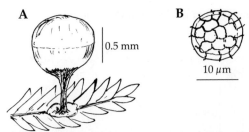

Fig. 231. *Craterium muscorum*: A: sporangium; B: spore.

FULIGO Haller
Stirp. Helv. **3**: 10. 1968.

Sporocarps large, aethalia or pseudoaethalia, usually with a well-developed cortex. The component sporangia or plasmodiocarps have calcareous walls which are seen as thick tubes within the aethalium. **Capillitium** of calcareous nodes connected by hyaline tubules. About 12 species, the type is *F. septica* (L.) F.H. Wigg.

Notes: the genus includes one of the most familiar, large and common myxomycetes and is usually clearly marked. However, smaller developments may lack a cortex and appear to be plasmodiocarpous; the transition to *Physarum* is seen through *gyrosa*, which is more often included in *Physarum*. Because the common species are rarely examined carefully the key includes four species (in parentheses) which have not yet been recorded in the British Isles but occur in Continental Europe. Careful checking of all material may reveal their presence in these islands.

KEY TO SPECIES

1	Sporocarp a rosette-like cluster of plasmodiocarps fused to form a pseudoaethalium, without a cortex	*gyrosa*
–	Sporocarp a true aethalium, with a cortex	2
2 (1)	Spores less than 9 μm diam, sculpture faint	3
–	Spores more than 9 μm diam, sculpture distinct	8
3 (2)	Cortex smooth, more or less glossy, persistent	4
–	Cortex rough, spongy, foamy or honeycombed, brittle, breaking away	6
4 (3)	Spores paler on one side, aethalium pale	*(laevis)*
–	Spores uniformly coloured, aethalia brightly coloured	5
5 (4)	Aethalium red or brown, spores globose, densely warted, capillitium of hyaline threads with spindle-shaped nodes	*(leviderma)*
–	Aethalium yellow, spores mostly oval, with scattered, irregular warts, capillitium with few or no hyaline threads and unattached mussel-shaped nodes	*(luteonitens)*
6 (3)	Aethalia white, internal walls and nodes white	*candida*
–	Aethalia coloured, at least internal walls yellow or red	7
7 (6)	Aethalia orange-brown to dark reddish-brown, nodes rust-coloured, spores 6–7 μm diam	*rufa*
–	Aethalia clear yellow or ochraceous, nodes yellow or white, spores 7–9 μm diam	*septica*

8 (2)   Spores 9–16 μm diam, cortex thin, or, if thicker, then aethalia elongate   9
–   Spores 15–20 μm diam, cortex thick, white   *megaspora*

9 (8)   Spores strongly elliptical   10
–   Spores globose   11

10 (9) Aethalia white, spores 10–12 x 14–16 μm with a broken reticulum   *cinerea*
–   Aethalia yellow, spores 9 x 10–11 μm   *(licenti)*

11 (9) Nodes white; on dead wood   *intermedia*
–   Nodes apricot: on terrestrial mosses   *muscorum*

Fuligo candida Pers.
Obs. Mycol. **1**: 92. 1796. Europe.
Syn. *Fuligo septica* var. *candida* (Pers.) R.E. Fr.

Sporocarps aethalia, pulvinate, white, to 5 cm in diam. **Hypothallus** white,
forming a margin to the aethalium. **Cortex** white, crumbly. Internal **peridia** white.
Capillitium of hyaline tubules and white nodes, these sometimes scanty or
absent. **Spores** in mass dark brown, pale lilac-brown in transmitted light, 7–9 μm
diam, finely warted. **Plasmodium** white. [Fig. 232]

Illustrations: E: pl. 68; L3: pl. 74; NB: 157.
Habitat: on fallen bark and rotten wood in woodland and hothouse litter,
occasionally overgrowing greenhouse plants.
Distribution: scattered, commonest in the south of England but reaching
Inverness [32, H4]. Widespread, but uncommon, in Europe and Japan.

Notes: maintained by many authors as a variety of *F. septica*, this differs constantly
in the white peridial lime within the aethalia and the white plasmodium. It differs
from *F. cinerea* and *F. intermedia* in its smaller spores and from *F. laevis* Pers. by its
rough cortex and white colour, the latter being cream or pale yellow, never white.

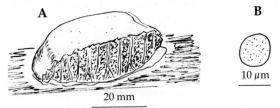

Fig. 232. *Fuligo candida*: A: aethalium; B: spore.

Fuligo cinerea (Schwein.) Morgan
J. Cinc. Soc. Nat. Hist. **19**: 33. 1896. Pennsylvania.

Sporocarps aethalia, often in small groups, pulvinate or elongate, white or pale
grey, to 6 cm long and 5 mm tall. **Hypothallus** of several layers, white, calcareous,

often protruding as a margin around aethalia. **Cortex** crumbly. Internal **peridia** white. **Capillitium** of hyaline tubules connecting to white nodes. **Spores** in mass black, dark purple brown in transmitted light, oval, 10–11 x 14–15 μm, warted and ridged, forming a broken reticulum. **Plasmodium** translucent white. [Fig. 233]

Illustrations: DM 2: 208; E: pl. 69; L3: pl. 75; MA: fig. 219; NB: 158.
Habitat: straw heaps, stable manure, dung heaps.
Distribution: once common, now rare, south of England north to Cheshire, few post-war records, last seen in 1974 [21]. Cosmopolitan.

Notes: the large, elliptical, reticulate spores and the often elongate aethalia mark out this species which is another victim of the changes in field management on arable farms. It could be mistaken for *Mucilago crustacea*, but that species has crystalline lime; from *F. candida* it is easily told by the spores.

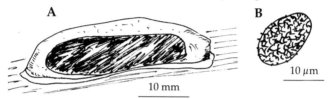

Fig. 233. *Fuligo cinerea*: A: aethalium; B: spore.

Fuligo gyrosa (Rostaf.) E. Jahn
Ber. Deutsch. Bot. Ges. **20**: 272. 1902. Germany.
Syn. *Physarum gyrosum* Rostaf.

Sporocarps pseudoaethalia of tightly massed plasmodiocarps forming a rosette, occasionally with a few free plasmodiocarps from the same plasmodium, laterally compressed, 1 mm tall, often in extensive developments of several square centimetres, pinkish-grey. **Hypothallus** transparent, reddish-brown. **Peridium** single, encrusted with rings of pink or red calcareous granules. **Capillitium** dominated by large, elongated white nodes which stretch across the width of the constituent plasmodiocarps, accompanied by a few small nodes. **Spores** in mass brown, pale lilac-brown in transmitted light, 7–10 μm diam, finely spinulose with some spinules in tight clusters. **Plasmodium** cream. [Fig. 234]

Illustrations: DM 2: 267; E: pl. 96; L3: pl. 52; MA: fig. 259; NB: 215.
Habitat: on potting compost and leaves of living plants in hothouses.
Distribution: rare, from Kent to Shropshire, and Edinburgh, all records from hothouses, few post-war records, last seen in 1974 [8]. Recorded from western Europe in hothouses, widespread in the tropics of Africa, Asia, South America and also in the eastern United States.

Notes: the brain-like clusters of plasmodiocarps are very like small ecorticate aethalia of *F. septica* before the colour develops. Removing this species from *Physarum* makes that genus marginally more homogeneous!

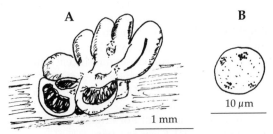

Fig. 234. *Fuligo gyrosa*: A: pseudoaethlium; B: spore.

Fuligo intermedia T. Macbr.
N. Am. Slime-Moulds edn 2. 30. 1922. Colorado.
Syn. *Fuligo cinerea* var. *ecorticata* G. Lister

Sporocarps aethalia, often in small groups, pulvinate, to 3 cm in diam and 1 cm tall, dirty white or pale grey, occasionally tinted with pale shades of brown, pink or yellow. **Hypothallus** membranous, of several layers, white. **Cortex** thin, brittle, crumbling away, often absent. Internal **peridia** white or tinged pale ochraceous. **Capillitium** of colourless tubes or with white or pale ochraceous nodes. **Spores** in mass dull dark brown, pale yellowish-brown in transmitted light, 10–12 μm diam, minutely warted. **Plasmodium** white. [Fig. 235]

Illustrations: DM 2: 209; MA: fig. 220; NB: 160.
Habitat: on dead wood, especially stumps.
Distribution: rare, known only from Sussex, Essex, Suffolk, Norfolk, Northants, Inverness, Co. Wicklow and Co. Meath, few recent records [6, H2]. Recorded from France, Germany, Italy, the Netherlands, North America and Pakistan.

Notes: a poorly defined species, or perhaps a mixture of several needing critical study; differs from *F. cinerea* in the paler, non-reticulate spores.

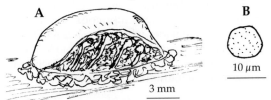

Fig. 235. *Fuligo intermedia*: A: aethalium; B: spore.

Fuligo megaspora Sturgis
Colo. Coll. Publ. Sci. **12**: 443. 1913. Colorado.

Sporocarps aethalia, pulvinate, up to 70 mm in diam, white. **Hypothallus** thick, white, calcareous. **Cortex** thick, spongy, calcareous. Internal **peridia** white. **Capillitium** sparse, of hyaline tubules with a few large, white, branching nodes. **Spores** in mass black but appearing grey because of the large amounts of white calcareous material around them, dark purplish-brown in transmitted light, 15–20 μm diam, strongly marked with tubercles which may form a partial net. **Plasmodium** white. [Fig. 236]

Illustrations: L3: pl. 202; MA: fig. 221.
Habitat: *Quercus ilex* litter.
Distribution: known only from a collection made at Kew, Surrey in 1965 [1].
Widespread in the Mediterranean region and in deserts and semi-arid vegetation
in the Americas, Africa and Asia.

Notes: the thick white cortex and enormous spores separate this typically desert
species.

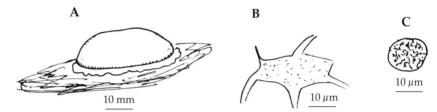

Fig. 236. *Fuligo megaspora*: A: aethalium; B: capillitium; C: spore.

Fuligo muscorum Alb. & Schwein.
Consp. Fung.: 86. 1805. Germany.

Sporocarps aethalia, pulvinate, usually about 1 cm diam but sometimes smaller
and may be to 5 x 1 cm, apricot. **Hypothallus** gelatinous and frothy, colourless or
pale orange. **Cortex** thin, sometimes with greenish tints, especially when young.
Internal **peridia** pale orange. **Capillitium** of small, spindle-shaped or branching,
pale orange nodes, connected by short hyaline tubules. **Spores** in mass dark
brown, yellow-brown in transmitted light, 11–13 μm diam, sparsely warted.
Plasmodium yellow or yellow-green becoming apricot before fruiting. [Fig. 237]

Illustrations: DM 2: 216; E: pl. 69; L3: pl. 77; MA: fig. 222.
Habitat: mosses on the forest floor, wet mossy rocks, occasionally on mosses on
mountain sides.
Distribution: Atlantic, frequent in Wales, Scotland and south-west Ireland, rare
elsewhere [55, H7]. Widespread in the cooler parts of Europe, North America,
Japan and Sri Lanka.

Notes: the apricot colour, habitat, large spores and especially the very
conspicuous plasmodium make this an easy species to identify.

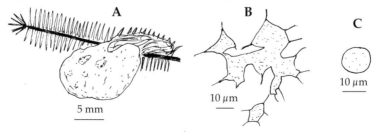

Fig. 237. *Fuligo muscorum*: A: aethalium on moss; B: capillitium; C: spore.

Fuligo rufa Pers.
Neues Mag. Bot. **1**: 88. 1794. Europe.
Syn. *Fuligo septica* var. *rufa* (Pers.) R.E. Fr.

Sporocarps aethalia, pulvinate, to 20 cm in diam and up to 3 cm thick, terra-cotta, brick-red to orange. **Hypothallus** many-layered, foamy, white. **Cortex** of two distinct spongy, foamy layers, crumbling away in large pieces. Internal **peridia** colourless or pale pink, not conspicuous. **Capillitium** an elastic network of colourless tubules connecting small, spindle-shaped reddish-brown nodes. **Spores** in mass dark brown, pale lilac-grey in transmitted light, 6–7 µm diam, finely warted. **Plasmodium** yellow. [Fig. 238]

Illustrations: DM 2: 220; E: pl. 68; L3: pl. 74; NB: 153.
Habitat: very rotten wood, especially stumps, sawdust, occasionally on rotting straw, often in exposed, sunny sites.
Distribution: scattered, mainly in the south, only in Flintshire in Wales and Perth and Inverness in Scotland, not recorded from Ireland [29]. Extra-British distribution doubtful because of confusion with other species, especially *F. septica*.

Notes: the slightly smaller spores, double-layered cortex and red calcareous matter separate this from *F. septica*. The double, spongy cortex separates it from *F. leviderma* Neubert, Nowotny & Baumann, which is the same colour but has a smooth, leathery cortex. The latter has been described from Germany and has been found in other parts of Europe and may be expected to occur with us.

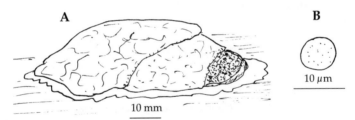

Fig. 238. *Fuligo rufa*: A: aethalium; B: spore.

Fuligo septica (L.) F.H. Wigg.
Prim. Fl. Holsat.: 112. 1780. France.
var. **septica** Flowers of Tan

Sporocarps aethalia, pulvinate, to 13 cm diam and 3 cm thick, ochraceous to lemon-yellow or greenish-yellow. **Hypothallus** white, of several layers, forming a margin around the aethalium. **Cortex** brittle, crumbling away; in very humid conditions, such as when a plasmodium is kept in moist chamber, the cortex may not develop and the sporocarp is brain-like with obvious plasmodiocarpous structures grouped closely together. Internal **peridia** white. **Capillitium** of colourless, branching tubules with small, white, spindle-shaped nodes. **Spores** in mass dark brown, pale lilac-grey in transmitted light, 7–9 µm diam, finely warted. **Plasmodium** yellow. [Fig. 239]

Illustrations: DM 2: 217; MA: fig. 223.
Habitat: on rotten wood, tan bark and sawdust.
Distribution: scattered, mostly in south-east England but extends north to Yorkshire [16]. Cosmopolitan.

var. **flava** (Pers) R.E. Fr.
Svensk Bot. Tidskr. **6**: 744. 1912. Europe.

Differs from the type variety in the brighter yellow cortex and the capillitial nodes yellow, not white.

Illustrations: DM 2: 218; E: pl. 68; L3: pl. 74; NB: 155.
Habitat: rotten wood, sawdust, forest litter and mosses (above buried wood).
Distribution: very common throughout the British Isles [110, H40, C]. Cosmopolitan.

Notes: the var. *flava* is one of the commonest and most familiar of all British and Irish myxomycetes, often looking like scrambled egg spilt on a log. The typical form seems to be commoner in warmer regions and, as in the rest of the genus, the species concepts should take these biogeographical considerations into account. Three non-British species are superficially similar: *F. licenti* Buchet has larger, oval spores; *F. laevis* Pers. has pale yellow or cream aethalia with a persistent, smooth cortex and spores which are paler on one side, and *F. luteonitens* L. Krieglst. & Nowotny has a smooth, shining cortical crust and oval spores.

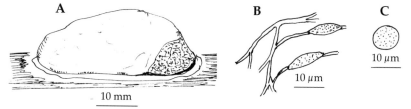

Fig. 239. *Fuligo septica*: A: aethalium; B: capillitium; C: spore.

LEOCARPUS Link
Ges. Nat. Freunde Berlin Mag. **3**: 25. 1809.

Sporocarps short-stalked sporangia. **Peridium** brittle, three layered, the outer thin and cartilaginous, the inner membranous and the middle thick and calcareous. **Columella** absent. **Capillitium** reticulate, badhamioid, part calcareous, part without granular inclusions, connected to the peridium and often forming a central pseudocolumella. Two species; the type is *L. fragilis* (Dicks.) Rostaf.

Leocarpus fragilis (Dicks.) Rostaf.
Mon.: 132. 1874. Hornsey, Middlesex.

Sporocarps short-stalked sporangia, crowded in large clusters, like bunches of grapes, ellipsoid to subglobose, to 4 mm tall and 0.6–1.6 mm diam, shining chestnut-brown, paler when freshly developed. **Hypothallus** pale ochraceous, common to a cluster and merging into the stalks. **Stalk** flat, weak, sometimes branched and bearing more than one sporangium, pale ochraceous to pale orange. **Peridium** as generic description, dehiscing by lobes, sometimes petaloid. **Capillitium** duplex, consisting of a network of pale, slender, branching, limeless threads and a second network of broad, yellow tubes with expansions, filled with calcareous granules, occasionally massed in the centre as a pseudocolumella. **Spores** in mass dark brown to nearly black, brown in transmitted light, 12–14 or 15–18 µm diam, paler on one side, finely warted. **Plasmodium** yellow. [Fig. 240]

Illustrations: DM 2: 222; E: pl. 106; L3: pl. 82; MA: fig. 201; NB: 238.
Habitat: leaf litter, especially of conifers, gorse and birch, often ascending a metre up trunks of small trees and clustering on vegetation some distance above the soil.
Distribution: very common throughout the British Isles [111, H39, C]. Cosmopolitan.

Notes: the bright yellow plasmodium emerging from the soil in conifer plantations is a familiar sight after the first rains of autumn. The clusters of sporangia are unmistakable. The only species with which this could be confused is *Physarum brunneolum*, but this has a single type of capillitium and small, round, white nodes. The different spore sizes may be linked to different ecology and could be linked to different genotypes, but no studies have been made. The large-spored form is rare and has not been specifically noted in the British Isles. There is also a form with spores in small clusters which has been described as *L. bisporus* Nann.-Bremek. & D.W. Mitchell; this too has not yet been reported from Britain.

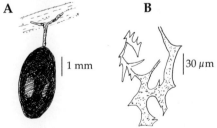

Fig. 240. *Leocarpus fragilis*: A: sporangium; B: capillitium.

PHYSARUM Pers.
Neues Mag. Bot. **1**: 88. 1794.

Sporocarps stalked or sessile sporangia or plasmodiocarps, rarely grouped into pseudoaethalia. **Hypothallus**, stalk and columella with or without calcareous deposits.
Peridium of one or two layers, usually covered with calcareous granules. **Capillitium** of hyaline tubules connecting calcareous nodes, forming a network or radiating from the columella or base of the sporangium. The largest genus of myxomycetes with about 150 species; the type is *P. viride* (Bull.) Pers.

Notes: as mentioned under other genera, the limits of *Physarum* are currently imprecise; it grades into *Badhamia*, *Craterium* and even *Fuligo*. Superficially, species may also resemble *Diderma*, but may be told by their calcareous capillitium, or *Didymium*, which has crystalline lime on the peridium.

KEY TO SPECIES

1	Sporocarps primarily plasmodiocarps or sessile sporangia	2
–	Sporocarps primarily stalked sporangia	26
2 (1)	Sporocarps forming elongate plasmodiocarps	3
–	Sporocarps forming short plasmodiocarps or sessile sporangia	10
3 (2)	Calcareous material in capillitium and on peridium yellow	4
–	Calcareous material white or grey	5
4 (3)	Peridium wrinkled, covered in scales, mostly yellow but with a few red or white scales, never green when young	*decipiens*
–	Peridium smooth, with orange, green and yellow scales, usually green when young	*auriscalpium*
5 (3)	Sporocarps strongly compressed laterally, dehiscing by a preformed fissure	6
–	Sporocarps not laterally compressed, dehiscence irregular	7
6 (5)	Spores with long spines, 10–12 µm diam	*echinosporum*
–	Spores minutely spinulose, 8–10 µm diam	*bivalve*
7 (5)	Peridium clearly double	*bitectum*
–	Peridium single	8
8 (7)	Spores pale, 6–8 µm diam	*sessile*
–	Spores more than 9 µm diam	9
9 (8)	Spores pale, 9–11 µm diam, peridium thin, lightly covered in calcareous flakes	*cinereum*
–	Spores dark, 10–12 µm diam, peridium thick, very calcareous	*vernum*

10 (2)	Capillitial lime orange-red, sporocarps red	*rubiginosum*
–	Capillitial lime yellow or white	11

11 (10)	Capillitial lime yellow	12
–	Capillitial lime white	21

12 (11)	Sporangia red, lime nodes yellow with red centres	*lateritium*
–	Sporangia predominantly yellow	13

13 (12)	Peridium clearly double	14
–	Peridium single, or apparently so under high power	17

14 (13)	Sporangia gregarious but not closely aggregated, without a sunken apex, usually with a weak stalk-like extension of the hypothallus; alpine	*albescens*
–	Sporangia closely aggregated, with a sunken lid-like apex surrounded by a rim, no stalk-like base; lowland	15

15 (14)	Peridium gelatinous when moist	*mucosum*
–	Peridium not gelatinous	16

16 (15)	Spores dark, strongly marked, 11–13 μm diam	*contextum*
–	Spores pale, almost smooth, 8–10 μm diam	*conglomeratum*

17 (13)	Sporangia heaped, small, greenish-yellow	*virescens*
–	Sporangia not heaped	18

18 (17)	Spores less than 9 μm diam	19
–	Spores more than 9 μm diam	20

19 (18)	Sporangia bright yellow	*nitens*
–	Sporangia olive-yellow to olive-brown	*obscurum*

20 (18)	Peridium wrinkled, covered in scales, mostly yellow but with a few red or white scales, never green when young	*decipiens*
–	Peridium smooth, with orange, green and yellow scales, usually green when young	*auriscalpium*

21 (11)	Peridium clearly double	*lividum*
–	Peridium single	22

22 (21)	Spores usually elliptical, encircled by a pale band; rare	*ovisporum*
–	Spores globose, without pale band	23

23 (22)	Sporangia dark grey to black, heaped	*confertum*
–	Sporangia pale, not heaped	24

24 (23) Capillitium scanty, peridium thin, both with little calcareous matter
nudum

– Capillitium abundant with well-developed nodes, peridium with
flakes or thick deposits of calcareous material
25

25 (24) Spores pale, 9–11 μm diam, peridium thin, lightly covered in
calcareous flakes; common
cinereum

– Spores dark, 10–12 μm diam, peridium thick, very calcareous
vernum

26 (1) Capillitium branching dichotomously, with cross connections, radiating
from the base of the sporangium, nodes spindle-shaped, rarely angular 27

– Capillitium forming a network, not dichotomously branched nor
radiating from the base of the sporangium, nodes round or angular,
rarely spindle-shaped
31

27 (26) Capillitial nodes yellow
28

– Capillitial nodes white
30

28 (27) Sporangia dusky or dark yellow, capillitial lime sparse,
nodes occasionally angular
flavicomum

– Sporangia blue, with yellow scales, bright yellow, rarely orange
or yellowish-grey, nodes always spindle-shaped
29

29 (28) Sporangia blue with yellow scales, spores 10–12 μm diam
bethelii

– Sporangia bright yellow, occasionally yellowish-grey or orange,
spores 7–9 μm diam
viride

30 (27) Sporangia erect, globose, pseudocolumella present
robustum

– Sporangia nodding, discoid, no pseudocolumella
nutans

31 (26) Sporangium with a true columella which is an extension of the stalk
32

– Sporangium with at most a pseudocolumella resulting from the
massing of capillitial nodes
39

32 (31) Columella large, well developed
33

– Columella small, a short, conical projection of the stalk
35

33 (32) Columella subglobose or club-shaped, not reaching centre of
sporangium
listeri

– Columella cylindrical, reaching apex of sporangium
34

34 (33) Columella calcareous, white or dark, with broad perpendicular capillitial
branches, sporangium white or grey, ovate to short cylindrical *crateriforme*

– Columella not calcareous, slender, orange, sporangium olivaceous,
long-ovate; on leaf litter
penetrale

35 (32) Sporangia yellow or orange
36

– Sporangia white, grey or brown
37

36 (35) Peridium, columella and stalk yellow   *citrinum*
–   Peridium orange, stalk orange-red   *pulcherripes*

37 (35) Peridium brown   *murinum*
–   Peridium white   38

38 (37) Nodes small, rounded, stalk smooth   *globuliferum*
–   Nodes large, angular, stalk grooved   *leucopus*

39 (31) Pseudocolumella present   40
–   Pseudocolumella absent   42

40 (39) Pseudocolumella spherical, free from base of sporangium,
        spores 6.5–7.5 μm diam   *nucleatum*
–   Pseudocolumella irregular, attached to base, spores 8–15 μm   41

41 (40) Sporangia not tightly packed, stalk robust, with included lime,
        spores 8–10 μm diam   *mutabile*
–   Sporangia closely massed, looking like *Diderma spumarioides*,
        stalk weak, flattened, spores 12–15 μm diam   *didermoides*

42 (39) Sporangia laterally compressed   43
–   Sporangia not laterally compressed   44

43 (42) Sporangia ovoid, fan-shaped, irregular, stalk stout, black,
        often dusted with white granules   *compressum*
–   Sporangia wedge-shaped, stalks weak   *straminipes*

44 (42) Sporangia funnel-shaped with a deep depression at the apex   *javanicum*
–   Sporangia globose, subglobose or slightly ovoid   45

45 (44) Stalk weak, an extension of the hypothallus, peridium yellow to
        tawny; alpine   *albescens*
–   Stalk normal, distinct   46

46 (45) Sporangia white or grey, nodes white   47
–   Sporangia coloured, nodes yellow or orange   53

47 (46) Stalks white, calcareous   48
–   Stalks dark, without internal lime   49

48 (47) Nodes small, rounded (usually with a columella), stalk smooth
                                                                                 globuliferum
–   Nodes large, angular, sporangia reminiscent of *Didymium squamulosum*,
        stalks grooved, hypothallus discoid, fluted   *leucopus*

49 (47) Sporangia small, with reddish base, stalk long, slender, reddish   *pusillum*
–   Sporangia larger, without reddish base, stalk shorter, stout,
        white or grey   50

50 (49) Sporangia clustered, stalks often fused, base of peridium not thickened
notabile
–   Sporangia not clustered, stalks free, base of peridium thickened   51

51 (50) Base of peridium ochraceous, stalk translucent, spores 11–13 μm diam
with pale band   *pusillopse*
–   Base of peridium not coloured, stalk opaque, spores 9–11 μm diam,
without pale band   52

52 (51) Peridium with circular plates separated by grooves, stalk with
internal lime   *scoticum*
–   Peridium without plates, stalk without lime   *leucophaeum*

53 (46) Sporangia iridescent blue or bronze   *psittacinum*
–   Sporangia not iridescent   54

54 (53) Peridium smooth, varnished brown, looking somewhat like
Leocarpus fragilis   *brunneolum*
–   Peridium not smooth or varnished, yellow or orange   55

55 (54) Stalk and base of peridium flesh-pink   *carneum*
–   Stalk and base of peridium not flesh-pink   56

56 (55) Peridium scaly, not granular   57
–   Peridium not scaly, with fine granules   58

57 (56) Stalks very short, peridial scales small, with red and green tints,
spores 9–12 μm diam   *auriscalpium*
–   Stalks longer, peridial scales large, pure yellow,
spores 10–13 μm diam   *limonium*

58 (56) Stalks short, sporangium with flattened top, nodes large, angular;
on bark   *oblatum*
–   Stalks long, sporangium rounded, nodes small; on bramble stems *galbeum*

Physarum albescens Ellis
in Macbride, *N. Am. Slime-Moulds* edn 2: 86. 1922. Colorado.
Syn. *Physarum fulvum* (T. Macbr.) G. Lister

Sporocarps short-stalked or sessile sporangia, gregarious or scattered, subglobose or roughly ovoid, 0.6–0.8 mm diam, pale yellow or reddish-brown. **Hypothallus** continuous under adjacent sporangia, veined, pale yellow. **Stalk** weak, flattened and thin, appearing as an extension of the hypothallus, to 0.5 mm long. **Peridium** of two layers, the inner membranous and the outer calcareous, persistent as a basal cup. **Capillitium** dense, dark yellow fading to white, with large, flattened angular nodes, often massed below into a pseudocolumella and darker than the outer and upper nodes. **Spores** black in mass, violet-brown in transmitted light, 12–15 μm diam, prominently warted. **Plasmodium** yellow. [Fig. 241]

Illustrations: DM 2: 235–7; L3: pl. 66: MA: fig. 231.
Habitat: on living stems of *Vaccinium myrtillus* at the edge of melting snow on mountains in the spring.
Distribution: known only from Glas Maol, Perthshire [1]. Recorded from the mountains of Europe, North America, north Africa, Japan and Australia but always uncommon.

Notes: this is a very distinctive species, the colour, capillitium and habitat making identification easy.

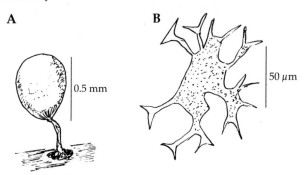

Fig. 241. *Physarum albescens:* A: sporangium; B: capillitium.

Physarum auriscalpium Cooke
Ann. Lyc. N.Y. **11**: 384. 1877. South Carolina.

Sporocarps short-stalked or sessile sporangia or short plasmodiocarps, orange, yellowish-brown, greenish, to 0.8 mm in diam and usually about 2 mm long when plasmodiocarpous. **Hypothallus** inconspicuous. **Stalk,** when present, dark, furrowed. **Peridium** smooth, membranous, covered with small calcareous scales, often concentrated on the upper portions leaving the base nearly limeless. **Capillitium** abundant, of large branching orange or yellow nodes connected by short colourless tubules, occasionally badhamioid. **Spores** black in mass, brown in transmitted light, minutely roughened, 9–12 μm diam. **Plasmodium** orange-yellow becoming bright green as the sporocarps develop. [Fig. 242]

Illustrations: E: pl. 88; L3: pl. 33; MA: fig. 234.
Habitat: predominantly on the bark of living trees but also found on fallen branches and occasionally on herbaceous litter.
Distribution: scattered from Devon and Kent northwards to Orkney, commoner in the west and north [26, H7]. Reported from Europe, North and central America, Hawaii and Japan but confused with related species.

Notes: frequently combined with *P. decipiens* and confused with *P. serpula,* this species is the only member of the complex which is ever stalked and the only one to occur on herbaceous substrates, usually in the stalked phase. The green colouration of the young sporocarps is possibly diagnostic and is regularly seen in bark cultures. See also the notes under *P. decipiens.*

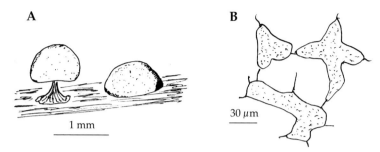

Fig. 242. *Physarum auriscalpium*: A: sporangia; B: capillitium.

Physarum bethelii T. Macbr.
in Lister, *Mycet.* edn 2: 57. 1911. Colorado.
Syn. *Physarum viride* var. *bethelii* (T. Macbr.) Sturgis

Sporocarps stalked sporangia, gregarious, 1–1.5 mm in height, sporangia usually nodding, flattened globes or thick discs, slightly umbilicate below, 0.6–0.8 mm diam, bronze. **Hypothallus** inconspicuous, brown. **Stalk** slender, dark brown to black, furrowed. **Peridium** membranous, blue, iridescent, sprinkled with yellow or white calcareous scales, the lower part persisting as a cup. **Capillitium** abundant, of delicate threads radiating from the top of the stalk and the base of the peridium, with scattered, pale yellow, spindle-shaped nodes. **Spores** black in mass, bright violet-brown in transmitted light, 10–11 µm diam, distinctly warted, with groups of larger warts. **Plasmodium** colourless or very pale brown. [Fig. 243]

Illustrations: DM 2: 242,2; L3: pl. 200; MA: fig. 235; NB: 191.
Habitat: moss on bark of living trees, rarely on fallen branches.
Distribution: rare, known from Jersey, Somerset, Wiltshire, Hampshire, Pembroke, Snowdonia, Lancashire and Berwickshire, in Ireland only from Co. Wexford [8, H1, C]. Elsewhere in North America, Europe, Chile and Japan.

Notes: the iridescent peridium and slightly larger spores separate this from *P. viride*, the yellow nodes from limeless forms of *P. nutans* and the shape of the sporangium and the nodes from most other species.

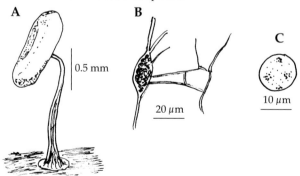

Fig. 243. *Physarum bethelii*: A: sporangium; B: capillitium; C: spore.

Physarum bitectum G. Lister
Mycet. edn 2: 78. 1911. Flitwick, Bedfordshire.

Sporocarps narrow, often long, plasmodiocarps to 6 mm long and 0.6 mm wide, or forming sessile sporangia, to 0.8 mm in diam, white or pale grey, rounded in section. **Hypothallus** inconspicuous. **Peridium** clearly double, the inner layer membranous, colourless or purple, the outer calcareous, splitting and folding back to reveal the inner layer, dehiscence irregular. **Capillitium** of large white nodes connected by short, colourless tubules. **Spores** in mass black, dark violet brown in transmitted light, 10–13 μm diam, with an irregular covering of coarse spines. **Plasmodium** white. [Fig. 244]

Illustrations: E: pl. 77; L3: pl. 51; MA: fig. 237; NB: 215.
Habitat: leaf litter, especially under bramble bushes.
Distribution: common in the south, with an easterly bias, thinning rapidly northwards to Aberdeen, rare in Wales and Scotland, absent from Ireland [53]. Probably cosmopolitan.

Notes: the clearly double peridium, the rounded cross-section and the prominent, white nodes are sufficient to separate this species.

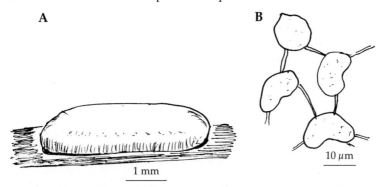

Fig. 244. *Physarum bitectum*: A: plasmodiocarp; B: capillitium.

Physarum bivalve Pers.
Annln. Bot. **15**: 5. 1795. France.
Syn. *Physarum sinuosum* (Bull.) Weinm.

Sporocarps elongate plasmodiocarps, strongly compressed laterally, white, 1 mm tall and to 20 mm long, often with very short plasmodiocarps or sessile sporangia in the development. **Hypothallus** white, inconspicuous. **Peridium** of two layers, the inner membranous, the outer calcareous, dehiscing by a preformed longitudinal split. **Capillitium** of large, rounded white nodes connected by a small-meshed network of short, colourless tubules. **Spores** in mass dark brown, lilac-brown in transmitted light, 8–10 μm diam, finely warted. **Plasmodium** white or pale grey. [Fig. 245]

Illustrations: DM 2: 245; E: pl. 97; L3: pl. 49; MA: fig. 238; NB: 217.

Habitat: leaf litter, especially of brambles and rosebay, found in sites where the phosphate content of the soil is high.

Distribution: common in the south, with an easterly trend, but occurring northwards to Ross-shire, although it is rare in Scotland; not seen in Ireland for over a century [96, H1, C]. Probably cosmopolitan.

Notes: the flattened, narrow plasmodiocarps can only be confused with *P. echinosporum* on the British list, but that, normally tropical, species can be easily told by its very spiny spores. A number of similarly shaped species occur in the warmer parts of the world but all have coloured lime somewhere in the fruit body.

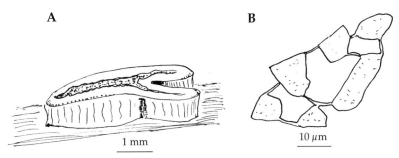

Fig. 245. *Physarum bivalve*: A: plasmodiocarp; B: capillitium.

Physarum brunneolum (Phill.) Massee
Mon. Myxog.: 280. 1892. California.

Sporocarps short-stalked or sessile sporangia, globose to top-shaped, 0.6–1.7 mm diam, shining dark yellowish-brown. **Hypothallus** small, dark. **Stalk** furrowed, dark. **Peridium** double, the outer layer cartilaginous, thick, crustose, smooth, the inner layer white, calcareous. **Capillitium** dense, of numerous large, white, rounded nodes with thin colourless tubules connecting them. **Spores** in mass black, dark brown in transmitted light, 8–10 µm diam, coarsely warted. **Plasmodium** yellow. [Fig. 246]

Illustrations: E: pl. 89; L3: pl. 69; MA: fig. 241.
Habitat: on dry leaf litter of thick-leaved trees.
Distribution: rare. Known in the British Isles from three collections: Kent, 1976; Cheshire, 1958 and Co. Down in 1917, always associated with long periods of hot, dry weather [2,H1]. Widespread in the Mediterranean region and areas with a similar climate in North and South America, Australia, the Canary Islands and Japan.

Notes: the only species with which this could be confused is *Leocarpus fragilis* but that has a very different capillitium, with jagged, yellowish nodes. This species is typical of the dry evergreen oak–pine forests of much of Mediterranean Europe.

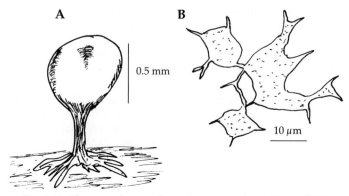

Fig. 246. *Physarum brunneolum*: A: sporangium; B: capillitium.

Physarum carneum G. Lister & Sturgis
J. Bot., Lond. **46**: 73. 1910. Colorado.

Sporocarps stalked sporangia, gregarious, subglobose, 0.4–0.6 mm diam, ochraceous yellow above, flesh-pink below. **Hypothallus** inconspicuous, flesh-coloured. **Stalk** short, to 0.4 mm high, flesh-coloured, translucent, widening at the base. **Peridium** membranous, pale yellow, evenly covered with calcareous granules. **Capillitium** dense, the nodes white, angular, connected by short colourless threads. **Spores** in mass black, purplish-brown in transmitted light, 8–9 μm diam, spinulose, paler on one side. **Plasmodium** yellow. [Fig. 247]

Illustrations: E: pl. 89; L3: pl. 204; MA: fig. 242.
Habitat: leafy litter under bramble thickets.
Distribution: known only from a series of collections made near Norwich between 1916 and 1922 [1]. Known from a few places in North America, Japan, Romania, Israel and the Canary Islands.

Notes: the flesh-coloured sporangia and stalks, not found in other species, should be enough to distinguish this rare species, should it ever occur again in Britain.

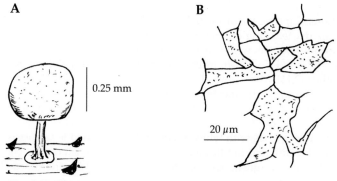

Fig. 247. *Physarum carneum*: A: sporangium; B: capillitium.

Physarum cinereum (Batsch) Pers.
Neues Mag. Bot. **1**: 89. 1794. Germany.

Sporocarps sessile sporangia or short to elongated plasmodiocarps, the sporangia often clustered or heaped, 0.3–0.5 mm broad, grey or white, or occasionally iridescent from lack of lime. **Hypothallus** inconspicuous, colourless. **Peridium** single, the amount of calcareous material varying from nil to a thick crust. **Capillitium** dense, with angular white nodes. **Spores** in mass purplish-brown, violet in transmitted light, 9–11 μm diam, minutely warted. **Plasmodium** white, often becoming bright yellow prior to fruiting, during which the young sporocarps are shining lilac-purple. [Fig. 248]

Illustrations: DM 2: 247; E: pl. 94: L3: pl. 47; MA: fig. 243; NB: 225.
Habitat: on lawns, grass litter of all kinds and leaf litter.
Distribution: common in the south, thinning northwards to Orkney [81, Hb, C]. Cosmopolitan.

Notes: the species most likely to be confused with this is *P. vernum* which has larger, darker, rougher spores, is usually more calcareous and has longer plasmodiocarps. Where the sporangia are heaped there is a resemblance to the rare *P. confertum* but this also has larger, darker spores and small, rounded nodes, rather than the large angular nodes of *P. cinereum*.

Fig. 248. *Physarum cinereum*: A: plasmodiocarp; B: capillitium.

Physarum citrinum Schumach.
Enum. Pl. Saell. **2**: 201. 1803. Germany.

Sporocarps stalked sporangia, subglobose with a slightly flattened base, 0.4–0.7 mm diam, clear lemon-yellow. **Hypothallus** small, discoid, yellow. **Stalk** calcareous, stout, furrowed, about 0.5 mm high. **Peridium** thin, covered evenly with calcareous scales. **Columella** small, conical, sometimes replaced by a pseudocolumella. **Capillitium** dense, delicate, with numerous small, yellow, rounded nodes, connected by a stiff, often branched, colourless threads. **Spores** black in mass, violet-brown in transmitted light, 8–10 μm diam, minutely dotted. **Plasmodium** yellow. [Fig. 249]

Illustrations: DM 2: 249; E: pl. 80; L3: pl. 20; MA: fig. 244.
Habitat: on moss on fallen wood and on terrestrial mosses.
Distribution: rare, northern and western, much commoner in the early part of the twentieth century [24]. Cosmopolitan, especially in temperate regions.

Notes: the clear yellow sporangia and small yellow nodes are useful indicators of this species which is now rarely found. The reasons for its apparent decline are unknown.

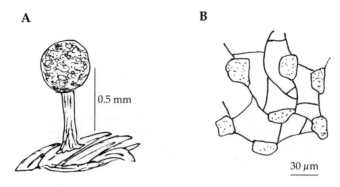

Fig. 249. *Physarum citrinum*: A: sporangium; B: capillitium.

Physarum compressum Alb. & Schwein.
Consp. Fung.: 97. 1805. Germany.

Sporocarps short-stalked or sessile sporangia or short plasmodiocarps, 0.8–1.3 mm diam, fan-shaped, irregularly subglobose, top-shaped or kidney-shaped, white or grey. **Hypothallus** inconspicuous. **Stalk** dark brown to black, or frosted with lime, short, stout, with distinct ridges. **Peridium** single, thickly covered with calcareous scales, dehiscing by an apical slit. **Capillitium** open, with variable white nodes. **Spores** black in mass, purple-brown in transmitted light, 10–13 μm diam, irregularly warted. **Plasmodium** white or grey. [Fig. 250]

Illustrations: DM 2: 251–2; E: pl. 92; L3: pl. 39; MA: fig. 245; NB: 209.
Habitat: on herbaceous waste, including compost heaps and crop residues, grass litter and straw heaps, not infrequently in cultures of tree bark after some weeks of culture.
Distribution: common and widespread, north to Orkney [75, H7, C]. Cosmopolitan.

Notes: a highly variable species and, because of this, it may resemble other members of the genus, including *P. robustum* and several tropical species. From all of these it may be distinguished by its round or angular nodes. There are several synonyms, which have not been applied to British material, and it is possible that there is a species aggregate involved but no detailed study has yet been made.

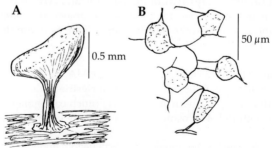

Fig. 250. *Physarum compressum*: A: sporangium; B: capillitium.

Physarum confertum T. Macbr.
N. Am. Slime-Moulds edn 2: 64. 1922. North Carolina.

Sporocarps sessile sporangia, heaped, subglobose, 0.2–0.4 mm diam, violet brown to black. **Hypothallus** inconspicuous, dark. **Peridium** single, thin, translucent, often without calcareous deposits but usually sprinkled with granules or decorated with a net. **Capillitium** sparse, with small, elongate nodes connected by limeless tubules, the junctions often without calcareous deposits. **Spores** black in mass, violet-brown in transmitted light, 10–13 μm diam, minutely warted. **Plasmodium** white, becoming pink then black as the sporocarps develop. [Fig. 251]

Illustrations: DM 2: 253; E: pl. 94; L3: pl. 64; MA: fig. 246; NB: 226.
Habitat: on moss and conifer litter.
Distribution: rare, known only from Sussex, Kent, Norfolk, Angus, Kincardine, Aberdeen and Sutherland [7]. Widespread, but not common, in Europe, and known from North America, Japan and parts of Africa.

Notes: the small, dark heaped sporangia are characteristic. Pale specimens fruiting on living grass could be mistaken for *P. cinereum* but that species has slightly larger sporangia, wider nodes and smaller spores, and is more frequently plasmodiocarpous.

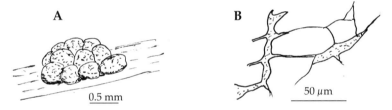

A

B

0.5 mm

50 μm

Fig. 251. *Physarum confertum*: A: sporangia; B: capillitium.

Physarum conglomeratum (Fr.) Rostaf.
Mon.: 108. 1874. Europe

Sporocarps sessile sporangia, crowded and often square in outline through mutual pressure, otherwise subglobose on a broad base, pale yellow, 0.3–0.5 mm diam. **Peridium** double, the outer layer limy, fragile, flattened at the apex and often with a rim-like margin around a sunken lid, the inner pale yellow, translucent, brittle. **Capillitium** with abundant yellow or white angular nodes, some connected by colourless tubules. **Spores** black in mass, pale violet-brown in transmitted light, 8–10 μm diam, almost smooth. **Plasmodium** pale yellow. [Fig. 252]

Illustrations: DM 2: 255; E: pl. 99; L3: pl. 56; NB: 219.
Habitat: leaf litter and moss in damp woods.
Distribution: uncommon, mostly southern, but with records from Yorkshire, Lancashire and Inverness; in Wales only in Flintshire and in Ireland only from Co. Mayo [20, H1]. Widespread in Europe and reported from South America, India and Japan.

Notes: the smaller, paler spores are the chief distinguishing feature from
P. contextum, which is more common and found in drier sites.

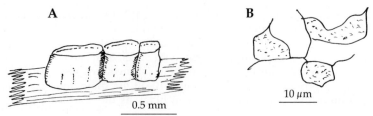

A

B

0.5 mm

10 μm

Fig. 252. *Physarum conglomeratum*: A: sporangia; B: capillitium.

Physarum contextum (Pers.) Pers.
Syn. Fung.: 168. 1810. Germany.

Sporocarps sessile sporangia, occasionally short plasmodiocarps, densely
crowded and sometimes appearing to form a pseudoaethalium but remaining
separate, angular or kidney-shaped, 0.3–0.6 mm wide, pale yellow. **Hypothallus**
inconspicuous, white. **Peridium** double, the outer layer thick and calcareous with
a distinct margin and depressed centre, the inner layer membranous, pale.
Capillitium dense, of white or pale yellow, angular nodes, sometimes aggregated
into a pseudocolumella. **Spores** black in mass, dark violet-brown in transmitted
light, 11–13 μm diam, strongly marked with spines or large warts. **Plasmodium**
yellow. [Fig. 253]

Illustrations: DM 2: 256; E: pl. 98; L3: pl. 55; MA: fig. 247; NB: 218.
Habitat: leaf litter and mosses.
Distribution: scattered, frequent only in the south but reaching Inverness [33].
Widely distributed in Europe, North America, Asia and Australia.

Notes: the larger, darker spores, more elongate sporangia and the frequent
presence of a pseudocolumella separate this rather neat species from
P. conglomeratum.

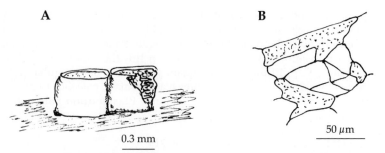

A

B

0.3 mm

50 μm

Fig. 253. *Physarum contextum*: A: sporangia; B: capillitium.

Physarum crateriforme Petch
Annln. R. Bot. Gard. Peradeniya **4**: 304. 1909. Sri Lanka.

Sporocarps short-stalked or sessile sporangia, globose to club-shaped or goblet-shaped, to 2 mm tall, 0.4–0.6 mm diam, greyish-white or very pale brown. **Hypothallus** thin, discoid, black. **Stalk** either completely black or black below and white above. **Peridium** membranous, the calcareous deposits often clustered, giving an uneven, mottled effect. **Columella** usually present, white, calcareous, reaching the apex of the sporangium, cylindrical or conical with broad conical outgrowths connected to the capillitium, looking like a ladder in section. **Capillitium** with rod-like nodes arranged vertically or large concretions attached to the columella. **Spores** in mass dark brown, lilac in transmitted light, 10–13 μm diam, densely spinulose. **Plasmodium** greyish-white or pale ochraceous. [Fig. 254]

Illustrations: E: pl. 92; L3: pl. 76; MA: fig. 248.
Habitat: bark of living trees, rarely on fallen branches.
Distribution: scattered, mostly western, north to Orkney, in Ireland only in Co. Wicklow [17, H1, C]. Widely distributed, but nowhere common, in Europe, North America, Belize, Asia and Nigeria.

Notes: the characteristic columella and large capillitial nodes, dark stalk and pale spores readily distinguish this species. In some developments in bark cultures a wide range of shapes may be found in the same dish, from small, globose sporangia, reminiscent of *P. robustum*, to tall, cylindrical forms looking like *P. compressum*; in all cases the columella is distinctive – it is rarely absent.

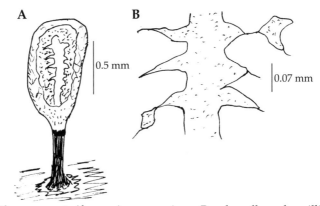

Fig. 254. *Physarum crateriforme*: A: sporangium; B: columella and capillitium.

Physarum decipiens M.A. Curtis
Am. J. Sci. II **6**: 352. 1848. South Carolina
Syn. *Badhamia decipiens* (M.A. Curtis) Berk.

Sporocarps sessile sporangia or plasmodiocarps, pulvinate or elongated, 0.3–0.7 mm wide, dull to bright yellow or orange. **Hypothallus** inconspicuous.

Peridium membranous with small, yellow calcareous scales. **Capillitium** of large angular yellow or orange nodes with a few short connecting tubules. **Spores** in mass black, pale violet-brown in transmitted light, 10–13 μm diam, minutely spinulose. **Plasmodium** yellow, or occasionally watery white. [Fig. 255]

Illustrations: DM 2: 259, 260; E: pl. 74; L3: pl. 7; MA: fig. 249.
Habitat: bark of living trees, especially associated with mosses.
Distribution: scattered, mostly in the west and north [16, H11, C]. Probably cosmopolitan but records difficult to evaluate because of confusion with related species.

Notes: part of a trio of similar species, it is said to be more sporangiate than *P. auriscalpium* or *P. serpula* Morgan, it lacks the green phase of the developing plasmodium, has paler and marginally larger spores than *P. auriscalpium* and the spores also lack the pale area seen in *P. serpula*. It is worth checking all material as a similar species is *P. lakhanpalii* Nann.-Bremek. & Y. Yamam., described from Switzerland and found elsewhere in Europe, which differs primarily in having clustered spores. The capillitium of *P. decipiens* is more badhamioid than the others but shows clearly the artificial nature of the division of *Badhamia* and *Physarum*.

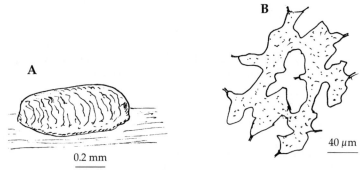

Fig. 255. *Physarum decipiens*: A: sporangium; B: capillitium.

Physarum didermoides (Pers.) Rostaf.
Mon.: 97. 1874. Sweden.

Sporocarps short-stalked or sessile sporangia, densely clustered or forming a pseudoaethalium, cylindrical to ovoid, 0.4–0.6 mm wide, white, becoming blue-grey with age. **Hypothallus** forming an extensive white, calcareous network under the whole development. **Stalk** white, weak, often flattened, sometimes fused with neighbours, a continuation of the hypothallus. **Peridium** double, the outer layer calcareous, fragile, falling away, the inner layer membranous, often with a purple tinge, the upper part of the peridium often remaining as a prominent cap. **Capillitium** abundant with numerous rounded or angular white nodes connected by colourless tubules, the nodes often massed as a pseudocolumella. **Spores** black in mass, dark purple-brown in transmitted light, 12–15 μm diam, densely spiny, sometimes angular or irregular in shape. **Plasmodium** white or pale grey. [Fig. 256]

Illustrations: DM 2: 261–2; E: pl. 91; L3: pl. 45: MA: fig. 252; NB: 214.
Habitat: straw heaps and straw bales, occasionally on other kinds of grass litter.
Distribution: rare, declining rapidly as the habitat disappears, not in Scotland, in Ireland only in Co. Dublin [28, H1]. Cosmopolitan and reportedly common in many parts of the world, including Europe.

Notes: the shape of the sporangia, the clusters of which resemble *Diderma spumarioides*, make this very distinctive. The only species with which it could be confused is *P. lividum*, which is, however, always sessile, is subglobose, has a single peridium and spores with a pale area on one side.

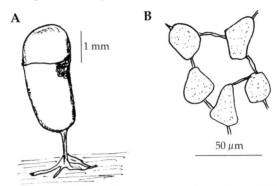

Fig. 256. *Physarum didermoides*: A: sporangium; B: capillitium.

Physarum echinosporum Lister
J. Bot., Lond. **37**: 147. 1899. Antigua.

Sporocarps elongate plasmodiocarps, laterally compressed, white. **Peridium** double, the outer layer smooth, calcareous, the inner membranous, pale purple, iridescent, dehiscing along a preformed apical split. **Capillitium** of dense white, angular nodes, connected by short colourless tubules. **Spores** black in mass, purple in transmitted light, 10–12 μm diam, marked with long spines forming ridges, but not reticulate. **Plasmodium** not seen. [Fig. 257]

Illustrations: L3: pl. 53; MA: fig. 254.
Habitat: on germinating seeds in hothouse.
Distribution: known only from a 1948 collection made on imported seeds from Kenya being grown at the Royal Botanic Gardens, Kew, therefore not strictly British [1]. Essentially a tropical species recorded from central and South America, the West Indies, Kenya, India, Indonesia and the Philippines.

Notes: closely resembles *P. bivalve* but differs in the iridescent inner peridium and the very spiny spores. May occur again on compost associated with imported tropical plants.

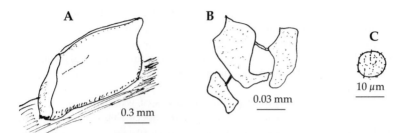

Fig. 257. *Physarum echinosporum*: A: plasmodiocarp; B: capillitium; C: spore.

Physarum flavicomum Berk.
J. Bot., Lond. **4**: 66. 1845. New South Wales.

Sporocarps stalked sporangia, gregarious, nodding, 1–2 mm tall, 0.3–0.6 mm diam, globose or lens-shaped, dusky yellow. **Hypothallus** small, discoid. **Stalk** slender, tapering, solid, twisted and grooved, reddish-brown. **Peridium** delicate, the calcareous material falling away except at the base, leaving an iridescent membrane. **Capillitium** dense, of branching colourless tubules with a few, small yellow nodes which are either spindle-shaped or angular and sometimes branched. **Spores** blackish-brown in mass, bright violet-brown in transmitted light, 8–10 μm diam. minutely dotted. **Plasmodium** yellow or yellowish-green. [Fig. 258]

Illustrations: DM 2: 264; E: pl. 86; L3: pl. 32; MA: fig. 255.
Habitat: on rotten wood.
Distribution: surprisingly, this is only known from a single, recent collection from Co. Wicklow [H1]. Widespread in the warmer parts of Europe, probably cosmopolitan.

Notes: closely resembles *P. viride* but is darker and the angular nodes in some collections will make it easy to separate. The peridial lime in *P. viride* is persistent, not deciduous, but the two species are clearly close.

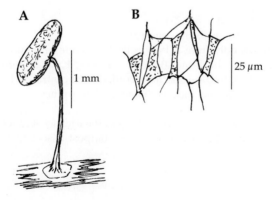

Fig. 258. *Physarum flavicomum*: A: sporangium; B: capillitium.

Physarum galbeum Wingate
in Macbride, *N. Am. Slime-Moulds*: 53. 1899. Pennsylvania.

Sporocarps stalked sporangia, globose to slightly pear-shaped, golden-yellow, 0.6–1.2 mm high, 0.3–0.5 mm diam. **Hypothallus** small, inconspicuous, discoid, orange. **Stalk** long, up to 0.8 mm long, slender, tapering, orange below, yellow above, furrowed. **Peridium** thin, the calcareous material patchy, falling away as flakes. **Capillitium** a small-meshed net of yellow threads with a few small, narrow, angular, yellow nodes. **Spores** pale brown in mass, yellow-brown in transmitted light, 7.5–10 µm diam, minutely warted with small clusters of warts. **Plasmodium** yellow. [Fig. 259]

Illustrations: E: pl. 86; L3: pl. 199; MA: fig. 257.
Habitat: on dead stems of brambles and rosebay.
Distribution: uncommon, southern, scattered northwards to the Isle of Man and Anglesey [14, H2]. Rare in Europe and uncommon in North America and Japan.

Notes: the pale, almost smooth spores and the distinct colour of the sporangia, together with the habitat separate this from other members of the genus. The only species with which it could be confused is *Craterium aureum*, which has larger nodes and a cap-like dehiscence.

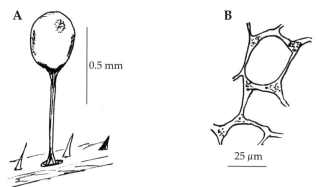

Fig. 259. *Physarum galbeum*: A: sporangium; B: capillitium.

Physarum globuliferum (Bull.) Pers.
Syn. Fung.: 175. 1801. France.

Sporocarps stalked sporangia, gregarious in large colonies, globose, 0.4–0.7 mm diam, 0.8–1.5 mm tall, white. **Hypothallus** inconspicuous. **Stalk** slender, white, furrowed, with enclosed calcareous material. **Peridium** membranous with patches of calcareous granules. **Columella** short, conical or blunt-tipped. **Capillitium** dense, delicate, with numerous junctions without nodes, nodes small, rounded, white. **Spores** dark greyish-brown in mass, violet in transmitted light, 7–9 µm diam, minutely warted, with small, faint clusters of warts. **Plasmodium** white. [Fig. 260]

Illustrations: DM 2: 265–6; E: pl. 79; L3: pl. 16; MA: fig. 258; NB: 198.
Habitat: rotten wood.
Distribution: rare, declining, from Kent to Inverness, in Ireland only in Co. Roscommon; last seen in 1983 [12, H1]. Cosmopolitan.

Notes: the calcareous stalk, pale spores and small white nodes separate this uncommon species. It differs from several other species only in the colour of the lime (e.g. *P. murinum*) and this may be due to uptake of appropriately coloured metallic salts from the substrate.

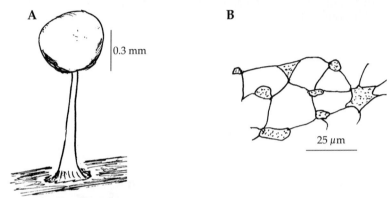

A

B

0.3 mm

25 µm

Fig. 260. *Physarum globuliferum*: A: sporangium; B: capillitium.

Physarum javanicum Racib.
Hedwigia **37**: 53. 1898. Indonesia

Sporocarps stalked sporangia, top-shaped with a depressed apex, 0.4–1 mm diam, 2–4 mm tall, white. **Hypothallus** small, discoid, white. **Stalk** long, slender, narrowing above, greyish-white, darker below. **Peridium** thin, unevenly covered with calcareous granules, the lower part remaining as an irregular cup. **Capillitium** dense, of spindle-shaped colourless tubes connecting small, white triangular nodes. **Spores** dark brown in mass, purple-brown in transmitted light, 9–10 µm diam, nearly smooth. **Plasmodium** not seen. [Fig. 261]

Illustrations: L3: pl. 197; MA: fig. 260.
Habitat: dead wood.
Distribution: known in the British Isles from a single collection made in 1934 at Westwick, Norfolk [1]. A tropical species known from the West Indies, Indonesia, Africa and South and central America; the British collection is one of several other casual occurrences during periods of hot weather, such as *Arcyria insignis* and *Physarum brunneolum*.

Notes: the shape of the sporangium and the unusual tubules in the capillitium will characterise this species if it is ever found again in the British Isles.

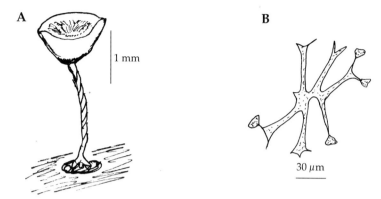

Fig. 261. *Physarum javanicum*: A: sporangium; B: capillitium.

Physarum lateritium (Berk. & Ravenel) Morgan
J. Cinc. Soc. Nat. Hist. **19**: 23. 1896. South Carolina.

Sporocarps sessile sporangia, rarely short plasmodiocarps, globose or subglobose, 0.3–0.7 mm diam, orange or red. **Peridium** thin, wrinkled, dotted with red calcareous scales. **Capillitium** delicate, of pale yellow tubules, the nodes often membranous, without calcareous granules, or filled with pale yellow lime, usually with red or deep yellow centres. **Spores** violet-brown in mass, clear violet in transmitted light, 7–9 μm diam, minutely warted. **Plasmodium** orange-yellow. [Fig. 262]

Illustrations: DM 2: 269,270; E: pl. 100; L3: pl. 60; MA: fig. 261; NB: 221.
Habitat: leaf litter.
Distribution: rare, scattered from Cornwall to Northumberland [9]. Recorded from the Americas, Asia, Europe and New Zealand but never common.

Notes: the red sporangia can only be confused, in the British Isles, with *P. rubiginosum*, which is larger and darker in all its parts.

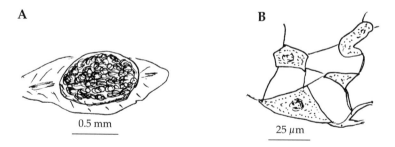

Fig. 262. *Physarum lateritium*: A: sporangium; B: capillitium.

Physarum leucophaeum Fr.
Symb. Gast.: 24. 1818. Sweden.
Syn. *Physarum nutans* var. *leucophaeum* (Fr.) Lister

Sporocarps stalked sporangia, erect, subglobose, 0.4–0.8 mm diam, 0.8–1.5 mm tall, white or bluish-grey. **Hypothallus** grey, reticulate. **Stalk** mid-brown to reddish-brown, often twisted, powdered with white. **Peridium** thin, membranous, usually thickly covered with calcareous granules, with a thickened base leaving a disc or shallow cup. **Capillitium** dense, delicate, with numerous white, rounded nodes or fewer, larger, angular or branching nodes. **Spores** black in mass, yellow-brown in transmitted light, 9–11 μm diam, minutely roughened. **Plasmodium** grey, in bark cultures sometimes brown. [Fig. 263]

Illustrations: DM 2: 271–2; L3: pl. 38; MA: fig. 262; NB: 195–6.
Habitat: on rotten wood, rarely on bark of living trees.
Distribution: very common throughout the British Isles [111, H33, C]. Probably cosmopolitan.

Notes: superficially resembles erect forms of *P. nutans* or *P. robustum* but does not have the capillitium radiating from the top of the stalk, neither does it have spindle-shaped nodes. Both *P. pusillopse* and *P. scoticum* have a persistent base to the peridium but this is ochraceous in *P. pusillopse* and *P. scoticum* has a calcareous stalk.

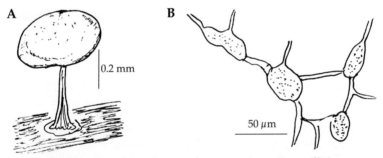

Fig. 263. *Physarum leucophaeum*: A: sporangium; B: capillitium.

Physarum leucopus Link
Ges. Nat. Freunde Berlin Mag. **3**: 27. 1809. Germany.

Sporocarps stalked sporangia, gregarious, globose, white, 0.4–0.5 mm diam. **Hypothallus** white, discoid. **Stalk** white, deeply furrowed, strongly calcareous. **Peridium** covered in small frost-like particles, closely resembling *Didymium squamulosum*. **Columella** represented by a small, white conical extension of the stalk, often absent. **Capillitium** an open net of short, colourless threads connecting large, angular, white nodes, these sometimes massed as a pseudocolumella. **Spores** black in mass, pale violet-brown in transmitted light, 8–10 μm diam, clearly warted. **Plasmodium** white, with occasional pastel tints. [Fig. 264]

Illustrations: DM 2: 274; E: pl. 78; L3: pl. 15; MA: fig. 263; NB: 196.
Habitat: leaf litter, rarely on wood.
Distribution: uncommon, mostly southern but reaching Argyll, not recorded in Wales or Ireland [29]. Cosmopolitan.

Notes: the close resemblance to *Didymium squamulosum* is easily dispelled by the presence of nodes in the capillitium. Specimens on wood could be mistaken for *P. robustum* but this has a less conspicuous hypothallus and quite different capillitium.

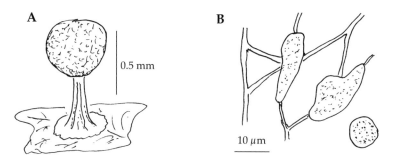

Fig. 264. *Physarum leucopus*: A: sporangium; B: capillitium.

Physarum limonium Nann.-Bremek.
Proc. K. Ned. Akad. Wet. C **69**: 257. 1966. Netherlands.

Sporocarps short-stalked sporangia, 0.8–1 mm diam, to 1.2 mm tall, globose, lemon-yellow. **Hypothallus** small, discoid, reddish-brown. **Stalk** to 0.7 mm tall, reddish-brown, slender, grooved. **Peridium** reddish-brown at the base and free of lime, pale yellow above and covered with round scales of yellow lime. **Capillitium** of large, irregular nodes, yellow or orange-yellow, with a few indistinct colourless threads, sometimes massed as a pseudocolumella. **Spores** dark brown in mass, lilac-grey in transmitted light, 10–13 μm diam, finely warted with groups of larger warts. **Plasmodium** yellow. [Fig. 265]

Illustrations: NB: 206.
Habitat: bark of living trees.
Distribution: rare, known only from Kent, Warwickshire, Cumbria, Perthshire, the Isle of Bute and Co. Wicklow [5, H1]. Recorded from France, Netherlands, Portugal, Spain and New Zealand.

Notes: grouped by some authors with *P. auriscalpium* but it lacks the greenish phase in development and also the multi-coloured reflections in the stalked form of that species. The spores are also very pale. The circular plates on the peridium are also seen in *P. scoticum*, but this is a greyish-white species and quite different internally.

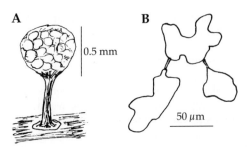

Fig. 265. *Physarum limonium*: A: sporangium; B: capillitium.

Physarum listeri T. Macbr.
in Macbride & Martin, *Myxom.*: 62. 1934. Italy.
Syn. *Physarum luteoalbum* Lister & G. Lister

Sporocarps stalked sporangia, subglobose, bright yellow, 0.8–1 mm diam.
Hypothallus of intertwined strands, white. **Stalk** thick, with a membranous outer
layer filled with calcareous material which is often crystalline, white below
becoming yellow or orange above, wider at the apex than the base, up to 1 mm
high. **Peridium** double, the outer calcareous, the inner membranous, dark
olivaceous, remaining as a collar round the apex of the stalk. **Columella** large,
subglobose or club-shaped, yellow. **Capillitium** of stiff yellow threads radiating
from the columella, branching and forming a net, with a few narrow yellow
nodes. **Spores** black in mass, dark purple-brown in transmitted light, 10–13 μm
diam, coarsely spiny. **Plasmodium** orange. [Fig. 266]

Illustrations: DM 2: 276; L3: pl. 24; MA: fig. 264.
Habitat: on conifer litter.
Distribution: rare, known only from Devon and Somerset, a record from Co.
Down may well be a mis-identification; last seen in 1919 [2, ?H1]. Recorded from
several European countries, from North America, Morocco, India and Pakistan,
but always rare.

Notes: the presence of crystalline lime and the capillitium being intermediate
between *Physarum* and *Diderma* support the notion that this very distinctive
species belongs in a different genus. Lack of material makes the erection of a new
genus premature.

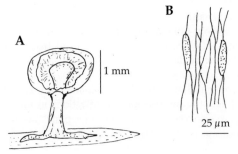

Fig. 266. *Physarum listeri*: A: sporangium; B: capillitium.

Physarum lividum Rostaf.
Mon.: 95. 1874. Poland.
Syn. *Physarum didermoides* var. *lividum* (Rostaf.) Lister

Sporocarps sessile sporangia, gregarious, globose, 0.3–0.6 mm diam, pale grey or bluish-grey, rough. **Hypothallus** colourless but sometimes encrusted with white lime. **Peridium** single, heavily encrusted with lime, rough, dehiscing irregularly leaving a basal cup with an irregular rim. **Capillitium** a close-meshed net of colourless tubules with numerous rounded, white nodes. **Spores** in mass black, dark purple-brown in transmitted light, 11–12 μm diam, with dark warts spread thinly over the surface and with a pale area to one side. **Plasmodium** watery white. [Fig. 267]

Illustrations: DM 2: 277; NB: 212.
Habitat: straw heaps, bales and other grass litter.
Distribution: rare, declining, north to Cheshire, last seen 1976 [12]. Recorded in several European countries and New Zealand.

Notes: similar in general appearance to *P. didermoides* but always sessile, globose, with a single peridial layer and spores with a pale area.

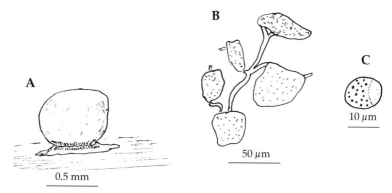

Fig. 267. *Physarum lividum*: A: sporangium; B: capillitium; C: spore.

Physarum mucosum Nann.-Bremek.
Med. Bot. Mus. Herb. Utrecht **150**: 782. 1958. Netherlands.

Sporocarps sessile sporangia or short plasmodiocarps, crowded, yellow to orange, fading to pale yellow, 0.6 mm wide, slimy when moist. **Hypothallus** membranous, pale brown. **Peridium** of three layers, the outer membranous, ochraceous, mucilaginous when moist, when dry adhering in wrinkles to the middle, brittle, yellow, calcareous layer, the inner layer membranous and largely lime-free; the upper parts forming a rim around the apex with a depressed lid-like centre. **Capillitium** with large angular, sometimes branched white or yellow nodes, usually forming a pseudocolumella. **Spores** black in mass, dark purple-brown in transmitted light, 13 μm diam, or ovoid and 12 x 14 μm, spiny. **Plasmodium** yellow. [Fig. 268]

Illustrations: NB: 218.
Habitat: decaying herbaceous stems.
Distribution: rare, known only from Kent, Perthshire and Inverness [3]. Recorded from Sweden and the Netherlands.

Notes: the more distinct rim and the mucilaginous peridium serve to separate this from the similar, especially when dry, *P. conglomeratum* and *P. contextum*. This species also occurs on stem rather than leaf litter and has not been found on mosses.

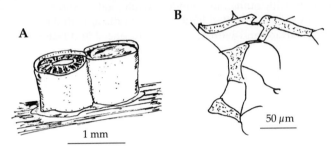

Fig. 268. *Physarum mucosum*: A: sporangia; B: capillitium.

Physarum murinum Lister
Mycet.: 41. 1894. Moffat, Dumfries-shire.

Sporocarps stalked sporangia, gregarious, to 1.5 mm tall, globose, 0.4–0.8 mm diam, pale reddish-brown to grey or ochraceous-brown. **Hypothallus** inconspicuous. **Stalk** with calcareous filling, grooved, brown. **Peridium** membranous, covered with pale brown, round scales, often leaving a collar–like base on dehiscence, not attached to the outer parts of the capillitium. **Capillitium** forming a strong, even net with numerous small, rounded brown nodes. **Spores** grey-brown in mass, lilac-grey in transmitted light, 8–10 μm diam, finely warted with small groups of smaller warts. **Plasmodium** cream. [Fig. 269]

Illustrations: DM 2: 278,280; L3: pl. 18; MA: fig. 270; NB: 200.
Habitat: rotten wood, especially of conifers..
Distribution: rare, known from Merioneth, Cumbria, Dumfries, Kincardine, Aberdeen, Inverness and Co. Down; last seen in 1927 [6, H1]. Widespread but not common in Europe and North America and also recorded from Costa Rica.

Notes: the brown colours are distinctive but this is little more than *P. globuliferum* with brown rather than white lime. It may represent a physiological race which takes up and incorporates a metallic pigment from the substrate, rather than a distinct species. It has been found in recent years in several European countries but, in spite of concentrated searching in its old haunts, has not been refound in the British Isles.

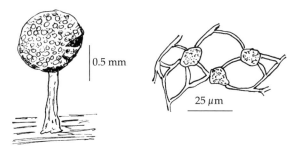

Fig. 269. *Physarum murinum*: A: sporangium; B: capillitium.

Physarum mutabile (Rostaf.) G. Lister
Mycet. edn 2: 53. 1911. Germany.

Sporocarps stalked, rarely sessile, sporangia or short plasmodiocarps, subglobose or top-shaped, 0.3–0.6 mm diam, the plasmodiocarps to 2 mm long, white or pale grey. **Hypothallus** membranous, pale yellow or brownish. **Stalk**, when present, yellow, with included lime. **Peridium** single, thin, with an even, smooth cover of white calcareous granules. **Columella** absent. **Capillitium** small-meshed, with small white, rounded nodes, usually with a conspicuous white pseudocolumella, cylindrical in the sporangia and linear in the plasmodiocarps. **Spores** black in mass, purple-brown in transmitted light, 7–10 μm diam, densely spinulose. **Plasmodium** pale grey. [Fig. 270]

Illustrations: E: pl. 82; L3: pl. 44; MA: fig. 271; NB: 223.
Habitat: on grass litter, living grass and on vegetation in dune slacks.
Distribution: uncommon, scattered from Cornwall to Moray (the only Scottish record), recently from Glamorgan, apparently absent from Ireland [14]. Widespread but not common in Europe, North America, Africa, Japan, Israel and Sri Lanka.

Notes: the shape of the sporangia is characteristic, reminiscent of *Craterium leucocephalum* but there is no lid, the pseudocolumella and very smooth peridium are also characteristic.

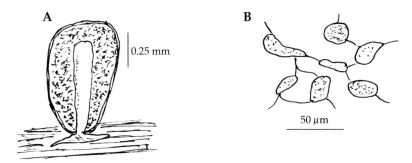

Fig. 270. *Physarum mutabile*: A: sporangium; B: capillitium.

Physarum nitens (Lister) Ing
Trans. Br. mycol. Soc. **78**: 444. 1982. Woburn Sands, Bedfordshire.
Syn. *Physarum virescens* var. *nitens* Lister

Sporocarps sessile sporangia, gregarious or clustered but not heaped, subglobose, 0.5–0.9 mm diam, bright yellow or orange. **Peridium** membranous, densely covered with calcareous granules but without circular discs. **Capillitium** a dense network of colourless tubules with angular yellow nodes. **Spores** in mass dark purple-brown, pale violet-brown in transmitted light, 7–9 µm diam, minutely spinulose. **Plasmodium** yellow, not becoming green. [Fig. 271]

Illustrations: DM 2: 283; L3: pl. 62; MA: fig. 265.
Habitat: leaf litter.
Distribution: rare, scattered from Somerset to Aberdeen, in Ireland only in Cork and Kerry [6, H2]. Reported from Germany, Czech Republic, Spain, Italy and Israel.

Notes: differs from *P. virescens* in the larger sporangia which are not heaped and the lack of yellow, circular discs in the peridium. North American material is different and probably refers to *P. luteolum* Peck. The species is probably less rare than the few records suggest as it may not have been separated from the widespread *P. virescens*.

A   B

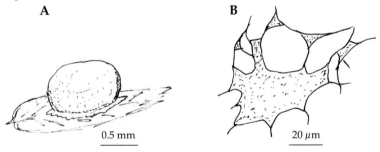

0.5 mm   20 µm

Fig. 271. *Physarum nitens*: A: sporangium; B: capillitium.

Physarum notabile T. Macbr.
N. Am. Slime-Moulds edn 2: 80. 1922. New York State.
Syn. *Physarum connatum* (Peck) G. Lister

Sporocarps stalked sporangia, occasionally sessile or forming short plasmodiocarps, gregarious, often in large developments, globose to kidney-shaped, often with to 10 sporangia joined by the stalks, 0.3–1 mm diam, white. **Hypothallus** continuous under the group, white. **Stalk** often mis-shapen, furrowed, dark but appearing white from the calcareous covering, sometimes absent. **Peridium** membranous, densely covered with white granules. **Capillitium** abundant, with large angular, white nodes connected by long colourless threads. **Spores** black in mass, olivaceous brown in transmitted light, 10–11.5 µm diam, minutely warted. **Plasmodium** white or pale grey. [Fig. 272]

Illustrations: DM 2: 284; E: pl. 93; L3: pl. 40; MA: fig. 273.
Habitat: on dead wood and, occasionally, on bark of living trees (not in the British Isles).
Distribution: rare, known only from Surrey, Hertfordshire, Bedfordshire and Buckinghamshire, always on the chalk [4]. Rare in Europe, Spain, Germany and the Ukraine, reported from Israel, not uncommon in east Asia, said to be common in the eastern United States and doubtfully recorded from New Zealand.

Notes: the joined sporangia, large angular nodes and distinctly smoky-olivaceous spores are diagnostic but the species is variable and sessile/plasmodiocarpous forms may be mistaken for forms of *P. compressum*, with much darker spores, so it is very important to check the spore colour carefully.

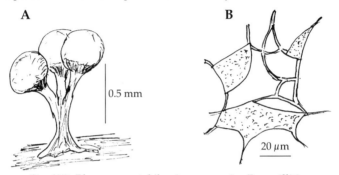

Fig. 272. *Physarum notabile*: A: sporangia; B: capillitium.

Physarum nucleatum Rex
Proc. Acad. Sci. Philad. **43**: 389. 1891. Pennsylvania.

Sporocarps stalked sporangia, globose, white, 0.3–0.5 mm diam, to 1.8 mm tall. **Hypothallus** inconspicuous. **Stalk** slender, yellowish-white, wrinkled. **Peridium** thin, covered with white granules, the base persisting as a collar on the stem. **Columella** usually lacking, sometimes a small projection from the top of the stalk. **Capillitium** dense, with small white, rounded nodes which are aggregated to form a spherical ball of lime in the centre of the sporangium looking like a pseudocolumella, but the nodes are not fused together. **Spores** in mass black, clear lilac in transmitted light, 6.5–7.5 µm diam, minutely spinulose. **Plasmodium** grey. [Fig. 273]

Illustrations: E: pl. 90; L3: pl. 35; MA: fig. 274.
Habitat: dead wood.
Distribution: rare, known only from Cornwall, Devon, Somerset and Kent, last seen 1963 [5]. Essentially a tropical species but also found around the Mediterranean, in the warmer parts of Central Europe, warm temperate North America, Japan, Australia and New Zealand.

Notes: the small long-stalked sporangia resemble *P. globuliferum* but the central ball of lime and the small, pale spores and the non-limy stalks separate it readily.

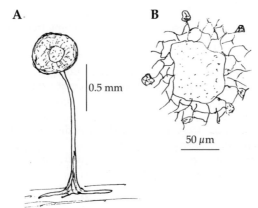

Fig. 273. *Physarum nucleatum*: A: sporangium; B: capillitium.

Physarum nudum T. Macbr.
in Peck & Gilbert, *Am. J. Bot.* **19**: 134. 1932. Washington.

Sporocarps sessile sporangia, gregarious, subglobose to pulvinate on a narrowed base, 0.3–0.5 mm diam, pale grey to almost black, when lime is absent. **Hypothallus** extensive, forming a network joining neighbouring sporangia. **Peridium** single, membranous, covered with thin layer of calcareous flakes or naked and iridescent. **Capillitium** delicate, with few narrow, white, calcareous nodes but with many lime-free junctions. **Spores** dark brown in mass, violet-brown in transmitted light, 10–12 µm diam, minutely spinulose, occasionally clustered in loose groups of up to 15 spores, then elliptical. **Plasmodium** yellow. [Fig. 274]

Illustrations: MA: fig. 275; NB: 197.
Habitat: leaf litter.
Distribution: rare, known only from Worcestershire and Angus [2]. Widely distributed in Europe, but never common, north-west United States, India and Australia.

Notes: a difficult species to characterise as it looks so much like a limeless *Badhamia*, but has a physaroid capillitium; the spore clusters have only been seen in Polish material. This may represent a lime-deficient sessile phase of something more familiar but is retained as a separate species on the basis of the delicate capillitium.

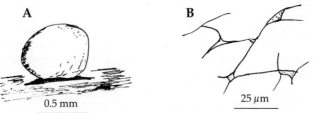

Fig. 274. *Physarum nudum*: A: sporangium; B: capillitium.

Physarum nutans Pers.
Annln. Bot. **15**: 6. 1795. France.

Sporocarps stalked sporangia, rarely sessile, gregarious, in large groups, nodding, lens-shaped, rarely flattened spheres, white or pale grey, 0.4–0.7 mm diam, to 1.5 mm tall. **Hypothallus** discoid but inconspicuous. **Stalk** long, usually twice the diameter of the sporangium, tapering, darker below but often pale ochraceous above. **Peridium** thin, the persistent base slightly thickened and ochraceous, the rest colourless, dehiscing into plates and, characteristically, into petaloid lobes. **Capillitium** radiating from the base with long meshes and small white spindle-shaped nodes. **Spores** in mass dark chocolate-brown, pale brown in transmitted light, 8–10.5 μm diam, minutely warted with groups of darker, small warts. **Plasmodium** colourless or pale brown. [Fig. 275]

Illustrations: DM 2: 286–7; E: pl. 91; L3: pl. 37; MA: fig. 276; NB: 192.
Habitat: usually on dead wood but frequently on bark of living trees in moist chamber, rarely on leaf litter or mosses.
Distribution: very common throughout the British Isles [112, H40, C]. Cosmopolitan.

Notes: the nodding, lenticular sporangia with petaloid dehiscence and the radiating capillitium with small white fusiform nodes are constant features of this otherwise variable and abundant species.

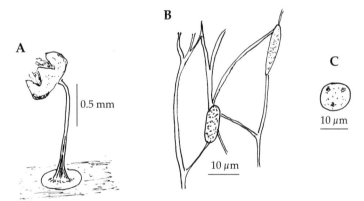

Fig. 275. *Physarum nutans*: A: sporangium; B: capillitium; C: spore.

Physarum oblatum T. Macbr.
Bull. Nat. Hist. Univ. Iowa **2**: 384. 1893. Iowa.
Syn. *Physarum maydis* (Morgan) Torrend

Sporocarps stalked sporangia, depressed-globose with a distinctly flattened top, 0.4–0.6 mm diam, to 1.5 mm tall, bright orange-yellow, with a darker base. **Hypothallus** inconspicuous. **Stalk** reddish-brown, translucent, furrowed. **Peridium** membranous above, thickened below and remaining as a cup.

Capillitium of angular, branching, orange nodes connected by colourless or yellow threads, these threads often absent. **Spores** in mass blackish-brown, violet brown in transmitted light, 9–13 µm diam, minutely spinulose with clusters of large warts. **Plasmodium** orange-yellow. [Fig. 276]

Illustrations: DM 2: 288; E: pl. 87; L3: pl. 32; MA: fig. 277.
Habitat: bark of living trees.
Distribution: frequent but scattered, mostly northern and western [27, H4, C]. Cosmopolitan.

Notes: the shape of the sporangium suggest *Craterium* but there is no trace of a lid; some bark cultures of *P. viride* come close but the capillitium is then very different. The large, bright spores and the large nodes, together with the usually flattened sporangia make this a fairly easy species to identify.

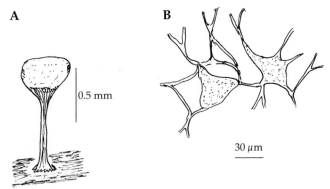

A

B

0.5 mm

30 µm

Fig. 276. *Physarum oblatum*: A: sporangium; B: capillitium.

Physarum obscurum (Lister) Ing
Trans. Br. mycol. Soc. **78**: 445. 1982. Charton, near Lyme Regis, Devon.
Syn. *Physarum virescens* var. *obscurum* Lister

Sporocarps sessile sporangia or short plasmodiocarps, gregarious but not heaped, 0.4–0.8 mm diam, greenish-grey, olive or yellowish, glossy. **Hypothallus** inconspicuous. **Peridium** membranous, colourless, often without calcareous deposits but usually with scattered granules, without circular yellow discs. **Capillitium** a network of threads with bright yellow angular nodes. **Spores** black in mass, pale violet-brown in transmitted light, 6–8 µm diam. **Plasmodium** yellow, not becoming green. [Fig. 277]

Illustrations: L3: pl. 61.
Habitat: leaf litter.
Distribution: uncommon, scattered from Devon north to Inverness [17, H2]. Known from several parts of Europe, North America and New Zealand.

Notes: the larger, olive, glossy, not heaped sporangia and the slightly smaller spores separate this from *P. virescens*, the colour from *P. nitens*.

A

B

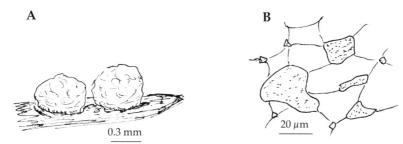

0.3 mm

20 μm

Fig. 277. *Physarum obscurum*: A: sporangia; B: capillitium.

Physarum ovisporum G. Lister
J. Bot., Lond. **59**: 90. 1921. Near Lyme Regis.

Sporocarps sessile sporangia or plasmodiocarps, pulvinate, white, 0.5–0.8 mm diam. **Peridium** roughened with calcareous granules, black at the base. **Capillitium** with numerous rounded, white nodes connected by short, colourless tubules. **Spores** black in mass, dark purple-brown in transmitted light, oval, 12–13 x 10–12 μm, occasionally globose, 9–11 μm diam, minutely warted and with a pale band through the long axis of the spore. **Plasmodium** white. [Fig. 278]

Illustrations: DM 2: 290; E: pl. 95; L3: pl. 202; MA: fig. 278.
Habitat: leaf litter and the bark of living trees.
Distribution: rare, known from Devon, Somerset, Dorset, Essex, Suffolk, Sutherland, Co. Cork and Co. Wicklow [6, H2]. Widespread, but uncommon, in Europe and recorded from North America and east Asia.

Notes: sometimes included in *P. vernum* but the spores are distinctive and the nodes rounded rather than angular. The plasmodiocarps are shorter and the base of the peridium is black, unlike *P. vernum* where there is no colour difference.

A

B

C

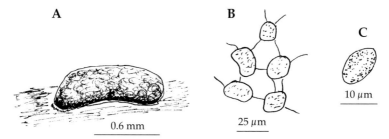

0.6 mm

25 μm

10 μm

Fig. 278. *Physarum ovisporum*: A: plasmodiocarp; B: capillitium; C: spore.

Physarum penetrale Rex
Proc. Acad. Sci. Philad. **43**: 389. 1891. Pennsylvania.

Sporocarps stalked sporangia, scattered, ellipsoid to pear-shaped, 0.4–0.6 mm diam, 1–2 mm tall, greenish-grey to yellowish-green, iridescent. **Hypothallus** inconspicuous. **Stalk** long, tapering, reddish-brown, translucent. **Peridium** thin, scantily covered with pale yellow granular scales, dehiscing in lobes. **Columella** a continuation of the stalk, pale brown, cylindrical reaching to at least three-quarters of the height of the sporangium. **Capillitium** dense, with small, round, pale yellow nodes. **Spores** in mass dark brown, brownish-lilac in transmitted light, 6–7 μm diam, very minutely spinulose with small clusters of spines. **Plasmodium** orange-yellow. [Fig. 279]

Illustrations: E: pl. 88; L3: pl. 36; MA: fig. 279.
Habitat: leaf litter.
Distribution: rare, known from Norfolk, Bedfordshire, Worcestershire, Dumfries, Perthshire, Inverness and Co. Wicklow, last seen in 1965 [6, H1]. Generally rare in North America, Europe, Asia and Africa.

Notes: the narrow, translucent columella, shape and colour of the sporangium and the small, pale spores make this rare species easy to identify.

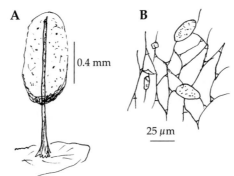

Fig. 279. *Physarum penetrale*: A: sporangium; B: capillitium.

Physarum psittacinum Ditmar
in Sturm, *Deutsch. Fl., Pilze* **1**: 125. 1817. Germany.

Sporocarps stalked sporangia, gregarious, often in large developments, globose, 0.5–0.8 mm diam, total height 1.2 mm, bronze, iridescent with blue reflections and mottled with orange. **Hypothallus** small, orange. **Stalk** brilliant orange or reddish-brown. **Peridium** membranous. **Capillitium** dense, with colourless or dark threads, which are often flattened, and brilliant orange nodes, sometimes forming a central mass. **Spores** dark brown in mass, pale brown in transmitted light, 8–10 μm diam, minutely warted, the warts often in groups. **Plasmodium** yellow or orange. [Fig. 280]

Illustrations: DM 2: 294; E: pl. 84; L3: pl. 29; MA: fig. 282; NB: 202.
Habitat: on rotten logs and stumps in ancient broad-leaved woodland, occasionally as a casual on bark of living trees..
Distribution: frequent, commoner in the south, thinning out northwards to Ross and Sutherland, in the north mostly on bark [47, H8, C]. Widespread in Europe, North America, Japan and the Philippines.

Notes: the brilliant orange stalk, iridescent bronze sporangia and orange nodes make this an unmistakable species; in bark cultures the colours are usually more subdued.

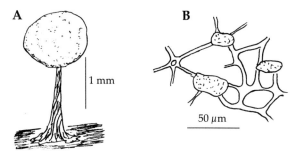

Fig. 280. *Physarum psittacinum*: A: sporangium; B: capillitium.

Physarum pulcherripes Peck
Bull. Buffalo Soc. Nat. Sci. **1**: 64. 1873. New York State.

Sporocarps stalked sporangia, globose, 0.4–0.6 mm diam, orange-brown to tawny, calcareous above, dark iridescent below, height 1–2 mm. **Hypothallus** well developed, dark reddish-brown. **Stalk** calcareous, slender, shades of red from pale red to reddish-brown. **Peridium** thin, falling away. **Columella** small, conical. **Capillitium** dense, somewhat elastic, small-meshed with small, rounded red or yellow nodes. **Spores** dark violet-grey in mass, pale lilac-brown in transmitted light, 8–10 μm diam, minutely warted, with clusters of darker warts. **Plasmodium** yellow. [Fig. 281]

Illustrations: L3: pl. 17; MA: fig. 284; NB: 199.
Habitat: dead wood.
Distribution: known from a single collection made in Rostrevor, Co. Down in 1916 [H1]. Rare in Europe, Germany, Netherlands and Spain, and recorded from Japan and Jamaica, otherwise widespread in North and central America.

Notes: a striking species; the combination of colours or peridium and nodes, the pale spores and the small columella are sufficient to identify this species. When the peridium has fallen away, and it is very fragile, the characters are less obvious.

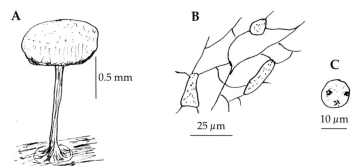

Fig. 281. *Physarum pulcherripes*: A: sporangium; B: capillitium; C: spore.

Physarum pusillopse D.W. Mitchell & Nann.-Bremek.
Proc. K. Ned. Akad. Wet. C **80**: 310. 1977. Bishopstone, Wiltshire.

Sporocarps stalked sporangia, gregarious, subglobose with a flat base, 0.8–1.2 mm diam, height 0.8–1.4 mm, white to pale buff. **Hypothallus** minute. **Stalk** stout, narrowing slightly upwards, wrinkled, dark reddish-brown, translucent. **Peridium** base ochraceous, thickened and radially striate, colourless and thin elsewhere and covered with small deposits of white lime, fragmenting. **Capillitium** a small-meshed net of narrow colourless tubules with many small, rounded white nodes, the whole attached to the peridium and falling away with it. **Spores** brown in mass, violet-grey in transmitted light, 11–13 μm diam, minutely warted and with small groups of larger warts and with a pale equatorial band. **Plasmodium** not seen. [Fig. 282]

Illustrations: original description.
Habitat: fallen bark.
Distribution: known from the type collection from Wiltshire and from Gloucestershire [2]. Otherwise recorded only from Germany.

Notes: this is superficially like *P. pusillum* but is larger and lacks the red base to the sporangium; it may also resemble *P. leucophaeum* but the larger spores with a pale band are distinctive as is the translucent stalk.

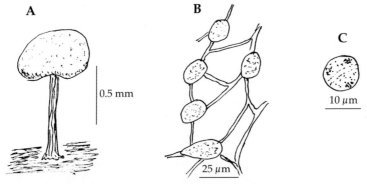

Fig. 282. *Physarum pusillopse*: A: sporangium; B: capillitium; C: spore.

Physarum pusillum (Berk. & M.A. Curtis) G. Lister
Mycet. edn 2: 54. 1911. South Carolina.

Sporocarps stalked, rarely sessile, sporangia, globose, 0.4–0.6 mm diam, to 2 mm tall, white with a red-brown base. **Hypothallus** discoid, brown, translucent. **Stalk** slender, reddish-brown, merging into the base of the sporangium. **Peridium** thin, wrinkled, thickly covered with white lime except the basal disc, which is thickened and persistent. **Capillitium** variable, with small, angular scattered nodes or, especially in the sessile forms, badhamioid. **Spores** black in mass, lilac-brown in transmitted light, 10–12 μm diam, minutely warted. **Plasmodium** watery white. [Fig. 283]

Illustrations: DM 2: 296; E: pl. 90: L3: pl. 43; MA: fig. 285; NB: 204.
Habitat: grass litter, including straw, reed-swamp litter, sand dune marram litter and thatch but also found frequently on the bark of living trees.
Distribution: frequent, scattered throughout the British Isles [48, H18]. Cosmopolitan.

Notes: the small white sporangia with a reddish base and stalks resemble the red-stalked *Didymium* species but lack the crystalline line and have a different capillitium. The sessile forms, often found in bark cultures, could be mistaken for *Badhamia panicea* but are usually accompanied by more typical, stalked forms.

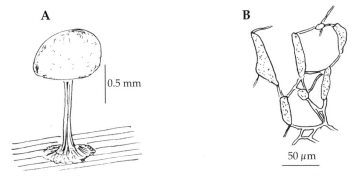

Fig. 283. *Physarum pusillum*: A: sporangium; B: capillitium.

Physarum robustum (Lister) Nann.-Bremek.
Proc. K. Ned. Akad. Wet. C **76**: 484. 1973. Near Lyme Regis, Devon.
Syn. *Physarum nutans* var. *nutans* Lister

Sporocarps stalked or sessile sporangia, occasionally short plasmodiocarps, subglobose, to 1.5 mm tall, 0.7–1 mm diam, the plasmodiocarps to 2 mm long, pale grey. **Hypothallus** discoid or continuous under a group, brown. **Stalk** short, no longer than the sporangial diameter, grooved, ochraceous above, darker below. **Peridium** single, colourless except at the base, where it is brown, and covered with white lime scales, again except round the base, where a collar is left around the top of the stalk. **Capillitium** radiating from the top of the stalk, forming a pseudocolumella in the centre of the sporangium, nodes spindle-shaped or slightly rectangular, white. **Spores** dark brown in mass, lilac in transmitted light, 9–12 µm diam, finely warted and often with groups of small warts. **Plasmodium** white, cream or grey. [Fig. 284]

Illustrations: DM 2: 297–8; NB: 193.
Habitat: dead wood and bark.
Distribution: common and widespread in the British Isles [59, H4]. Widespread in Europe and also recorded from Japan and New Zealand.

Notes: most likely to be confused with *P. leucophaeum* but has a radiating capillitium, pseudocolumella, spindle-shaped nodes and pale spores.

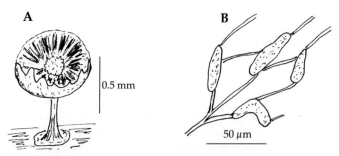

Fig. 284. *Physarum robustum*: A: sporangium; B: capillitium.

Physarum rubiginosum Fr.
Symb. Gast.: 21. 1817. Sweden

Sporocarps sessile sporangia, gregarious, subglobose or pulvinate, 0.5–0.8 mm diam, reddish-brown or scarlet, occasionally olive-brown without red tints. **Hypothallus** inconspicuous. **Peridium** thin, wrinkled, thickly encrusted with lime, often in scales. **Capillitium** dense, with large, angular, branched orange to rust-red nodes together with numerous small nodes, often with a reddish centre and paler outside. **Spores** charcoal grey in mass, greyish-brown in transmitted light, 9–12 μm diam, minutely spinulose. **Plasmodium** orange-red or scarlet. [Fig. 285]

Illustrations: L3: pl. 59; MA: fig. 288.
Habitat: moss and leafy litter.
Distribution: rare, known only from Gloucestershire, Staffordshire and Inverness; last record 1977 [3]. Recorded widely in Europe and North America but not common.

Notes: distinguished from *P. lateritium* by its larger size, brighter colours, the large nodes and the darker, larger spores.

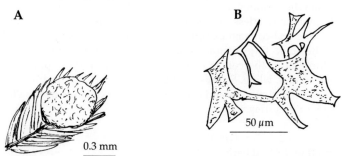

Fig. 285. *Physarum rubiginosum*: A: sporangium; B: capillitium.

Physarum scoticum Ing
Trans. Br. mycol. Soc. **78**: 442. 1982. Aros Park, Mull.

Sporocarps stalked sporangia, scattered, globose, 0.6–0.9 mm diam, 1.3–1.7 mm tall, greyish-white. **Hypothallus** inconspicuous. **Stalk** calcareous, orange-yellow. **Peridium** thick, with circular plates of lime, with marked grooves where the plates meet, the base persisting as a cup. **Capillitium** a dense network of colourless threads connecting irregular, angular nodes which are white in mass but pale yellow in transmitted light. **Spores** black in mass, pale lilac-brown in transmitted light, 9.5–10.5 μm diam, very minutely roughened. **Plasmodium** not seen. [Fig. 286]

Illustrations: original description.
Habitat: on moss-covered rotten wood.
Distribution: known from five collections, all made by the late Malcolm Clark, from the island of Mull [1]. Possibly endemic.

Notes: this odd species bears a slight resemblance to indehisced *Diderma floriforme* but has a typically physaroid capillitium. It is not unlike *P. leucophaeum* but has larger sporangia, a bright stalk and large angular nodes. It is similar to *P. pusillopse* but lacks the ochraceous base to the peridium and, in any case, has a calcareous stalk.

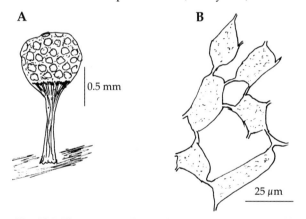

A

0.5 mm

B

25 μm

Fig. 286. *Physarum scoticum*: A: sporangium; B: capillitium.

Physarum sessile Brandza
Ann. Sci. Univ. Jassy **11**: 116. 1921. Romania.

Sporocarps sessile sporangia, globose, 0.4–1 mm diam, or sinuous plasmodiocarps 2–10 mm long, grey. **Peridium** single, fragile, composed of colourless calcareous granules. **Columella** often present in sporangiate forms, white, globose. **Capillitium** abundant, persistent, of round nodes filled with granules identical to those in the peridium, connected by colourless filaments. **Spores** dark brown in mass, pale violet-brown in transmitted light, 6–8 μm diam. **Plasmodium** greyish-white. [Fig. 287]

Illustrations: E: pl. 96.
Habitat: leaf litter and once on bark in moist chamber.
Distribution: rare, known only from Norfolk, Renfrew and Co. Derry [2.H1]. Said to be abundant in Romania and widespread in Europe; also recorded from North and South America, Asia and north Africa.

Notes: rather like *P. cinereum* but differs in the rounded nodes and the small, violet spores.

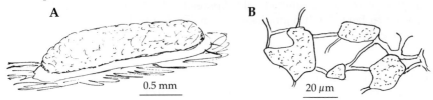

Fig. 287. *Physarum sessile*: A: plasmodiocarp; B: capillitium.

Physarum straminipes Lister
J. Bot., Lond. **36**: 163. 1898. Dunstable, Bedfordshire.

Sporocarps short-stalked or sessile sporangia, gregarious, subglobose, ovoid or wedge-shaped, to 2 mm tall, 0.5–1 mm diam, greyish-white. **Hypothallus** extensive, forming a network, white or pale ochraceous. **Stalk** weak, flattened, slender, sometimes branched, continuous with the hypothallus. **Peridium** double, the outer layer calcareous, covered with scattered flakes of lime, persisting as a cup, the inner membranous. **Capillitium** dense, a rigid mass of white, rounded or lobed nodes which are frequently massed as a loose pseudocolumella. **Spores** black in mass, dark yellowish-brown in transmitted light, 10–14 μm diam, prominently warted in clusters separated by a series of pale lines forming a net. **Plasmodium** white. [Fig. 288]

Illustrations: L3: pl. 42; MA: fig. 293; NB: 207.
Habitat: straw heaps, bales and other grass litter.
Distribution: rare, although once fairly common, and has declined rapidly with the loss of its straw heap habitat, the records are scattered from Somerset to Aberdeen [25, H2]. Widespread but no longer common in Europe, the Americas and New Zealand, probably confined to temperate regions.

Notes: the odd shape of the sporangia, the characteristic stalks and dense capillitium, together with the unusual spores make this an easy species to identify. It could be confused with certain forms of *P. compressum* but the spores will confirm it.

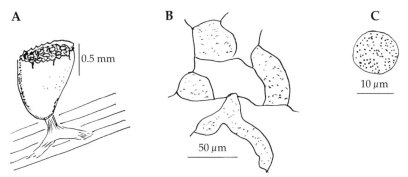

Fig. 288. *Physarum straminipes*: A: sporangium; B: capillitium; C: spore.

Physarum vernum Sommerf.
in Fries, *Syst. Mycol.* **3**: 146. 1829. Norway.

Sporocarps sessile sporangia or plasmodiocarps, 0.5–0.8 mm diam or wide, the plasmodiocarps to 20 mm long, rough, white. **Hypothallus** membranous, only conspicuous when impregnated with lime, then white. **Peridium** single, thickly encrusted with white calcareous granules. Capillitium of large, angular, branching white nodes connected by short colourless tubules, the nodes sometimes grouped as a pseudocolumella. **Spores** black in mass, dark purplish-brown in transmitted light, 10–12 μm diam, warted. **Plasmodium** white. [Fig. 289]

Illustrations: DM 2: 303–5; E: pl. 95; L3: pl. 48; MA: fig. 299; NB: 224.
Habitat: on leaf litter in both lowland and alpine situations.
Distribution: uncommon, scattered across the British Isles [38, H4]. Probably cosmopolitan.

Notes: this is one of the most conspicuous species in early spring at the edge of melting snow in the Alps. It is most likely to be confused with *P. cinereum* but it more often forms long plasmodiocarps, is much limier and has larger and darker spores. There is no obvious difference between the lowland and alpine forms.

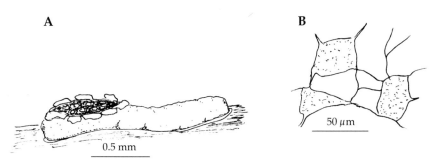

Fig. 289. *Physarum vernum*: A: plasmodiocarp; B: capillitium.

Physarum virescens Ditmar
in Sturm, *Deutsch. Fl. Pilze* **1**: 127. 1817. Germany.

Sporocarps sessile sporangia, heaped in large clusters, subglobose or slightly taller than wide, 0.2–0.4 mm diam, yellow, rarely grey, passing through a green phase when young. **Hypothallus** colourless or pale brown, common to a cluster. **Peridium** single, usually with circular yellow, crystalline plates. **Capillitium** a fragile net with numerous small, angular and branched yellow nodes. **Spores** brown in mass, pale lilac-brown in transmitted light, 7–10 μm diam, warted and often with groups of larger warts. **Plasmodium** bright yellow, becoming green on fruiting. [Fig. 290]

Illustrations: DM 2: 397–8; E: pl. 101; L3: pl. 61; MA: fig. 300; NB: 227.
Habitat: on terrestrial mosses in damp forest.
Distribution: frequent, but distinctly northern and western [65, H10]. Widespread in Europe and reported from North America, Japan, Indonesia and India.

Notes: the bright yellow heaps of small sporangia developing through the green phase and the habitat are sufficient to separate this species. Others, such as *P. confertum*, are heaped but the colours involved are distinctive. The circular plates in the peridium are characteristic but do not always appear.

Fig. 290. *Physarum virescens*: A: sporangia on moss; B: capillitium.

Physarum viride (Bull.) Pers.
Annln Bot. **15**: 6. 1795. France.
var. **viride**

Sporocarps stalked sporangia, gregarious, lens-shaped, 0.3–0.6 mm diam and 0.1–0.15 mm thick, height 1.5 mm, bright yellow but with a greenish tinge. **Hypothallus** discoid, small, inconspicuous. **Stalk** long, slender, tapering, often twisted, dark below and paler above, variously coloured but often with a reddish tinge, usually in the middle section. **Peridium** single, encrusted with yellow lime scales, dehiscing via a series of cracks and then into petaloid lobes. **Capillitium** radiating from the top of the stalk, sparingly branched and forming elongate meshes, with a few yellow, spindle-shaped nodes. **Spores** dark brown in mass, pale lilac-brown in transmitted light, 7–8 μm diam, finely warted and with groups of larger warts. **Plasmodium** yellow. [Fig. 291]

Illustrations: DM 2: 309; E: pl. 85; L3: pl. 81; MA: fig. 301; NB: 190.
Habitat: on small, fallen branches, especially of conifer or oak, quite often in bark cultures in moist chamber.

Distribution: common throughout the British Isles [110, H25, C]. Cosmopolitan.

Notes: the bright yellow lens-shaped sporangia with yellow, spindle-shaped nodes are sufficient to separate this common and beautiful species. It could be mistaken for *P. galbeum* but that has a very different capillitium and the same is also true for *P. oblatum*, which may resemble it in bark cultures.

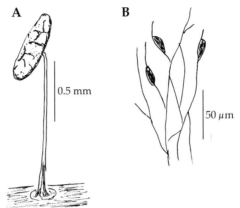

A   B

0.5 mm

50 µm

Fig. 291. *Physarum viride*: A: sporangium; B: capillitium.

var. **aurantium** (Bull.) Lister
Mycet.: 47. 1894. France.

Differs from the type variety in having bright orange sporangia, which are slightly larger and fatter.

Illustrations: DM 2: 311; E: pl. 85.
Distribution: rare, scattered from Cornwall to Aberdeen, not in Wales or Ireland [17].

Notes: this is the common form in the tropics of both hemispheres but it is also widespread in the warmer parts of the temperate region.

var. **incanum** Lister
Mycet.: 47. 1894. Czech Republic.

Differs from the type variety in its grey sporangia.

Illustrations: DM 2: 312.
Distribution: uncommon, scattered from Sussex north to Aberdeen, not in Wales, in Ireland only in Co. Down [21, H1]. Recorded from various parts of Europe, Africa and Japan.

Notes: this could easily be mistaken for a slender form of *P. nutans* but the yellow nodes are diagnostic.

WILLKOMMLANGEA Kuntze
Rev. Gen. Pl. **2**: 875. 1891.

Sporocarps worm-like, branching or net-forming plasmodiocarps. **Capillitium** duplex, with a series of perpendicular calcareous plates forming cross walls connected to a net of tubules and calcareous nodes. A single species, *W. reticulata* (Alb. & Schwein.) Kuntze

Willkommlangea reticulata (Alb. & Schwein.) Kuntze
Rev. Gen. Pl. **2**: 875. 1891. Germany.
Syn. *Cienkowskia reticulata* (Alb. & Schwein.) Rostaf.

Sporocarps plasmodiocarps, 0.3–0.5 mm wide, slightly flattened, long, reticulate, worm-like, orange-yellow with dark red spots, showing a series of pale transverse lines, segmenting the plasmodiocarp like an earthworm. **Peridium** membranous, coated with yellow or ochraceous granules, dehiscing by a longitudinal split which allows the capillitium to spill out. **Capillitium** with white plates perpendicular to the axis of the plasmodiocarp, attached to which is a series of colourless tubules forming small meshes, with or without small, linear calcareous nodes; when limeless the capillitium is yellow or colourless, when nodes are filled the structures appear white. **Spores** dark brown in mass, pale lilac-brown in transmitted light, 8–10 µm diam, densely covered in small warts. **Plasmodium** orange-yellow or scarlet, rather thick and slow to mature. [Fig. 292]

Illustrations: E: pl. 195; L3: pl. 70; MA: fig. 200; NB: 182.
Habitat: on bark of living trees, less often on fallen wood or sticks.
Distribution: uncommon, scattered from Cornwall to Aberdeen, with a westerly bias [17, H11]. Cosmopolitan.

Notes: the worm-like shape is emphasised by the 'segmentation' by the capillitial plates. The colour is distinctive and the plasmodium becomes a familiar 'pet' when bark cultures are slow to sporulate.

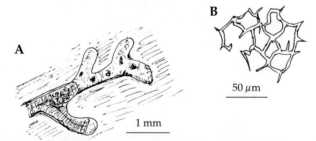

Fig. 292. *Willkommlangea reticulata*: A: plasmodiocarp; B: capillitium.

ELAEOMYXACEAE Hagelst. ex M.L. Farr & H.W. Keller
Mycologia **74**: 857. 1982

Sporocarps with calcareous matter replaced by oil droplets or wax globules. **Peridium** iridescent. A single genus.

ELAEOMYXA Hagelst.
Mycologia **34**: 593. 1942.

Sporocarps stalked sporangia with oil or wax inclusions in the stalk, columella or the capillitium. **Capillitium** of branching and anastomosing threads. Two species; the type is *E. miyazakiensis* (Emoto) Hagelst.

Notes: the genus is close to *Diachea* and was originally included in it, only the replacement of calcareous material by oil or wax separates it. Hagelstein was convinced that this was sufficient to make it the type of a distinct family and later authors have agreed.

Elaeomyxa cerifera (G. Lister) Hagelst.
Mycologia **34**: 593. 1942. Norway.
Syn. *Diachea cerifera* G. Lister

Sporocarps stalked sporangia, rarely sessile, subglobose, 0.7–1.2 mm diam, 0.7–1.8 mm tall, brownish-purple, brilliantly iridescent with blue reflections. **Stalk** pale, becoming brown or black, to 0.5 mm thick, the darker specimens with wax globules in the stem, typical material also has a thick, yellow, waxy collar at the apex. **Peridium** membranous, persisting below as a shallow cup. **Columella** absent or suggested by the thick, convex apex of the stalk, from which the capillitium arises. **Capillitium** of stiff, branching threads giving more or less parallel main branches, the tips pale. **Spores** black in mass, dark grey in transmitted light, 10–13 μm diam, minutely but distinctly spinulose. **Plasmodium** white. [Fig. 293]

Illustrations: E: pl. 51; L3: 212; MA: fig. 130.
Habitat: on the thallus of *Pellia epiphylla* on the bank of a stream.
Distribution: rare, only known from a single gathering made in autumn 1920 near Porlock Weir, Somerset [1]. Recorded from France, Germany, Switzerland, Portugal, Norway, Romania, Lebanon, Libya, Nepal and Japan, but always rare.

Notes: this is one of the most spectacularly coloured myxomycetes and the large, iridescent sporangia, with or without wax, nearly always associated with liverworts or mosses, are unmistakable. The relationship with *Diachea* is easily seen in the general appearance and in the structure of the stalk, albeit without lime, and, especially of the capillitium. It has not been seen recently in most of the countries in this list; this may be because it is more likely to be found in mountain woods.

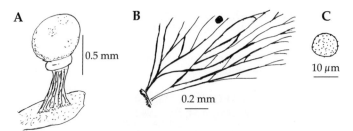

Fig. 293. *Elaeomyxa cerifera*: A: sporangium; B: capillitium; C: spore.

DIDYMIACEAE Rostaf. ex Cooke
Contr. Mycol. Br.: 29. 1877.

Sporocarps stalked or sessile sporangia, plasmodiocarps of aethalia. **Peridium** coated with calcium carbonate, either as compacted granules or crystalline, the crystals being stellate, loose as powdery covering, or compacted together to form either an egg-shell crust or small scales. **Capillitium** usually without calcareous deposits, if present these are small and quite unlike the nodes typical of *Physaraceae*, the threads slender, either colourless or purple-brown. Eight genera, only the tropical *Physarina* is not represented here.

Notes: it is clear from her notes that Nannenga-Bremekamp had intended to divide the family to separate those genera with crystalline lime from those without. Because the calcium carbonate may recrystallise after being moistened, especially in snow-line species, the presence of crystals is not sufficient to make such a division. In any case, the boundaries between the genera are so confused that it makes more sense to maintain larger groups until adequate genetic studies have been made.

KEY TO GENERA

1	Sporocarp a plasmodiocarp completely free of calcareous material, capillitium of vertical, parallel, thin bars	*Trabrooksia*
–	Calcareous deposits in peridium, stalk and columella, rarely in capillitium	2
2 (1)	Peridium without lime	*Diachea*
–	Peridium with calcareous deposits	3
3 (2)	Calcareous material in peridium granular	*Diderma*
–	Calcareous material in peridium crystalline	4
4 (3)	Sporocarp an aethalium	*Mucilago*
–	Sporocarp sporangium or plasmodiocarp	5
5 (4)	Peridial lime in the form of stellate crystals which may be aggregated into an egg-shell crust	*Didymium*
–	Peridial lime in the form of crystalline scales or plates	6

6 (5)   Peridial scales abundant   *Lepidoderma*
–   Peridial scales scanty, confined to the base of the sporangium
        and often difficult to see   *Leptoderma*

DIACHEA Fr.
Syst. Orb. Veg.: 143. 1825.

Sporocarps stalked, rarely sessile, sporangia. **Peridium** free of calcareous material, iridescent. **Hypothallus**, stalk and columella strongly calcareous. **Capillitium** of branching, anastomosing, purple threads. Thirteen species, mostly tropical; the type is *D. leucopodia* (Bull.) Rostaf. (syn. *D. elegans* (Trentep.) Fr.).

Notes: the previous placing of the genus in *Stemonitales* is not supported by its abundant lime nor its sporangial development, both characters requiring its return to *Physarales*.

KEY TO SPECIES

1   Sporangia cylindrical, columella cylindrical, spores warted   *leucopodia*
–   Sporangia globose, columella short, spores reticulate   *subsessilis*

Diachea leucopodia (Bull.) Rostaf.
Mon.: 190. 1874. France.

Sporocarps stalked sporangia, gregarious, cylindrical or elliptical, 0.4–0.6 mm diam, 1–2 mm tall, metallic blue, bronze or purple. **Hypothallus** white, calcareous, forming a conspicuous network. **Stalk** stout, white, calcareous, up to half total height. **Peridium** membranous. **Columella** cylindrical, thick, calcareous, almost reaching the apex of the sporangium. **Capillitium** of purple-brown, branching and anastomosing threads, pale at the tips, arising from the whole length of the columella. **Spores** black in mass, dull lilac in transmitted light, 8–11 μm diam, minutely warted. **Plasmodium** white. [Fig. 294]

Illustrations: DM 2: 27; E: pl. 52; L3: pl. 99; MA: fig. 133; NB: 300.
Habitat: on leaf litter and on stems of dead and living plants, several centimetres above the ground.
Distribution: common in the south of England, thinning out northwards, rare in Scotland, not in Ireland [70]. Cosmopolitan, but especially common in warmer regions.

Notes: this is an unmistakable species, and one of the most beautiful. It may occur in very large developments, covering several square metres of herbaceous litter. The ability of the plasmodium to climb stems is legendary and there is an historic photograph of the species fruiting on a spider's orb web!

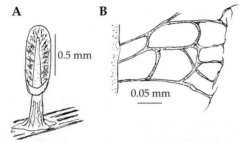

Fig. 294. *Diachea leucopodia*: A: sporangium; B: capillitium.

Diachea subsessilis Peck
Ann. Rep. N.Y. State Mus. **31**: 41. 1879. New York State.

Sporocarps stalked, rarely sessile, sporangia, gregarious, 0.4–0.8 mm diam, 0.6–1 mm in height, iridescent blue or green, often with grey tones. **Hypothallus** forming a network, white and calcareous. **Stalk** white, rarely grey or pale brown, conical, shorter than the sporangial diameter. **Peridium** membranous. **Columella** conical, short. **Capillitium** of branching and anastomosing, light purple-brown threads, radiating from the columella, pale at the tips. **Spores** nearly black in mass, pale brown in transmitted light, 8–11 µm diam, delicately reticulate with minute spines. **Plasmodium** yellow. [Fig. 295]

Illustrations: DM 2: 29; E: pl. 51; L3: pl. 100; MA: fig. 136.
Habitat: leaf litter.
Distribution: uncommon, scattered from the Isle of Wight north to Perthshire, not recorded for Wales or Ireland [11]. Widespread, but not common, in Europe and recorded in North and South America and several parts of Asia.

Notes: the stalk is always present in British material and the iridescent, globose sporangium on a stout, white stalk is diagnostic; the reticulate spores will confirm. The literature sometimes quotes *D. leucopodia* as being subglobose, this is not my experience. This is another species that may occur in very large developments; for example, at Holme Fen in 1974, it covered at least a hectare of the fen.

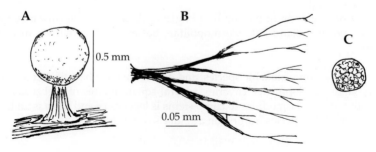

Fig. 295. *Diachea subsessilis*: A: sporangium; B: capillitium; C: spore.

DIDERMA Pers.
Neues Mag. Bot. **1**: 89. 1794.

Sporocarps stalked or sessile sporangia or plasmodiocarps. **Peridium** usually double, sometimes single or triple, either cartilaginous or brittle, impregnated with calcium carbonate as granules. **Columella** usually well developed, calcareous. **Capillitium** of slender, branching and anastomosing threads, usually limeless but ins few cases replaced by calcareous columns. Over 70 species; the type is *D. globosum* Pers.

KEY TO SPECIES

1	Peridium cartilaginous, tough, dehiscence usually by lobes	2
–	Peridium calcareous, fragile, dehiscence irregular	9
2 (1)	Peridium of three layers, the middle calcareous	3
–	Peridium of two layers, without the calcareous middle layer	4
3 (2)	Middle layer crystalline	*trevelyanii*
–	Middle layer granular	*asteroides*
4 (2)	Sporangia stalked; on wood or moss	5
–	Sporangia sessile; on moss	8
5 (4)	Sporangia bright orange; on moss on wet rocks	*lucidum*
–	Sporangia grey, white or pale brown; on wood	6
6 (5)	Sporangia pale brown	*radiatum*
–	Sporangia grey or white	7
7 (6)	Sporangia white or grey, columella hemispherical, dehiscence irregular; on twigs and bramble stems	*umbilicatum*
–	Sporangia grey, columella club-shaped, dehiscence by lobes; on wood	*floriforme*
8 (5)	Sporangia yellow-ochraceous, capillitium dark, spores pale, 9–11 µm diam	*ochraceum*
–	Sporangia pink-ochraceous, capillitium pale, spores dark, 12–13 µm diam; (rare)	*sauteri*
9 (1)	Peridium single, or apparently so	10
–	Peridium clearly double	12
10 (9)	Sporangia with reddish, yellow or brown shades	*simplex*
–	Sporangia white, grey or pale pink	11
11 (10)	Sporangia stalked, columella reddish, stalked	*montanum*
–	Sporangia sessile, columella white, sessile	*cinereum*

12 (9)   Sporangia stalked, disc-shaped, white   *hemisphaericum*
–   Sporocarps sessile, rarely with a constricted, stalk-like base   13

13 (12) Sporocarps broad plasmodiocarps, often reticulate or forming a ring   14
–   Sporocarps short plasmodiocarps or sessile sporangia   16

14 (13) Plasmodiocarps very thin, less than 0.1 mm tall, forming perforated
            plates   *platycarpum*
–   Plasmodiocarps thicker, not forming perforated plates   15

15 (14) Columella reduced to an orange base to the sporocarp, spores dark,
            9–10 µm diam   *deplanatum*
–   Columella flattened, white to pale brown, not orange, spores pale,
            7–9 µm diam   *effusum*

16 (13) Hypothallus a well developed white crust on which the sporangia are
            densely clustered   17
–   Hypothallus inconspicuous or sporangia not clustered   21

17 (16) Columella white; lowland   18
–   Columella distinctly coloured; alpine   20

18 (17) Columella cylindrical   *cingulatum*
–   Columella subglobose   19

19 (18) Hypothallus thick, sporangia embedded, peridial layers fragmenting,
            not separating   *spumarioides*
–   Hypothallus thin, sporangia not embedded, peridial layers separating
                                                                                    globosum

20 (17) Columella pink, spores 14–17 µm diam   *lyallii*
–   Columella orange, spores 11–12 µm diam   *alpinum*

21 (16) Sporangia white or pale grey   22
–   Sporangia pink or beige   23

22 (21) Sporangia clustered, white; alpine   *niveum*
–   Sporangia flattened, or short plasmodiocarps; on moss on trees
                                                                                chondrioderma

23 (21) Sporangia pink, porcelain-like, flattened   *testaceum*
–   Sporangia beige or ochraceous, clustered, subglobose   *donkii*

Diderma alpinum Meyl.
Bull. Soc. Vaud. Sci. Nat. **51**: 261. 1917. Switzerland.

Sporocarps sessile sporangia or short plasmodiocarps, clustered and closely appressed, 0.7–1 mm diam, pulvinate, slightly flattened. **Hypothallus** conspicuous, white, calcareous. **Peridium** double, the outer, white calcareous layer separating easily from the inner, smooth, pinkish-white layer; when there is a deficiency of lime the sporangia are dark, glossy brown. **Columella** pulvinate, ochraceous-orange, occupying much of the base of the sporangium, the basal wall of which is lined with an orange membrane. **Capillitium** of dark branching, slightly anastomosing threads, marked with dark beads. **Spores** black in mass, purple-brown in transmitted light, 11–12 μm diam, distinctly spiny. **Plasmodium** white. [Fig. 296]

Illustrations: DM 2: 38; E: pl. 109; MA: fig. 304.
Habitat: on vegetation at the edge of melting snow on mountains in the spring.
Distribution: known from several mountains in the Scottish Highlands and not uncommon locally [7]. Widespread in the mountains of Europe, North America, Asia and Australia.

Notes: closely resembles *D. niveum* but it is usually plasmodiocarpous and closely appressed, slightly flattened; the hypothallus is also usually conspicuous and calcareous. It is also more likely to occur in a glossy, limeless form than *D. niveum*. Many authors have suggested that it is merely a plasmodiocarp form of the commoner species but the features that separate them are constant.

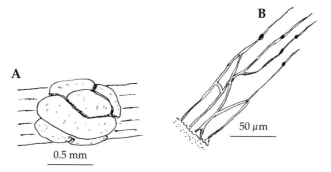

Fig. 296. *Diderma alpinum*: A: sporangia; B: capillitium.

Diderma asteroides (Lister & G. Lister) G. Lister
Mycet. edn 2: 113. 1911. Italy.

Sporocarps sessile or very short-stalked sporangia, hemispherical, the apex pointed when young, 0.2–0.8 mm diam, reddish-brown, marked by radial lines of dehiscence. **Hypothallus** white, small. **Stalk**, when present, white, merely a bump in the hypothallus. **Peridium** of three layers, the outer cartilaginous, closely attached to the middle pale, calcareous layer, the inner layer membranous and

separate; the whole peridium splits lobes and resembles a minute *Geastrum*.
Columella globose, pale to ochraceous, with a rough surface. **Capillitium** of
slender, purplish threads with pale tips. **Spores** black in mass, grey-violet in
transmitted light, 10–12 μm diam, warted. **Plasmodium** yellow. [Fig. 297]

Illustrations: DM 2: 41; L3: pl. 97; MA: fig. 305; NB: 261.
Habitat: leaf litter, especially of hard-leaved trees, such as holly.
Distribution: rare, scattered from Somerset and Surrey to Inverness; last recorded
in 1975 [9]. Recorded from several parts of Europe but probably commonest in the
Mediterranean region, in evergreen forests, known from the Canary Islands,
North and central America, Israel, India and Australia.

Notes: the reddish exterior of the young sporangia and the open, earthstar-like
older sporangia are unmistakable.

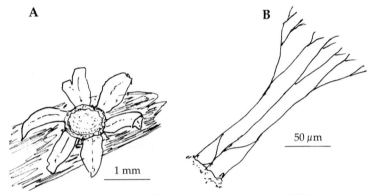

Fig. 297. *Diderma asteroides*: A: sporangium;   B: capillitium.

Diderma chondrioderma (de Bary & Rostaf.) G. Lister
Mycet. edn 3: 258. 1925. Poland.
Syn. *Diderma arboreum* G. Lister & Petch

Sporocarps sessile sporangia or short plasmodiocarps, scattered, discoid, or, more
often, expanded into plate-like plasmodiocarps, 1–3 mm diam, white or purplish-
grey. **Hypothallus** inconspicuous. **Peridium** single, membranous, covered in a
thin layer of white granules, often very sparsely distributed and sometimes
absent altogether. **Columella** flesh-coloured, often scanty. **Capillitium** of coarse
threads, with a few small expansions at junctions, sometimes appearing like rods.
Spores dark grey in mass, pale purplish-grey in transmitted light, 12–13 μm
diam, minutely spinulose. **Plasmodium** white, becoming violet as the sporangia
develop. [Fig. 298]

Illustrations: E: pl. 108; L3: pl. 206; MA: fig. 306.
Habitat: on moss on the bark of living trees.
Distribution: uncommon, scattered, mostly western and northern [30, H14].
Widespread in Europe, and known from several parts of Asia, Australia, New

Zealand and Africa, but said to be rare in North America, although recently isolated from Virginia.

Notes: the flattened, rounded plasmodiocarps and the simple rod-like capillitium, together with the habitat, should avoid confusion with other species. The only possible errors would involve missing the crystals on the peridium of superficially similar species of *Didymium*, but most of these have darker spores.

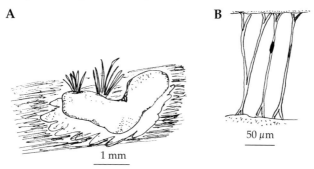

Fig. 298. *Diderma chondrioderma*: A: plasmodiocarp; B: capillitium.

Diderma cinereum Morgan
J. Cinc. Soc. Nat. Hist. **16**: 154. 1894. Ohio.

Sporocarps sessile sporangia, gregarious, subglobose, somewhat depressed, 0.3–0.5 mm diam, pearl-grey. **Hypothallus** inconspicuous. **Peridium** apparently single, thin, smooth, crustose, dehiscing irregularly. **Capillitium** of slender, dark threads, sparsely branched, easily detached from the columella. **Spores** black in mass, dark violet-grey in transmitted light, 9–11 µm diam, minutely warted. **Plasmodium** not seen. [Fig. 299]

Illustrations: MA: fig. 307; NB: 247.
Habitat: on mosses and leaf litter.
Distribution: rare, known only from Surrey and Worcestershire, last seen in 1984 [2]. Recorded from France, Germany, Netherlands, Spain, Sweden, Japan and North America.

Notes: similar to *D. spumarioides* but differs in its single peridium, deciduous capillitium and the dark grey spores.

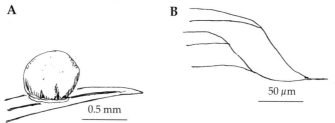

Fig. 299. *Diderma cinereum*: A: sporangium; B: capillitium.

Diderma cingulatum Nann.-Bremek.
Proc. K. Ned. Akad. Wet. C **71**: 191. 1968. Netherlands.

Sporocarps sessile sporangia, closely clustered and embedded in a limy hypothallus, taller than wide, to 1 mm tall and 0.3–0.5 mm diam, white. **Hypothallus** a thick white crust under the cluster and forming a cushion around the base of individual sporangia. **Peridium** of two layers, the outer thick and calcareous, brittle, the inner membranous, the whole fragmenting. **Columella** cylindrical or club-shaped, white, calcareous, almost reaching the apex of the sporangium. **Capillitium** abundant, slender, thicker at the base, purple with pale tips, branching dichotomously but hardly anastomosing. **Spore** dark brown in mass, purple-brown in transmitted light, 13–14 μm diam, densely warted, with a few fine ridges and a prominent white line round the middle of the spore. **Plasmodium** not seen. [Fig. 300]

Illustrations: DM 2: 45; NB: 251.
Habitat: leaf litter and encrusting the stems of herbaceous plants in damp places.
Distribution: known from a single collection from Crawley, Sussex in 1922 [1]. Known from several parts of Europe, China and North America.

Notes: superficially similar to *D. spumarioides* but easily separated by the cylindrical columella and banded spores.

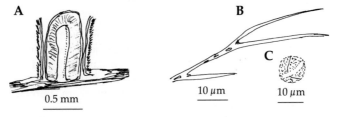

Fig. 300. *Diderma cingulatum*: A: section through sporangium; B: capillitium; C: spore.

Diderma deplanatum Fr.
Syst. Mycol. **3**: 110. 1829. Germany.

Sporocarps short plasmodiocarps which are curved or ring-shaped, or sessile sporangia, scattered, pulvinate, flattened, 1–1.5 mm diam, white or cream. **Hypothallus** inconspicuous. **Peridium** double, the outer layer smooth, crustose, thick, brittle, the inner membranous, iridescent, deep orange in the base. **Columella** lacking, represented by the thickened, orange base of the sporocarp. **Capillitium** of dark purple threads, which are scarcely branched, with a few bead-like swellings. **Spores** dark brownish-black in mass, dark yellow-brown in transmitted light, 9.5–10 μm diam, minutely spinulose. **Plasmodium** white. [Fig. 301]

Illustrations: DM 2: 48; E: pl. 111; L3: pl. 87; MA: fig. 311; NB: 243.
Habitat: on mosses and leaf litter.

Distribution: frequent, scattered north to Orkney [38, H8]. Widespread in Europe, North and central America, Asia and New Zealand.

Notes: the intense orange base of the sporocarp which replaces a columella in this species is very distinctive and separates it from *D. effusum*, which is both sporangiate and plasmodiocarpous but usually has a distinct columella, at least when forming sporangia or short plasmodiocarps. This species was at one time included in *D. niveum*, as the lowland form, but that species has a well-developed columella, is sporangiate and not flattened, only the orange colours of the inner walls are shared.

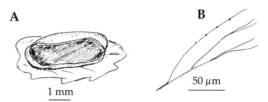

Fig. 301. *Diderma deplanatum*: A: plasmodiocarp; B: capillitium.

Diderma donkii Nann.-Bremek.
Proc. K. Ned. Akad. Wet. C **76**: 482. 1973. Netherlands.

Sporocarps sessile sporangia, clustered, subglobose and flattened, dirty cream darkening to ochraceous, beige or pale khaki, 0.3–1.2 mm diam, only 0.2 mm tall. **Hypothallus** inconspicuous. **Peridium** double, the outer dull, wrinkled, or smooth, calcareous, the inner membranous, colourless. **Columella** red-brown, thin, flat, covering most of the base of the sporangium, or missing. **Capillitium** of thin, colourless threads which branch dichotomously, and a second set which are purple-brown and thicker at the centre. **Spores** dark brown in mass, purple-grey in transmitted light, 8–10 μm diam, paler on one side, warted with small groups of larger warts. **Plasmodium** creamy buff. [Fig. 302]

Illustrations: DM 2: 50; NB: 249.
Habitat: leaf litter.
Distribution: rare, England only, north to Yorkshire [11]. Reported from Germany, Netherlands, Austria, Belgium, Japan and New Zealand.

Notes: the distinctive colour and the thickened central portions of the capillitial threads separate this from the other pale, flattened litter-inhabiting species.

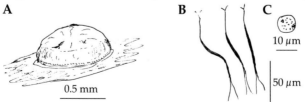

Fig. 302. *Diderma donkii*: A: sporangium; B: capillitium; C: spore.

Diderma effusum (Schwein.) Morgan
J. Cinc. Soc. Nat. Hist. **16**: 155. 1874. North Carolina.

Sporocarps sessile sporangia or broadly effused or reticulate plasmodiocarps, gregarious, flattened, to 0.4 mm tall, from 0.6 mm to several centimetres long, white, apparently formed from merged sporangia. **Hypothallus** inconspicuous, membranous, shared by the whole sporocarp. **Peridium** of two layers, the outer, smooth, eggshell-like, the inner membranous, colourless. **Columella** depressed-pulvinate, white to pale brown. **Capillitium** threads abundant, colourless or pale lilac-brown, hardly branched with few cross-walls, sometimes expanding through gaps in the dehisced peridium. **Spores** brown in mass, lilac-brown in transmitted light, 7–9 μm diam, almost smooth but with very fine, pale warts. **Plasmodium** white. [Fig. 303]

Illustrations: DM 2: 51; E: pl. 107; L3: pl. 83; MA: fig. 312; NB: 244.
Habitat: leaf litter, especially of beech, occasionally in bark cultures in moist chamber.
Distribution: widespread and generally common in the British Isles [67, H5, C]. Cosmopolitan.

Notes: the presence of a columella separates this from *D. deplanatum* and the thicker plasmodiocarps from *D. platycarpum*.

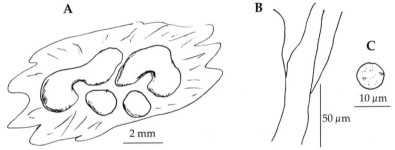

Fig. 303. *Diderma effusum*: A: plasmodiocarps; B: capillitium; C: spore.

Diderma floriforme (Bull.) Pers.
Neues Mag. Bot. **1**: 89. 1794. France.

Sporocarps stalked sporangia, gregarious subglobose, 0.7–1 mm diam, to 2 mm tall, pearl-grey to greyish-beige, shining. **Hypothallus** extensive but not conspicuous. **Stalk** longer than sporangial diameter, thick grooved, calcareous, pale ochraceous. **Peridium** double, the outer cartilaginous but also calcareous, the inner membranous, the whole dehiscing in a petaloid fashion, revealing the pale brown inner surface of the peridium. **Columella** club-shaped, reaching well in to the middle of the sporangium, reddish ochraceous, rough. **Capillitium** abundant, the threads thin, sparsely branched, purple-brown with bead-like swellings. **Spores** dark brown in mass, dark purple-brown in transmitted light, 10–11 μm diam, with large, dark scattered warts, sometimes with a thin line. **Plasmodium** off-white. [Fig. 304]

Illustrations: DM 2: 52–4; E: pl. 113; L3: pl. 92; MA: fig. 313; NB: 258.
Habitat: on rotten logs and fallen branches in ancient, broad-leaved forest.
Distribution: frequent in the south, rare in the north, the last Scottish record, near Edinburgh, was in the 18th century [39, H2]. Widely distributed in north temperate regions.

Notes: the grey, globose young sporangia, dehiscing in petaloid fashion, and the prominent club-shaped columella are diagnostic.

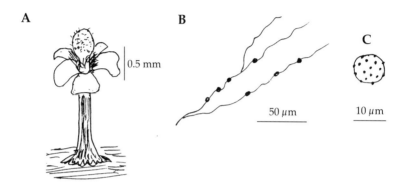

Fig. 304. *Diderma floriforme*: A: sporangium; B: capillitium; C: spore.

Diderma globosum Pers.
Neues Mag. Bot. **1**: 89. 1794. Europe.

Sporocarps sessile sporangia, closely clustered, subglobose, slightly flattened, 0.5–1 mm diam, white or pale grey. **Hypothallus** membranous, inconspicuous. **Peridium** double, the layers not closely attached, the outer a smooth, calcareous crust, the inner membranous. **Columella** subglobose, small, white, calcareous. **Capillitium** of thin, colourless or purple-brown threads, dichotomously branched but hardly anastomosing. **Spores** dark brown in mass, dark purple-brown in transmitted light, 9–12 μm diam, densely and finely warted, often with small clusters of darker warts. **Plasmodium** white. [Fig. 305]

Illustrations: E: pl. 109; L3: pl. 85; MA: fig. 314; NB: 250.
Habitat: on leaf litter and encrusting living stems and leaves in damp places, especially in species-rich fens and marshes.
Distribution: frequent in the south of England, rare in Scotland [41, H3]. Widespread in Europe, North and South America, east Asia, Australia and New Zealand.

Notes: in the past confused with *D. spumarioides* but, as now understood, it differs in lacking a thick, embedding hypothallus and has darker spores. It may be confused with *D. cinereum* but that is pearly grey, not white.

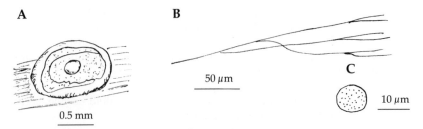

Fig. 305. *Diderma globosum*: A: sporangium; B: capillitium; C: spore.

Diderma hemisphaericum (Bull.) Hornem.
Fl. Dan. **33**: 13. 1829. France.

Sporocarps stalked sporangia, discoid, 0.5–1.5 mm diam, to 0.02 mm thick and to 1.3 mm tall, white, smooth, except sometimes in the centre of the disc. **Hypothallus** discoid, membranous, sometimes with white lime. **Stalk** thick, short but may reach 1 mm, sometimes almost absent and the sporangia then appear sessile, ochraceous but with sufficient lime to make it appear white. **Peridium** double, the outer layer calcareous, brittle, fragmenting to leave the grey reflecting inner, membranous layer. **Columella** large, discoid, pale or dark brown, calcareous. **Capillitium** elastic, of thin, colourless threads branching dichotomously but with few anastomoses. **Spores** pale brown in mass, pale pinkish-grey in transmitted light, 7–9 µm diam, densely covered with small pale warts with groups of larger warts. **Plasmodium** white. [Fig. 306]

Illustrations: DM 2: 56; E: pl. 107; L3: pl. 83; MA: fig. 315; NB: 252.
Habitat: on plant litter in damp places.
Distribution: frequent in the south, rare northwards but reaches Orkney [60. H5, C]. Cosmopolitan.

Notes: the discoid sporangia are unmistakable, only *Didymium applanatum*, which has a white stalk, is superficially similar, but that, of course, has crystalline lime on the peridium.

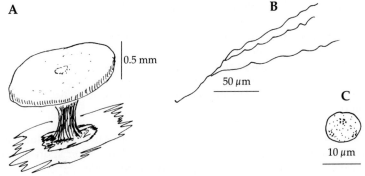

Fig. 306. *Diderma hemisphaericum*: A: sporangium; B: capillitium; C: spore.

Diderma lucidum Berk. & Broome
Ann. Mag. Nat. Hist., ser. III. **7**: 380. 1861. Dolgarrog, Caernarfon.

Sporocarps stalked sporangia, subglobose, brilliant vermilion, shining, 0.6–0.8 mm diam. **Hypothallus** inconspicuous. **Stalk** slender, dark brown to black, to 0.5 mm high. **Peridium** double, the outer layer smooth, orange-yellow with a small amount of calcareous material, the inner membranous, yellow; dehiscing by 4 or 5 lobes which develop pale margins. **Columella** subglobose, short-stalked, white or ochraceous, calcareous. **Capillitium** dark, reticulate, with expanded junctions. **Spores** black in mass dark grey-brown in transmitted light, 13–15 μm diam, densely spiny. **Plasmodium** orange-yellow. [Fig. 307]

Illustrations: E: pl. 111; L3: pl. 98; MA: fig. 317.
Habitat: on mosses on wet rocks, especially near waterfalls; also on wet mossy rocks in dense Atlantic oakwoods where the humidity is constantly high.
Distribution: rare: known from Cornwall, the English Lake District, Snowdonia (several sites) western Scotland and Co. Cork, Co. Kerry and Co. Wicklow [8, H3]. Only known with certainty outside the British Isles from Japan.

Notes: the colour of the sporangium and the characteristics of the capillitium should prevent confusion with any other myxomycete. It grows with *D. ochraceum*, *Lepidoderma tigrinum* and *Lamproderma columbinum* in several ravines in Snowdonia and is a constant species in the ravine myxomycete association. It was listed as having originally been found at Trefriw but the label on the type, although in faint pencil, makes it certain that it was found in the ravine of the Afon Porth Ilwyd, which runs along the north side of the Coed Dolgarrog National Nature Reserve in the Conwy valley. It has been found in the same place in recent years. There must still be considerable doubt about an old record from Sri Lanka.

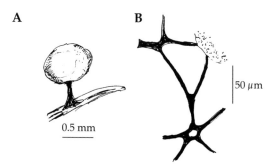

Fig. 307. *Diderma lucidum*: A: sporangium on moss; B: capillitium.

Diderma lyallii (Massee) T. Macbr.
N. Am. Slime-Moulds: 99. 1899. Washington State.

Sporocarps short-stalked or sessile sporangia, crowded, subglobose, 1–1.5 mm diam, white or tinted with very pale yellow or pink. **Hypothallus** well-developed, white, calcareous. **Stalk** short, stout, furrowed, an extension of the hypothallus. **Peridium** double, the outer layer thick, heavily calcareous, the inner layer membranous, opaque, pink or buff. **Columella** large, club-shaped, calcareous, reaching half-way into the sporangium, white, flesh-pink or very pale brown, never with orange shades. **Capillitium** stiff, branching and anastomosing threads, expanded at junctions, pale or dark. **Spores** black in mass, dark purple-brown in transmitted light, 14–17 μm diam, coarsely spiny, the spines blunt, but may be to 1.5 μm long. **Plasmodium** white. [Fig. 308]

Illustrations: DM 2: 58; E: pl. 110; L3: pl. 90; MA: fig. 318.
Habitat: vegetation at the edge of melting snow on mountains in the spring.
Distribution: rare, so far only in Perthshire and the Cairngorms [3]. Widespread in alpine areas of North America, Chile, Europe, Asia and north Africa, but less common than other alpine species of the genus.

Notes: easily separated from *D. niveum* by the pale columella and very large spores; the peridium is also much thicker and more encrusted and creamier. The stalks are present in all British collections but are often absent in material from the Alps and Pyrenees.

A   B   C

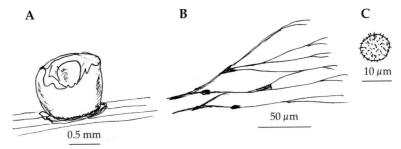

Fig. 308. *Diderma lyallii*: A: sporangium; B: capillitium; C: spore.

Diderma montanum (Meyl.) Meyl.
Ann. Cons. Jard. Bot. Genève **16**: 311. 1913. Switzerland.

Sporocarps short-stalked sporangia, depressed globose, 0.6–0.8 mm diam, pearl or pinkish-grey to nearly white, smooth or slightly wrinkled. **Hypothallus** inconspicuous. **Stalk** stout, pale or yellowish-brown, calcareous, to 0.8 mm high. **Peridium** double, the outer wall calcareous, the inner membranous and reddish-brown towards the base. **Columella** prominent, stalked, white or reddish-brown, subglobose. **Capillitium** of slender purplish threads with a few branches and anastomoses, especially towards the tips. **Spores** black in mass, pale purple brown in transmitted light, 8–10 μm diam, densely and minutely spinulose. **Plasmodium** white. [Fig. 309]

Illustrations: DM 2: 61; E: pl. 106; L3: pl. 207; MA: fig. 319; NB: 254.
Habitat: mosses, leaves and herbaceous plant litter.
Distribution: uncommon, scattered from Devon to the Isle of Man, Arran and Mull, in Ireland only in Co. Wicklow [23, H1]. Widespread in Europe, North America, north Africa, Pakistan and Japan, but nowhere common.

Notes: although described from the Jura mountains this is mostly a forest species and is lowland in the British Isles. The combination of the pinkish colour, prominent, often reddish columella and short stalks separate it from most species in the genus but it does bear a superficial resemblance to *D. umbilicatum*, which is larger, whiter, and has larger spores.

A   B

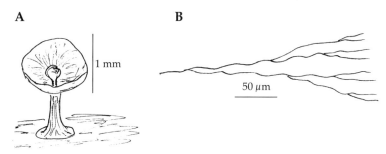

Fig. 309. *Diderma montanum*: A: sporangium; B: capillitium.

Diderma niveum (Rostaf.) T. Macbr.
N. Am. Slime-Moulds: 100. 1899. France.

Sporocarps sessile sporangia, closely clustered, subglobose, 0.7–2.2 mm diam, white. **Hypothallus** white, but largely hidden beneath groups of sporangia and not embedding them. **Peridium** double, the outer layer calcareous, fragile, the inner delicate, often iridescent, yellowish or orange below. **Columella** globose, large, ochraceous to deep orange. **Capillitium** elastic, abundant, surviving long after the peridium has fragmented, with threads which are either coarse, purplish with pale tips or delicate, colourless with bead-like swellings; in both cases with few branches or anastomoses. **Spores** black in mass, violet-brown in transmitted light, 9–11 µm diam, minutely roughened. **Plasmodium** white. [Fig. 310]

Illustrations: DM 2: 65; E: pl. 110; L3: pl. 89; MA: fig. 321.
Habitat: living and dead vegetation at the edge of melting snow on mountains in the spring, reaching down into the forest zone (but not in the British Isles).
Distribution: frequent on the mountains of the English Lake District and the Scottish Highlands but apparently absent from Snowdonia [11]. Abundant in all mountain regions, including Antarctica, wherever a deep snowpack develops for at least three months, the commonest snowline myxomycete.

Notes: easily separated from *D. lyallii* which has a thick hypothallus and much larger spores and a pale columella; it is more difficult to separate from *D. alpinum* but that too has a more obvious hypothallus and has bolster-shaped sporangia, or, more often, short, closely clustered plasmodiocarps. In the Alps several closely related taxa have been described. *D. microcarpum* Meyl. is very similar to *D. niveum* but has much smaller sporangia, always less than 1 mm in diam, occurs in smaller clusters and has an inner peridium which is calcareous rather than iridescent and a thinner hypothallus; its spores are 10–12.5 µm diam. *D. niveum* var. *niveum* has spores 9–12 μm diam. *D. niveum* var. *ferrugineum* Meylan has larger spores, 13–14 μm diam, dark capillitium and a dark orange-brown outer peridium, beneath the calcareous covering. It may well be best regarded as a distinct species. *D. niveum* f. *endoleuca* Meyl. has a white columella and spores 10–12 μm diam. All the British material fits into var. *niveum*.

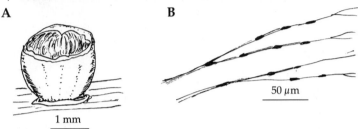

Fig. 310. *Diderma niveum*: A: sporangium; B: capillitium.

Diderma ochraceum Hoffm.
Deutsch. Fl. **2**: pl. 9. 1795. Germany.

Sporocarps sessile sporangia to curved or ring-shaped plasmodiocarps, scattered, or, more often, clustered, 0.4–1 mm diam, subglobose when sporangiate, deep ochraceous. **Hypothallus** inconspicuous. **Peridium** double, the outer layer cartilaginous, smooth or slightly wrinkled, obviously calcareous, the inner membranous, yellow. **Columella** inconspicuous. **Capillitium** abundant, of delicate, brown, simple threads, colourless at the base. **Spores** black in mass, dark yellowish-brown in transmitted light, 9–11 μm diam, minutely spinulose. **Plasmodium** lemon-yellow. [Fig. 311]

Illustrations: E: pl. 114; L3: pl. 96; MA: fig. 322; NB: 260.
Habitat: on mosses on wet rocks.
Distribution: uncommon, predominantly western and northern [31, H3]. Widespread in Europe, North America, north Africa and Japan.

Notes: the ochraceous colour, ring-shaped plasmodiocarps encircling moss shoots in the characteristic ravine habitat make this species easy to identify.

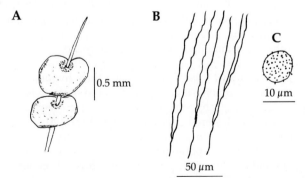

Fig. 311. *Diderma ochraceum*: A: sporangia; B: capillitium; C: spore.

Diderma platycarpum Nann.-Bremek.
Proc. K. Ned. Akad. Wet. C **69**: 359. 1966. Netherlands.

Sporocarps thin, broadly effused plasmodiocarps, forming white, perforated plates, to 0.2 mm thick and 10–20 mm diam. **Hypothallus** inconspicuous. **Peridium** double, the outer fragile and calcareous, the inner membranous. **Columella** absent. **Capillitium** abundant, of thin, colourless, dichotomously branching threads with few cross-connections. **Spores** in mass dark brown, pale rosy brown in transmitted light, subglobose (rather than globose) 10–11 µm diam, almost smooth, but in fact with fine, pale warts and groups of larger warts. **Plasmodium** yellow. [Fig. 312]

Illustrations: NB: 242.
Habitat: leaf litter.
Distribution: known only from a recent collection form Argyll [1]. Reported from Belgium, Spain, the Netherlands, the Galapagos Islands, Java and Japan, but clearly rare.

Notes: easily separated from all other plasmodiocarpous species of *Diderma* by its paper-thin sporocarps and from superficially similar species of *Didymium* by the lack of peridial crystals.

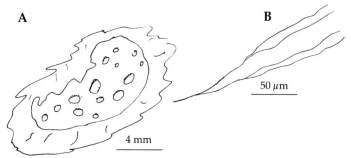

Fig. 312. *Diderma platycarpum*: A: plasmodiocarp; B: capillitium.

Diderma radiatum (L.) Morgan
J. Cinc. Soc. Nat. Hist **16**: 151. 1894. Sweden.

Sporocarps short-stalked sporangia, scattered or grouped, globose or slightly flattened, 0.6–1.4 mm diam, brown, mottled or marked with pale lines. **Hypothallus** inconspicuous, brown. **Stalk** brown, furrowed, calcareous. **Peridium** double, the outer layer cartilaginous, the inner membranous, dehiscing into petal-like lobes. **Columella** large, hemispherical to subglobose, orange-brown to reddish-brown. **Capillitium** abundant, of brown threads, pale at the tips, hardly branching. **Spores** forming a tight, hemispherical, black mass around the columella, well separated from the peridium, purple-brown in transmitted light, 9–12 µm diam, distinctly warted. **Plasmodium** yellow. [Fig. 313]

Illustrations: DM 2: 73; E: pl. 114; L3: pl. 94; MA: fig. 323.

Habitat: on dead wood, mostly of small size, especially twigs or large bramble stems.

Distribution: rare, from Devon northwards to Northumberland and Perthshire [19]. Cosmopolitan but many records include *D. umbilicatum*.

Notes: the brown, stalked sporangia can only be confused with *D. trevelyanii* but that has a middle, crystalline peridial layer and frequently is without a columella, also the unopened sporangium is ellipsoid rather than globose.

Fig. 313. *Diderma radiatum*: A: sporangium; B: capillitium.

Diderma sauteri (Rostaf.) T. Macbr.
N. Am. Slime-Moulds: 103. 1899. Austria.

Sporocarps sessile sporangia, clustered, 0.6–1 mm diam, pinkish-grey to reddish-brown. **Hypothallus** inconspicuous. **Peridium** double, the outer layer cartilaginous, smooth, separate from the inner, membranous layer which is grey or iridescent. **Columella** small, often no more than a thickened, reddish base to the sporangium. **Capillitium** scanty, the threads pale violet or colourless but always with reddish-brown bases where they are attached to the columella, giving the appearance of long spines. **Spores** black in mass, dark brown in transmitted light, 12–13 μm diam, spinulose. **Plasmodium** white. [Fig. 314]

Illustrations: L3: pl. 95.
Habitat: on moss on wet rocks in Atlantic woodland.
Distribution: rare, known only from Mull, nearby Argyll and Co. Tipperary [2, H1]. Recorded from Austria, Portugal, Romania and North America.

Notes: closest to *D. ochraceum* but separated by its pinkish colour, pale capillitium and larger, darker spores.

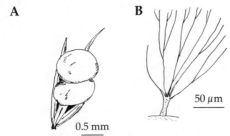

Fig. 314. *Diderma sauteri*: A: sporangia on moss; B: capillitium.

Diderma simplex (Schröt.) G. Lister
Mycet. edn 2: 107. 1911. Poland.

Sporocarps sessile sporangia, clustered or heaped, 0.2–0.8 mm diam, subglobose, pulvinate or flattened, brown, brick-red, ochraceous or khaki. **Hypothallus** extensive, coloured as the sporangia. **Peridium** single, calcareous, smooth or slightly wrinkled. **Columella** rarely more than a thickened base to the sporangium. **Capillitium** scanty, of delicate pale threads. **Spores** dark brown in mass, pale violet-brown in transmitted light, 9–11 μm diam, minutely warted, sometimes with clusters of larger warts. **Plasmodium** orange-brown. [Fig. 315]

Illustrations: DM 2: 76; E: pl. 113; L3: pl. 88; MA; fig. 326.
Habitat: heather litter on heaths and moors and birch litter in woodland.
Distribution: uncommon, scattered from the Isle of Wight north to Inverness, in Ireland only in Co. Offaly [16, H1]. Widespread in Europe, North America, Asia and north Africa, but never common.

Notes: few myxomycetes are found in heather litter and this brown *Diderma* with a single peridium is not difficult to identify. The var. *echinulatum* Meylan, with yellow sporangia and spiny spores is probably best treated as a separate species; it has not been found in the British Isles.

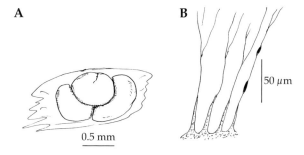

Fig. 315. *Diderma simplex*: A: sporangia; B: capillitium.

Diderma spumarioides (Fr.) Fr.
Syst. Mycol. **3**: 104. 1829. Europe.

Sporocarps sessile sporangia, densely clustered, globose, 0.4–0.8 mm diam, white, deeply embedded in the thick, white, calcareous **hypothallus**. **Peridium** double, the outer layer thickly calcareous, rough, fragile, closely attached to the inner, membranous, grey layer. **Columella** convex or hemispherical, white, calcareous. **Capillitium** abundant, of brown threads with pale tips, hardly branching or anastomosing. **Spores** black in mass, pale yellow-brown in transmitted light, 8–11 μm diam, minutely warted. **Plasmodium** white. [Fig. 316]

Illustrations: DM 2: 77; E: pl. 104; L3: pl. 84; MA: fig. 327; NB: 248.
Habitat: most abundant in the mossy grasslands in fixed, coastal dunes, but also characteristic of dry tree-leaf litter on chalk and limestone.

Distribution: frequent, scattered from the Channel Islands north to Orkney [58, H4, C]. Cosmopolitan.

Notes: separated from *D. globosum* by the closely appressed peridial layers and the thick, embedding hypothallus, and from *D. cinereum* in the rough peridium, hypothallus and spore colour. This species is abundant in the litter of evergreen oak woodland in the Mediterranean and occupies a similar ecological niche in the chalk woodlands of the south of England.

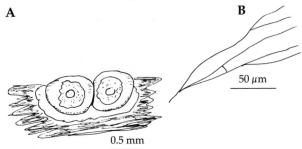

A   B

50 μm

0.5 mm

Fig. 316. *Diderma spumarioides*: A: sporangia; B: capillitium.

Diderma testaceum (Schrad.) Pers.
Syn. Fung.: 167. 1801. Germany.

Sporocarps sessile sporangia, gregarious, hemispherical or depressed globose, 0.7–1 mm diam, flesh-coloured or pinkish, smooth. **Hypothallus** inconspicuous. **Peridium** double, the outer layer porcelain-like, the separate, inner layer membranous, pinkish or whitish-grey. **Columella** conical, prominent, pinkish-brown, rough. **Capillitium** abundant, the pale, delicate threads hardly branched. **Spores** black in mass, pale brown in transmitted light, 8–9 μm diam, nearly smooth. **Plasmodium** yellowish-buff. [Fig. 317]

Illustrations: DM 2: 80; E: pl. 112; L3: pl. 87; MA: fig. 329; NB: 246.
Habitat: leaf litter.
Distribution: uncommon, scattered from Cornwall north to Cheshire, in Scotland only in Dumfries (last century), not recorded from Ireland [18]. Recorded from Europe, the Americas, Asia and north Africa.

Notes: the pink, porcelain peridium is distinctive but faded specimens could easily be mistaken for *Didymium difforme* but the crystalline lime and the ornamented spores of the latter should avoid mis-identification.

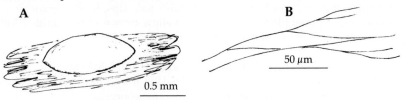

A   B

50 μm

0.5 mm

Fig. 317. *Diderma testaceum*: A: sporangium; B: capillitium.

Diderma trevelyanii (Grev.) Fr.
Syst. Mycol. **3**: 105. 1829. Near Edinburgh, Midlothian.

Sporocarps stalked sporangia, scattered or in small groups, globose or slightly ovoid, 0.8–1.5 mm diam, pale reddish-brown. **Hypothallus** dark, inconspicuous. **Stalk** stout, reddish-brown. **Peridium** of three layers, the outer cartilaginous, the middle with transparent crystals, the inner membranous; the lines of dehiscence are marked as pale zones and the peridium splits into stellate lobes. **Columella** varies from a large subglobose structure on a thin stalk to a few granules on the base of the sporangium. **Capillitium** abundant, of coarse, brown threads with nodular swellings, branching and anastomosing . **Spores** in mass black, dark brown in transmitted light, 11–12 μm diam, minutely warted. **Plasmodium** yellow-brown. [Fig. 318]

Illustrations: DM 2: 82; L3: pl. 91; MA: fig. 330; NB: 259.
Habitat: on twiggy litter of conifers, rhododendron and birch.
Distribution: rare, scattered from Somerset to Aberdeen, last record 1980 [18]. Widely recorded in Europe, North America, north Africa, Chile, India and Nepal.

Notes: the crystalline middle peridial layer and the stalked sporangia should separate this from *D. asteroides*; the lighter colour and narrower lobes of the dehisced sporangium should distinguish it from *D. radiatum*. An alpine form with mottled peridium, usually sessile, has been separated as *D. nivale* (Meyl.) Nowotny, Neubert & Baumann, it has not been found in Scotland.

A   B

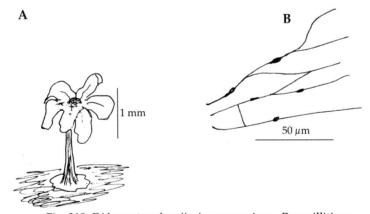

Fig. 318. *Diderma trevelyanii*: A: sporangium; B: capillitium.

Diderma umbilicatum Pers.
Syn. Fung.: 165. 1801. France.
Syn. *Diderma radiatum* var. *umbilicatum* (Pers.) Morgan
var. **umbilicatum**

Sporocarps stalked sporangia, in small groups, subglobose, slightly flattened, usually umbilicate below, 0.5–1.3 mm diam, to 1.5 mm tall. white or pale grey, slightly shiny. **Hypothallus** inconspicuous. **Stalk** short, thick, reddish-brown but covered with white lime. **Peridium** appearing single, calcareous, dehiscing irregularly, leaving a cup with a frayed margin. **Columella** large, subglobose, covering most of the sporangial base, usually white or pale brown, occasionally darker, rough or spiky. **Capillitium** of simple purple-brown threads. **Spores** dark brown in mass, purple-brown in transmitted light, 9–12 μm diam, densely warted. **Plasmodium** white. [Fig. 319]

Illustrations: DM 2: 83; L3: pl. 93; NB: 256.
Habitat: on twigs and small, rotten branches.
Distribution: frequent, scattered from Cornwall to Inverness, in Ireland only in Co. Galway [47, H1]. Probably cosmopolitan but not always recorded independently of *D. radiatum*.

Notes: the large, pale sporangia and conspicuous pale columella, together with the thick stalks allow this species to be separated easily from other members of the genus. It was considered to be synonymous with *D. radiatum* until quite recently but is completely different – irregular dehiscence, non-cartilaginous peridium, pale columella and stout stalks are all characters not present in *D. radiatum*.

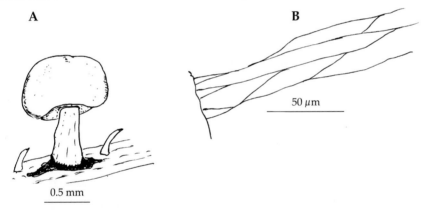

Fig. 319. *Diderma umbilicatum*: A: sporangium; B: capillitium.

var. **macrosporum** Meyl.
Bull. Soc. Vaud. Sci. Nat. **56**: 68. 1925. Switzerland.

Differs from the type variety by the larger, paler spores which are 14–15 μm diam.

Habitat: on moss on tree trunks.
Distribution: rare, known from Cumbria and Sutherland [2]. Recorded from Austria, Germany, the Netherlands, Switzerland and Australia.

DIDYMIUM Schrad.
Nov. Gen. Pl.: 20. 1797.

Sporocarps stalked or sessile sporangia or plasmodiocarps. **Peridium** covered with a powder of stellate crystals of calcium carbonate or an egg-shell crust of aggregated crystals. **Columella** frequently present, if absent, a pseudocolumella may be present. **Capillitium** of slender threads which are usually dichotomously branched and may anastomose, sometimes with bead-like swellings, nodules or ·expansions, but rarely with calcareous inclusions. Over 70 species; the type is *D. melanospermum* (Pers.) T. Macbr.

Notes: the genus *Squamuloderma* Kowalski was described for species without a capillitium. Several species have reduced threads and it is probably better to include all these in *Didymium*. Some specimens with long stalks which are yellow/orange have been referred to *D. iridis*. This is not keyed here, see p. 325.

KEY TO SPECIES

1	Peridium covered with a smooth, egg-shell crust of compacted calcareous crystals, with or without a powdery covering on top	2
–	Peridium covered with scattered, stellate crystals	7
2 (1)	Sporangia hemispherical, with a thick, short stalk, and a domed columella	*vaccinum*
–	Sporocarps sessile or plasmodiocarpous	3
3 (2)	Peridium covered with a sprinkling of crystals	4
–	Peridium without a sprinkling of crystals	5
4 (3)	Spores with large, dark warts, often arranged in a reticulate pattern, 10–12 µm diam	*trachysporum*
–	Spores with small, pale warts, 8–10 µm diam	*listeri*
5 (3)	Sporocarps with vertical pillars which show through as small pits in the peridium	*tubulatum*
–	Sporocarps without pillars	6
6 (5)	Capillitium flexible, expanding, spores with wavy ridges or an incomplete net	*comatum*
–	Capillitium stiff, not expanding, spores without ridges or a net, but, especially when dry, with fine, dark lines	*difforme*
7 (1)	Sporocarps sessile sporangia or plasmodiocarps	8
–	Sporocarps stalked sporangia	15
8 (7)	Capillitium with large yellow vesicles	*serpula*
–	Capillitium without vesicles	9
9 (8)	Plasmodiocarps with vertical, calcareous pillars, capillitium scanty or absent	*sturgisii*
–	Sporocarps without vertical pillars, capillitium abundant	10

10 (9)   Sporocarps ochraceous   *ochroideum*
–   Sporocarps white or grey   11

11 (10) Sporangiate, columella hemispherical, white   *squamulosum*
–   Plasmodiocarpous, columella absent   12

12 (11) Plasmodiocarp dark grey, broad, forming a network of strands
         fused into a perforated sheet, peridial crystals black   *perforatum*
–   Plasmodiocarps pale grey or white, not forming a perforated sheet,
         crystals colourless   13

13 (12) Plasmodiocarps often ring-shaped, on a narrow base, spores pale,
         minutely warted, less than 10 μm diam   *anellus*
–   Plasmodiocarps usually elongate, on a broad base, spores dark,
         strongly warted, more than 10 μm diam   14

14 (13) Spores 14–16 μm diam, warty-reticulate; alpine   *nivicola*
–   Spores 10–12 μm diam, warts in rows; alpine and lowland   *dubium*

15 (7)   Stalks short, usually less than half total height   16
–   Stalks long, at least three-quarters total height   22

16 (15) Sporangia clustered, on shared, weak stalks, with a common crust over
         the whole group and approaching a pseudoaethalium in appearance
                                                                         crustaceum
–   Sporangia separate, stalk normal, without a common crust   17

17 (16) Stalk bright orange   *laxifilum*
–   Stalk white or black   18

18 (17) Stalk white   19
–   Stalk black   20

19 (18) Sporangia discoid, columella absent   *applanatum*
–   Sporangia subglobose, columella subglobose   *squamulosum*

20 (18) Sporangia discoid, columella absent   *clavus*
–   Sporangia subglobose, columella brown   21

21 (20) Spores dark, 10–14 μm diam   *melanospermum*
–   Spores pale, 8–10 μm diam   *minus*

22 (15) Peridium dark, mottled in transmitted light, columella brown,
         stalk usually black   *nigripes*
–   Peridium pale, not mottled, columella pale, sometimes absent or replaced
         by a pseudocolumella, stalk orange, reddish-brown, yellow or paler   23

23 (22) Stalk containing calcareous nodules   24
–   Stalk without calcareous nodules   25

24 (23)	Stalk white or pale yellow, stout	*macrospermum*
–	Stalk reddish-brown, slender	*pertusum*

25 (23)	Columella and pseudocolumella lacking	26
–	Columella or pseudocolumella present	27

26 (25)	Crystals on the peridium smaller than the spores	*elegantissimum*
–	Crystals on the peridium more than twice the diameter of the spores	
		crassicolle

27 (25)	True columella, an extension of the stalk, present	28
–	Pseudocolumella present, resting on the basal plate of the peridium	29

28 (27)	Sporangia erect, stalk reddish-brown, peridial crystals smaller than the spores, spores almost smooth	*ovoideum*
–	Sporangia nodding, stalk ochraceous, peridial crystals larger than the spores, spores warted, with groups of larger warts	*verrucosporum*

29 (27)	Stalk narrowing upwards, sporangia often nodding, spores with obvious groups of larger warts	*bahiense*
–	Stalk of uniform width, sporangia erect, spores uniformly marked	30

30 (29)	Peridial crystals larger than the spores	*megalosporum*
–	Peridial crystals smaller than the spores	*eximium*

Didymium anellus Morgan
J. Cinc. Sci. Nat. Hist. **16**: 148. 1894. Ohio.

Sporocarps plasmodiocarps which may be broad or ring-shaped, several mm long, white or pale grey, the surface pitted. **Hypothallus** delicate, inconspicuous. **Peridium** single, membranous, rather sparsely covered with crystals, dehiscence circumscissile. **Columella** absent or suggested by the brownish base of the sporocarp. **Capillitium** abundant of branching and anastomosing slender, dark threads which form an elastic net. **Spores** dark brown in mass, violet-brown in transmitted light, 8–10 μm diam, minutely warted with clusters of larger warts. **Plasmodium** transparent. [Fig. 320]

Illustrations: DM 2: 96; E: pl. 115; L3: pl. 110: MA: fig. 332; NB: 273.
Habitat: leaf litter and also regularly found on the underside of the leaves of *Petasites* and *Tussilago*.
Distribution: frequent, mainly southern, from Cornwall north to Cumbria [23]. Widespread in Europe and recorded from North America and Asia.

Notes: the capillitium forms a more obvious net in this species than in most of the genus and this, together with the single peridium should enable the species to be identified. The ring-shaped plasmodiocarps with a hollow centre are the most frequent form in the British Isles.

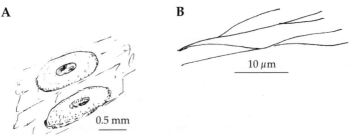

Fig. 320. *Didymium anellus*: A: sporangia; B: capillitium.

Didymium applanatum Nann.-Bremek.
Proc. K. Ned. Akad. Wet. C **75**: 352. 1972. Netherlands.

Sporocarps short-stalked sporangia, discoid, white, gregarious, 1 mm diam, 0.1–0.2 mm thick and to 1.2 mm tall, with a wide umbilicus around the stalk junction. **Hypothallus** membranous, shared by adjacent sporangia. **Stalk** thick, white, furrowed, to 1 mm high. **Peridium** membranous, the basal plate thickened, dehiscing by a circumscissile split, then fragmenting. **Columella** absent. **Capillitium** scant, the colourless threads dichotomously branched but scarcely anastomosing. **Spores** dark brown in mass, lilac-grey in transmitted light, 10.5 μm diam, densely and finely warted with groups of larger warts. **Plasmodium** not seen. [Fig. 321]

Illustrations: NB: 282.
Habitat: on washed-up debris of aquatic plants at the edge of ponds.
Distribution: known from one site each in Devon and Worcestershire [2]. Otherwise only recorded in France and the Netherlands.

Notes: this species bears a strong resemblance to *Diderma hemisphaericum* but can be readily separated by the presence of crystals on the peridium; it is also like a white form of *Didymium clavus* but lacks the black stalk of that species and is slightly more robust. It might also be mistaken for a flattened *D. squamulosum* but that has a white columella. Whether this is an aquatic myxomycete is not established but the sporangia are found within a few centimetres of open water so this cannot be ruled out.

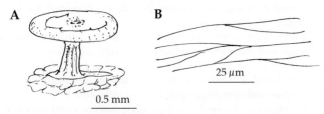

Fig. 321. *Didymium applanatum*: A: sporangium; B: capillitium.

Didymium clavus (Alb. & Schwein.) Rabenh.
Deutsch. Krypt.-Fl. **1**: 280. 1844. Germany.

Sporocarps short-stalked sporangia, gregarious, discoid, 0.5–1 mm diam, 0.2 mm thick and to 1 mm tall, grey, with a wide, black umbilicus at the base. **Hypothallus** discoid, dark brown or black. **Stalk** not tapering, black, to 0.8 mm tall. **Peridium** thin, with a thickened basal plate, brown with a dusting of white, stellate crystals which are larger than the spores. **Columella** absent. **Capillitium** abundant, sparingly branched, radiating out from the basal plate, usually colourless. **Spores** dark brown in mass, almost colourless in transmitted light, 6–8 µm diam, almost smooth but finely and distantly warted. **Plasmodium** colourless or grey. [Fig. 322]

Illustrations: DM 2: 101; E: pl. 119; L3: pl. 108; MA: fig. 333; NB: 283.
Habitat: in leaf litter, especially of broad-leaved trees, very rarely as a casual on bark of living trees in moist chamber culture.
Distribution: common, recorded from most parts of the British Isles but there are gaps in southern Scotland and Ireland [87, H5, C]. Probably cosmopolitan.

Notes: this is a very distinctive species and is not likely to be confused with anything else.

A   B

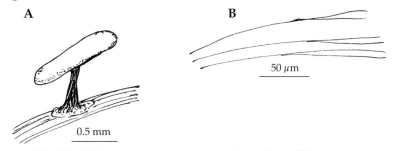

50 µm

0.5 mm

Fig. 322. *Didymium clavus*: A: sporangium; B: capillitium.

Didymium comatum (Lister) Nann.-Bremek.
Proc. K. Ned. Akad. Wet. C **69**: 361. 1966. Japan.
Syn. *Didymium difforme* var. *comatum* Lister

Sporocarps sessile sporangia or plasmodiocarps, to 0.2 mm tall and varying from 0.2 mm diam to elongated structures 10 mm long, flattened, smooth, white, occasionally stained with reddish-yellow streaks or dots. **Hypothallus** inconspicuous. **Peridium** double, the outer eggshell-like, the inner membranous colourless or purple, not iridescent, dehiscing via a circumscissile split, the upper portion forming a lid. **Columella** absent but the base of the sporangium has a deposit of pale calcareous material. **Capillitium** abundant, elastic, of slender, pale brown, threads which branch dichotomously, often with small bead-like swellings, after dehiscence expanding into a woolly mass. **Spores** dark brown in mass, pale lilac-brown in transmitted light, 10–13 µm diam, densely warted, the warts arranged in ridges or forming a broken net. **Plasmodium** colourless. [Fig. 323]

Illustrations: L3: pl. 104; NB: 266.
Habitat: straw, grass litter and herbaceous waste.
Distribution: rare, scattered from Cornwall to Aberdeen, in Ireland only in Co. Down [11, H1]. Recorded from several parts of Europe, North America and Japan.

Notes: grows with *D. difforme* but easily distinguished by the very elastic capillitium which projects in a fuzzy plume and the ridged spores. Not always separated by other workers, this is probably commoner than the records suggest.

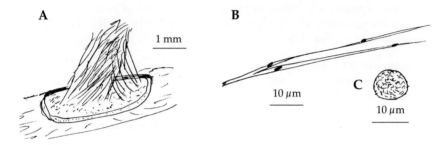

Fig. 323. *Didymium comatum*: A: sporangium; B: capillitium; C: spore.

Didymium crustaceum Fr.
Syst. Mycol. **3**: 124. 1829. Europe.

Sporocarps stalked sporangia, clustered on shared stalks and covered with a common, white, calcareous crust, individual sporangia 0.7–2 mm diam. **Hypothallus** membranous, shared by a cluster, often calcareous but not prominent. **Stalk** weak, white, calcareous. **Peridium** double, the outer layer fragile and calcareous, forming the shared covering, the inner membranous, covered with crystals. **Columella** absent. **Capillitium** stiff, little branched, pale brown. **Spores** black in mass, lilac-brown in transmitted light, 10–14 μm diam, minutely warted or spinulose. **Plasmodium** white. [Fig. 324]

Illustrations: DM 2: 103; E: pl. 121; L3: pl. 111; MA: fig. 334.
Habitat: leaf litter, especially in hedge bottoms.
Distribution: uncommon and apparently becoming rarer, scattered from Devon north to Orkney [20]. Recorded from several European countries, North America, Hawaii, India and Japan.

Notes: the covering of the sporangia is rather like the cortex of *Fuligo* but the sporangia are never fused and the 'cortex' is not always present, and in any case, it is fragile and disappears quickly. Without it the sporangia could be mistaken for rather robust *D. squamulosum* but that has a columella. When closely massed it can resemble *Diderma spumarioides*, but that can be told by the absence of crystalline lime and the presence of a columella.

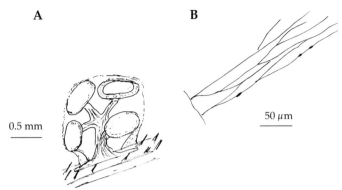

A   B

0.5 mm

50 μm

Fig. 324. *Didymium crustaceum*: A: sporangium; B: capillitium.

Didymium difforme (Pers.) Gray
Nat. Arr. Brit. Plants **1**: 571. 1821. Europe.

Sporocarps sessile sporangia or plasmodiocarps, gregarious, 0.1–0.3 mm tall, to 1 mm wide and to 1 mm long, smooth, white or pale ochraceous. **Hypothallus** inconspicuous. **Peridium** double, the outer layer an egg-shell crust, the inner pale purple, shining iridescent, dehiscing to form a rough lid and base. **Columella** absent but the base of the sporangium is often covered with white lime instead of the usual dark, shining surface. **Capillitium** of stiff, non-elastic thick, threads, sparsely branched, pale brown or colourless, often with bead-like swellings. **Spores** densely black in mass, dark purple-brown in transmitted light, paler on one side, 11–14 μm diam, densely covered with fine warts and with two fine, dark lines at the sides of the pale area; the dry spore, in a fresh mount, is wrinkled and angular and as it swells develops a reticulum, which disappears as the spherical shape is achieved. **Plasmodium** colourless or pale grey, but thin and often difficult to see. [Fig. 325]

Illustrations: DM 2: 106; E: pl. 116; L3: pl. 104; MA: fig. 336; NB: 268.
Habitat: on herbaceous plant litter of all kinds, especially old nettle stems; occasionally in bark cultures, especially of young trees, and found in water cultures of bulbs and roots of garden plants in nurseries, etc.
Distribution: one of the commonest of all myxomycetes, found throughout the British Isles [111, H38, C]. Cosmopolitan.

Notes: the egg-shell peridium is found in several species of the genus but only *D. difforme* has a purple, iridescent inner layer that shines through a broken area. It can be mistaken for small forms of *Diderma effusum* but that does not have crystalline lime and the base of the sporangium is orange. The closely related *D. comatum* and *D. tubulatum* can be separated easily on capillitium characteristics, that of *D. comatum* is very elastic, that of *D. tubulatum* has columns; both have different spores. The plasmodium of this species is truly aquatic and can survive for weeks in water cultures of bacteria or in water pots with hyacinth bulbs. As a common soil organism it is less likely to be inhibited by wet conditions than some other species. It is also highly characteristic of the dead stems of the previous year's growth of nettles, suggesting a connection with the high phosphate levels required by nettles.

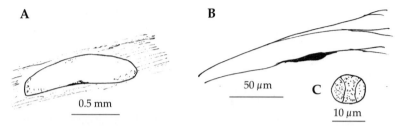

Fig. 325. *Didymium difforme*: A: sporangium; B: capillitium; C: spore.

Didymium dubium Rostaf.
Mon.: 152. 1874. Czech Republic
Syn. *Didymium wilczeckii* Meyl.

Sporocarps plasmodiocarps, bolster-shaped or long and narrow, sometimes doubled back on themselves, to 0.3 mm high, 1–7 mm wide and to 15 mm long, grey or darker, depending on the amount of peridial encrustation. **Hypothallus** inconspicuous. **Peridium** single, membranous, frosted with a cover of stellate lime crystals about the size of the spores. **Columella** absent but the floor of the sporocarp often shows a calcareous layer. **Capillitium** radiating from the base, thin, branched, wavy, colourless, forming an open net, elastic and protruding when the peridium is broken. **Spores** dark brown in mass, pale lilac-grey in transmitted light, 10–12 μm diam, densely warted. **Plasmodium** yellow. [Fig. 326]

Illustrations: DM 2: 109,111; E: pl. 116; L3: pl. 194 (as *wilczeckii*); MA: fig. 337; NB: 275–6.
Habitat: on plant litter in lowland and alpine situations.
Distribution: rare, recorded only from Sussex, Kent, Gloucestershire, Worcestershire, Warwickshire, Perthshire and Inverness [7]. Widely recorded in Europe, North America and Japan and possibly cosmopolitan, at least in temperate regions.

Notes: this is a very confused species, some of the collections have been separated as *D. listeri*, which has an egg-shell crust covered with a powder of crystals. Many of the alpine collections are now regarded as *D. nivicola*, which has larger, more sharply marked spores and a flaky peridial covering. Others have been referred to *D. leptotrichum* (Racib.) Massee which is an even more confused taxon! In the British Isles the lowland and alpine forms may represent different taxa, but our few alpine gatherings are typical *D. dubium* – we have more records of *D. nivicola* in Scotland than of *D. dubium*. The lowland collections may be better placed in *D. leptotrichum* but it will be necessary to examine the type of that species before a final decision can be made. The suggestion that *D. leptotrichum* and *D. nivicola* are conspecific has been made on several occasions but seems unlikely.

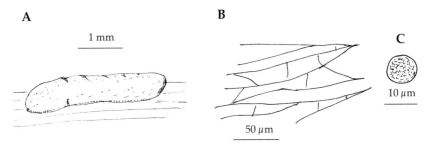

Fig. 326. *Didymium dubium*: A: plasmodiocarp; B: capillitium; C: spore.

Didymium iridis (Ditmar) Fr.
Syst. Mycol. **3**: 120. 1829. Germany.

A number of taxa with long stalks which are yellow or reddish-brown have been described by many authors over a long period of time. These were grouped by Lister (1925) as varieties of *D. nigripes*, either as var. *xanthopus* (Ditm.) Lister or var. *eximium* (Peck) Lister, but all were included by Martin & Alexopoulos (1969) under *D. iridis*. The great variation in colour, spore size and markings, presence or absence of a columella or pseudocolumella and the different sizes of peridial crystals have made it possible to characterise a number of *morphological* species, some of which are described below. The situation is complicated by the genetics of the group. Key research in the United States has demonstrated a small number of *biological* species which can be identified by their ability to form fertile crosses in culture. These do not correspond to the morphological species, whose range of variation is sometimes seen within a single biological species. Nevertheless some of the morphotypes appear to represent biologically distinct entities. While a fuller evaluation of all the morphotypes is being undertaken it seems appropriate to include them all under the umbrella of *D. iridis* – the typical form of which does not occur in the British Isles and is rare in Europe.

Illustrations: E: pl. 120; L3: pl. 102; MA: fig. 343.
Habitat: rotting herbaceous material.
Distribution: the aggregate species is widespread in the British Isles [104, H5, C]. Cosmopolitan.

Notes: the differences between the eight 'microspecies' below are set out in the main key to *Didymium*. Only records based on material that has been studied recently is included – a number of older records, where material was not available, are subsumed under the aggregate.

Didymium bahiense Gottsb.
Nova Hedwigia **16**: 365. 1968. Brazil.

Sporocarps stalked sporangia, gregarious, appearing subglobose but actually discoid and reflexed around the top of the stalk, forming a deep umbilicus,

0.2–0.7 mm diam, to 2 mm tall, white. **Hypothallus** small, discoid, very dark red, appearing black. **Stalk** long, slender and tapering, dark at the base, paler above, in transmitted light translucent orange-red-brown below and pale ochraceous above, without calcareous deposits. **Peridium** mostly thin and colourless except for a thickened ochraceous basal plate, on which sits the pseudocolumella; the peridium is dusted with white, stellate crystals about the same size as the spores. **Columella** absent, but a discoid, white pseudocolumella is present. **Capillitium** abundant, the threads branching freely and with some anastomoses, brown with pale tips and small, dark, bead-like swellings. **Spores** dark brown in mass, pale brown to dark lilac-grey in transmitted light, 10–12 μm diam, warted, with groups of larger warts. **Plasmodium** brown, but in the developing sporangia it is white. [Fig. 327]

Illustrations: DM 2: 99; NB: 292.
Habitat: on rotting herbaceous debris, rarely as a casual on bark in moist chambers.
Distribution: the commonest member of the aggregate in the British Isles [98, H5, C]. Probably cosmopolitan, certainly the commonest member of the aggregate in Europe.

Notes: the prominent, white pseudocolumella, the reddish, tapering stalk and the spores with prominent groups of warts make this fairly easy to separate. Three varieties have been described: var. *microsporum* Hochsg., Gottsb. & Nann.-Bremek. with spores 8–9 μm, var. *bahiense*, with spores 10–12 μm, and var. *europaeum* Nann.-Bremek., with spores 12–14 μm diam. The last two have been found in the British Isles but have not been specifically recorded.

Didymium crassicolle Ing
Trans. Br. mycol. Soc. **78**: 443. 1982. Brentwood, Essex.

Sporocarps stalked sporangia, gregarious, subglobose, widely umbilicate below, 0.4–0.6 mm diam, height to 1.4 mm, white. **Hypothallus** thin, discoid, orange. **Stalk** bright orange, widened and flattened just below the sporangium, ending abruptly in the base of the sporangium, without calcareous deposits. **Peridium** membranous, pale yellow, covered with white stellate crystals to 25 μm long, each with long, thin spines. **Columella** and pseudocolumella absent. **Capillitium** delicate, of colourless threads, sparsely branched with few cross-connections. **Spores** black in mass, pale purple-brown in transmitted light, 7.5–10 μm diam, uniformly and strongly warted. **Plasmodium** orange-yellow. [Fig. 328]

Illustrations: original description.
Habitat: forest leaf litter.
Distribution: rare, known only from three collections, in Essex, Warwickshire and Perthshire [3]. Not yet identified outside the British Isles.

Notes: the orange stalk which distinctly widens below the sporangium, the absence of columella or pseudocolumella and the large, slender stellate crystals on the peridium separate this species readily.

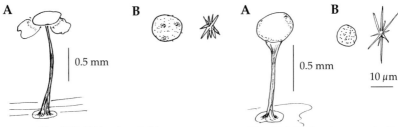

Fig. 327. *Didymium bahiense*:
A: sporangium;
B: spore and peridial crystal.

Fig. 328. *Didymium crassicolle*:
A: sporangium;
B: spore and peridial crystal.

Didymium elegantissimum Massee
Mon.: 234. 1892. Scarborough, Yorkshire.

Sporocarps stalked sporangia, subglobose, 0.4–0.5 mm diam, 1.4 mm tall, white.
Hypothallus discoid, small, orange. **Stalk** cylindrical, i.e. not tapering,
translucent orange or reddish-brown, furrowed, without calcareous deposits.
Peridium thin, the basal plate slightly thickened and pleated, covered with very
small, prismatic crystals, which are less star-shaped than usual for the genus and
much smaller than the spores. **Columella** and pseudocolumella absent.
Capillitium with numerous small nodules which are not calcareous. **Spores** in
mass dark brown, pale lilac in transmitted light, 8–11 µm diam, evenly warted.
Plasmodium not seen. [Fig. 329]

Illustrations: original description.
Habitat: leaf litter.
Distribution: rare, apparently only known form the type material, collected in the
19th century from Scarborough [1].

Notes: the absence of a pseudo- or true columella and the small, almost
rectangular peridial crystals are the key characters. It would be of considerable
interest if this were to be refound.

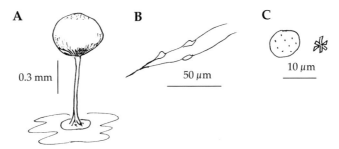

Fig. 329. *Didymium elegantissimum*:
A: sporangium; B: capillitium; C: spore and peridial crystal.

Didymium eximium Peck
Ann. Rep. N.Y. State Mus. **31**: 41. 1897. United States.

Sporocarps stalked sporangia, gregarious, discoid but wrapped around an umbilicus and appearing irregular, often like a saddle, 0.3–0.8 mm diam, 1.5 mm tall, pale ochraceous or pale grey. **Hypothallus** discoid, brown, shining. **Stalk** tapering, grooved, reddish-brown, in transmitted light ochraceous or orange-ochraceous, darker towards the base, without calcareous deposits. **Peridium** colourless or pale yellow, with a thickened yellow basal plate on which sits a rough, ochraceous pseudocolumella; the peridium covered with white or pale ochraceous stellate crystals which are much smaller than the spores. **Columella** absent, replaced by the pseudocolumella. **Capillitium** sparse, the threads sparingly branched with few cross-connections, pale or dark, with some dark broad, rather than bead-like, expansions. **Spores** dark brown in mass, pale lilac-brown in transmitted light, 9–10 μm diam, almost smooth but evenly warted with pale, small warts, sometimes paler on one side. **Plasmodium** colourless to yellow. [Fig. 330]

Illustrations: DM 2: 112; L3: pl. 102; NB: 291.
Habitat: leaf litter.
Distribution: uncommon, scattered from Cornwall to Aberdeen [13]. Recorded widely in Europe, north Africa and Japan and also found in North America.

Notes: characterised by the pseudocolumella, uniformly marked spores and small peridial crystals.

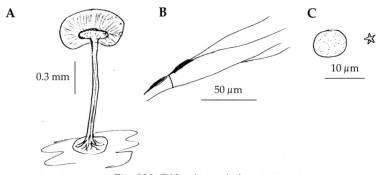

A   B   C

0.3 mm   50 μm   10 μm

Fig. 330. *Didymium eximium*:
A: sporangium; B: capillitium; C: spore and peridial crystal.

Didymium megalosporum Berk. & M.A. Curt.
Grevillea **2**: 53. 1873. South Carolina

Sporocarps stalked sporangia, gregarious, discoid but folded back around a deep umbilicus and appearing subglobose, rarely irregularly saddle-shaped, 0.4–0.7 mm diam, to 1.8 mm tall, pale grey, pale ochraceous-grey, or, rarely, white. **Hypothallus** discoid, brown, shining. **Stalk** cylindrical, grooved, reddish-brown, dark at the base, translucent and orange-red-brown in transmitted light, without calcareous deposits. **Peridium** very pale yellow, with a thicker yellow basal plate on which sits an ochraceous pseudocolumella; peridium covered with white or pale yellow stellate crystals which are at least as long as the spores and up to twice the diam. **Columella** absent, replaced by the pseudocolumella. **Capillitium** abundant, radiating out from the basal plate, thick, dichotomously branched with few cross-connections, purple-brown with pale tips and dark linear swellings. **Spores** dark brown in mass, pale lilac-brown in transmitted light, 9–10 μm diam, densely and evenly warted, sometimes paler on one side. **Plasmodium** colourless or yellow. [Fig. 331]

Illustrations: DM 2: 116–17; E: pl. 120; MA: fig. 338; NB: 290.
Habitat: on plant remains, including fallen tree fruits, also found on herbivore dung.
Distribution: frequent, from Devon to Inverness [24]. Widespread in Europe, Africa, Asia and North America.

Notes: the pseudocolumella is rough and usually coloured rather than white; this character, together with the uniformly marked spores, non-tapering stalk and large peridial crystals separate this species. It is, however, close to *D. eximium* and differs in the more abundant, thicker capillitium and the larger peridial crystals.

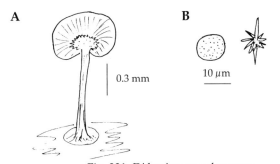

Fig. 331. *Didymium megalosporum*:
A: sporangium; B: spore and peridial crystal.

Didymium ovoideum Nann.-Bremek.
Med. Bot. Mus. Herb. Utrechte **150**: 780. 1958. Netherlands.

Sporocarps stalked sporangia, gregarious, subglobose, decidedly taller than wide, 0.4–0.5 mm diam, 0.8–1 mm tall, with a small umbilicus, white, or, in the absence of lime, shining bronze. **Hypothallus** discoid, pale brown. **Stalk** slender, cylindrical, grooved, reddish-brown, translucent pale orange-brown in transmitted light, without calcareous deposits. **Peridium** tough, colourless or pale yellow but reflecting a bronze iridescence, covered with stellate crystals which are the same size as the spores or smaller; dehiscing to leave a small collar. **Columella** reaching the centre of the sporangium, globose or a similar shape to the sporangium itself, usually white. **Capillitium** radiating from the columella, dichotomously branched with a few cross-connections and darker, thicker regions. **Spores** brown in mass, pale lilac-brown in transmitted light, 7–8 μm diam, almost smooth but very finely warted. **Plasmodium** yellow. [Fig. 332]

Illustrations: DM 2: 126; MA: fig. 350; NB: 289.
Habitat: leaf litter.
Distribution: rare, southern, from Surrey to Lincolnshire [8]. Recorded widely in Europe and found in China, Japan and North America.

Notes: the shape of the sporangia and the columella and the almost smooth spores are good characters. This species apparently breeds true and is regarded as a biological as well as a morphological species.

Didymium pertusum Berk.
in Smith, *Engl. Fl.* **5**: 313. 1836. Appin, Argyll.

Sporocarps stalked sporangia, scattered, subglobose, 0.6–0.8 mm diam, to 3 mm tall, white. **Hypothallus** reddish-brown, discoid. **Stalk** grooved, slightly tapering, reddish, orange-red-brown in transmitted light, filled with calcareous nodules. **Peridium** thin, pale yellow, with a thickened basal plate, covered with very slender stellate crystals which are smaller than the spores. **Columella** absent, but a small reddish-brown columella-like structure has been reported from the Netherlands, but not found in British collections. **Capillitium** of very slender colourless threads branching and forming an open net. **Spores** brown in mass, lilac-brown in transmitted light, 10–13 μm diam, warted. **Plasmodium** not seen. [Fig. 333]

Illustrations: NB: 287.
Habitat: leaf litter.
Distribution: rare, scattered from Sussex to Argyll, few recent records [7]. Only recorded from the Netherlands outside the British Isles.

Notes: the calcareous stalks separate this species from all others in the complex. The lime is easily seen by using lactophenol to mount specimens rather than Hoyer's medium, when bubbles of gas appear around the granules. This is why lactophenol is not used as a mountant for calcareous myxomycetes! It is clear that the interpretations of this taxon vary; suffice it to say that the British collections conform to the original description.

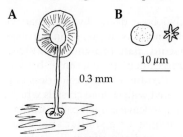

Fig. 332. *Didymium ovoideum*:
A: sporangium;
B: spore and peridial crystal.

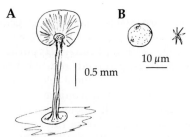

Fig. 333. *Didymium pertusum*:
A: sporangium;
B: spore and peridial crystal.

Didymium verrucosporum A.L. Welden
Mycologia **46**: 98. 1954. Panama.

Sporocarps stalked sporangia, gregarious, subglobose, with a small umbilicus round the stalk, nodding, 0.3–0.4 mm diam, 0.8–1.8 mm tall, white or very pale grey. **Hypothallus** discoid, purple-brown. Stalk long, thin, tapering, ochraceous, without calcareous deposits. **Peridium** colourless or pale yellow, covered with stellate crystals which are larger than the spores. **Columella** subglobose, white, about one-third of the diam of the sporangium. **Capillitium** of lilac-brown threads, scarcely branched or anastomosing, colourless at the tips. **Spores** dark purple brown in mass, lilac-brown in transmitted light, 7–10 μm diam, warted with groups of larger warts. **Plasmodium** white. [Fig. 334]

Illustrations: MA: fig. 358; NB: 293.
Habitat: leaf and other herbaceous litter.
Distribution: uncommon, scattered from Sussex to Yorkshire [12]. Widely distributed in Europe, the Americas, Asia, Africa and Australia, but can hardly be said to be cosmopolitan.

Notes: the nodding sporangia with a distinct columella, pale stalks and large peridial crystals make this fairly easy to identify.

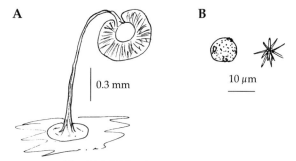

A

B

0.3 mm

10 μm

Fig. 334. *Didymium verrucosporum*:
A: sporangium; B: spore and peridial crystal.

Didymium laxifilum G. Lister & R. Ross
Essex Nat. **27**: 263. 1943. Loughton, Essex.

Sporocarps short-stalked sporangia, gregarious, subglobose, flattened and deeply umbilicate below, 0.5–0.8 mm diam, white; height 1.5 mm. **Hypothallus** discoid, orange, very conspicuous. **Stalk** bright orange. **Peridium** membranous, dark, densely covered with crystals which appear white but are very pale yellow in transmitted light. **Columella** large, white, hemispherical, stalked. **Capillitium** a network of thick, dark branching threads with wide expansions at the junctions of branches. **Spores** dark purplish black in mass, dark brown in transmitted light, 9–11 μm diam, minutely warted with a pale, smooth area. **Plasmodium** greenish-yellow. [Fig. 335]

Illustrations: MA: 364.
Habitat: deep in leaf litter, especially of sweet chestnut.
Distribution: not uncommon in the Home Counties, also recorded from Devon and Hampshire [9]. Very characteristic of the evergreen oak woods of the Mediterranean; recorded from North America as a possible synonym of *D. aurantipes* T.E. Brooks & Kowlaski, but also from Iowa in its own right.

Notes: the bright orange stalk, white peridium and columella and the netted capillitium are key characters.

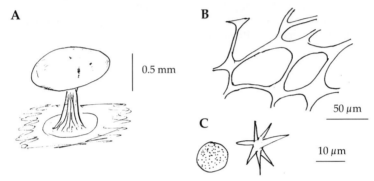

Fig. 335. *Didymium laxifilum*:
A: sporangium; B: capillitium; C: spore and peridial crystal.

Didymium listeri Massee
Mon. Myxog.: 244. 1892. Lyme Regis, Dorset.

Sporocarps plasmodiocarps or sessile sporangia, pulvinate, 0.3–0.5 mm high, to 15 mm long, white. **Hypothallus** inconspicuous. **Peridium** double, the outer layer eggshell-like with a powdery layer of stellate crystals, the inner delicate, membranous. **Columella** absent or represented by a thickened calcareous base to the sporocarp. **Capillitium** abundant, of stiff, dark brown threads connected by transverse bars, joined by pale tips to the peridium. **Spores** blackish-brown in mass, violet-brown in transmitted light, 9–11 µm diam, minutely roughened. **Plasmodium** watery white. [Fig. 336]

Illustrations: L3: pl. 105 (as *dubium*); MA: fig. 345.
Habitat: leaf litter.
Distribution: rare, from Devon to Lincolnshire, in Wales only in Glamorgan, in Scotland only in Inverness, not in Ireland [15]. Widely distributed in Europe, North and South America and Asia, recorded from Israel.

Notes: the powder of crystals over an egg-shell crust is characteristic and separates it from *D. dubium* and allies; the inelastic capillitium and smaller, paler spores are also significant. The only other species with the same peridial covering is *D. trachysporum* but that has very different spores.

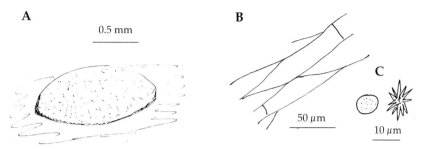

Fig. 336. *Didymium listeri*:
A: plasmodiocarp; B: capillitium; C: spore and peridial crystal.

Didymium macrospermum Rostaf.
Mon.: 161. 1874. Europe.

Sporocarps long-stalked sporangia, depressed globose, often somewhat irregular in outline, white, 0.6–0.8 mm diam, up to 2.4 mm height. **Hypothallus** white, discoid. **Stalk** long, stout, narrowing upwards, white or pale yellow, containing calcareous nodules. **Peridium** membranous, covered with white crystals. **Columella** discoid to globose, white. **Capillitium** of thin, hardly branched threads, pale violet-brown with pale tips. **Spores** dark brown in mass, pale violet brown in transmitted light, 12–13.5 μm diam, covered with long, pointed spines. **Plasmodium** not seen. [Fig. 337]

Illustrations: none.
Habitat: grass litter.
Distribution: known only from two collections, from Norfolk in 1935 and Warwickshire in 1915 [2]. Recorded from Poland.

Notes: this is like a long-stalked *D. squamulosum* but has larger spores which are strongly aculeate. It would be worthwhile examining all collections of *D. squamulosum* with long stalks and irregularly-shaped sporangia and checking the spores. This species has not been seen anywhere in the world for over fifty years.

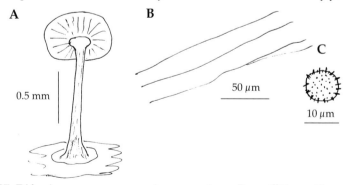

Fig. 337. *Didymium macrospermum*: A: sporangium; B: capillitium; C: spore.

Didymium melanospermum (Pers.) T. Macbr.
N. Am. Slime-Moulds: 88. 1899. Europe.

Sporocarps short-stalked sporangia, gregarious, subglobose or slightly flattened, deeply umbilicate below, 0.5–1 mm diam, to 1 mm tall, white. **Hypothallus** dark, inconspicuous. **Stalk** dark brown or black, stout, short, rarely absent (more often the short stalk is completely hidden by the deep umbilicus and the sporangium sits directly on the substrate). **Peridium** firm, brown, frosted with crystals, looking as if it were dusted with flour. **Columella** large, hemispherical brown, calcareous. **Capillitium** of wavy threads, pale or brown, little branched, some thin, some much thicker, often with dark nodular swellings. **Spores** black in mass, purplish-brown in transmitted light, 10–14 μm diam, warted. **Plasmodium** colourless or grey. [Fig. 338]

Illustrations: DM 2: 119; E: pl. 120; L3: pl. 112; MA: fig. 346; NB: 284.
Habitat: leaf and twig litter, especially of conifers and gorse, less commonly on wood.
Distribution: common throughout the British Isles [110, H10, C]. Cosmopolitan.

Notes: the dark stalk and columella separate this from all except *D. minus* and *D. nigripes*, the latter has a very long stalk, and *D. minus* has smaller, paler spores.

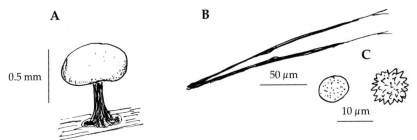

Fig. 338. *Didymium melanospermum*:
A: sporangium; B: capillitium; C: spore and peridial crystal.

Didymium minus (Lister) Morgan
J. Cinc. Soc. Nat. Hist. **16**: 145. 1894. Lyme Regis, Dorset.
Syn. *Didymium melanospermum* var. *minus* Lister

Sporocarps short-stalked sporangia, gregarious, depressed-globose, umbilicate below, 0.4–0.6 mm diam, to 0.8 mm in total height, white. **Hypothallus** dark, discoid. **Stalk** slender, black or dark brown, usually about the same length or shorter than the sporangial diam. **Peridium** membranous, delicate, frosted with crystals. **Columella** globose or depressed-globose, dark brown. **Capillitium** delicate, colourless, branching with few anastomoses. **Spores** black in mass, dark violet brown in transmitted light, 8–10 μm diam, minutely and densely warted, the warts often in clusters. **Plasmodium** dark purplish-grey. [Fig. 339]

Illustrations: DM 2: 123; L3: pl. 112; MA: fig. 347; NB: 285.

Habitat: on dead herbaceous stems, less often in leaf litter.
Distribution: frequent, scattered from Devon to Aberdeen, rare in Ireland [44, H3]. Cosmopolitan.

Notes: separated from *D. melanospermum* by its smaller size, smaller and paler spores and from *D. nigripes* by the short stalk.

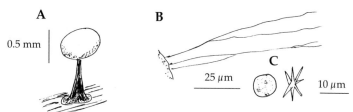

Fig. 339. *Didymium minus*:
A: sporangium; B: capillitium; C: spore and peridial crystal.

Didymium nigripes (Link) Fr.
Syst. Mycol. **3**: 119. 1829. Germany.

Sporocarps long-stalked sporangia, globose, umbilicate below, 0.3–0.5 mm diam, height 1.5 mm, white. **Hypothallus** discoid, black. **Stalk** slender, dark brown to black, often slightly paler towards the top. **Peridium** membranous, grey-brown, mottled, thickly covered with white crystals. **Columella** subglobose, dark brown, calcareous. **Capillitium** delicate, of brown or colourless threads with a few thickened areas, little branched. **Spores** dark brown in mass, pale violet-brown in transmitted light, 7–10 μm diam, minutely warted with clusters of larger warts. **Plasmodium** grey or colourless. [Fig. 340]

Illustrations: DM 2: 122–3; E: pl. 120; L3: pl. 102; MA: fig. 348; NB; 286.
Habitat: leaf litter, especially of holly, and dead herbaceous stems.
Distribution: common throughout the British Isles [109, H18, C]. Cosmopolitan.

Notes: the neat, long-stalked white sporangia contrasting with the black stalks are readily identified. There is a strong relationship with the *D. iridis* group but *D. nigripes* rarely has a pale stalk or columella and the mottled peridium is also not found in the *D. iridis* complex.

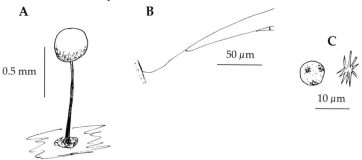

Fig. 340. *Didymium nigripes*:
A: sporangium; B: capillitium; C: spore and peridial crystal.

Didymium nivicola Meyl.
Bull. Soc. Vaud. Sci. Nat. **57**: 40. 1929. Switzerland.

Sporocarps elongate, narrow plasmodiocarps or pulvinate, sessile sporangia, to 2 mm wide, white or pale grey. **Hypothallus** inconspicuous. **Peridium** double, the inner membranous, brown, shining, the outer clothed in white flakes, sometimes the lime is re-crystallised after wetting and may form a more irregular crust, sometimes stained yellow. **Columella** absent but replaced by a calcareous base to the sporocarp. **Capillitium** an inelastic network of pale threads with small bead-like swellings. **Spores** black in mass, dark brown in transmitted light, 14–16 μm diam, covered in large warts to 1 μm high, often forming a broken reticulation. **Plasmodium** colourless. [Fig. 341]

Illustrations: DM 2: 124.
Habitat: vegetation at the edge of melting snow on mountains in the spring.
Distribution: rare, from a few localities in the Scottish Highlands [6]. Widely reported from the Alps and recorded from Japan; also, with some uncertainty, from North America.

Notes: this is an obligately alpine species of the *D. dubium* complex that has been confused with lowland taxa, partly because earlier taxonomists ignored the significance of ecological characters. This species can be separated from *D. dubium sensu stricto* by the larger, more reticulate spores, the inelastic capillitium and the regular occurrence of calcareous flakes on the peridium, rather than the powdery coating of *D. dubium*. The yellow staining of specimens growing close to actively melting snow seems to associated with the solution and re-crystallisation of the lime.

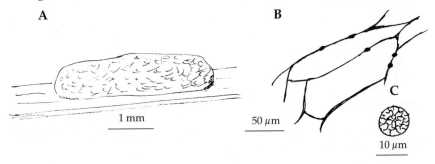

A

B

C

1 mm   50 μm   10 μm

Fig. 341. *Didymium nivicola*: A: plasmodiocarp; B: capillitium; C: spore.

Didymium ochroideum G. Lister
J. Bot., Lond. **69**: 297. 1931. Japan.

Sporocarps sessile sporangia or short plasmodiocarps, pulvinate, 0.2–0.5 mm broad, pale brown or ochraceous. **Hypothallus** sparse, pale orange. **Peridium** membranous, thickly covered with pale yellow stellate crystals. **Columella** orange, convex but flattened, occupying most of the sporocarp floor. **Capillitium** a loose net of slender, yellow-brown threads. **Spores** dark brown in mass, pale purple-grey in transmitted light, 6–7 μm diam, minutely roughened. **Plasmodium** white. [Fig. 342].

Illustrations: E: pl. 28; MA: fig. 349.
Habitat: plant litter in damp places (in other countries it also occurs on dung and mosses).
Distribution: rare, only known form a single collection made in Warwickshire in 1975 [1]. Recorded from Italy, Austria, Norway, India, Japan and North America.

Notes: the dull brownish sporocarps with yellow lime crystals are very distinctive.

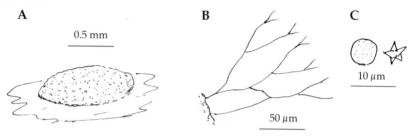

Fig. 342. *Didymium ochroideum*:
A: plasmodiocarp; B: capillitium; C: spore and peridial crystal.

Didymium perforatum Yamash.
J. Sci. Hiroshima Univ. B2 **3**: 33. 1936. Japan.

Sporocarps effused plasmodiocarps, forming extensive fructifications, to 200 mm long and 100 mm wide, more usually sizes being 2 cm diam, the sporocarps made up of sinuous, elongate plasmodiocarps fused into a sheet with gaps – perforations - in the sheet, dark grey. **Hypothallus** inconspicuous. **Peridium** membranous, grey, iridescent, covered with dark grey crystals (described as yellow in some texts). **Columella** absent. **Capillitium** a dark network of threads with nodular thickenings, the meshes small, scarcely larger than the spores. **Spores** black in mass, violet-brown in transmitted light, 10–11 μm diam, with large, distant spines. **Plasmodium** not seen. [Fig. 343]

Illustrations: E: pl. 118; MA: fig. 351.
Habitat: the British collection was from the mossy bark of a mature sycamore tree, the other collections are from leaf litter.
Distribution: known only from a collection made on the Isle of Arran in September 1998 [1]. Recorded from India, Japan, Pakistan and Kansas.

Notes: there is some discrepancy between the description above and that in Martin & Alexopoulos (1969), but only in the size of the sporocarp and the colour of the lime crystals. Nannenga-Bremekamp (1991) agrees that they are black but says that the spores have large warts rather than spines. The Arran material, which is very extensive, has dark grey to black crystals and spiny spores.

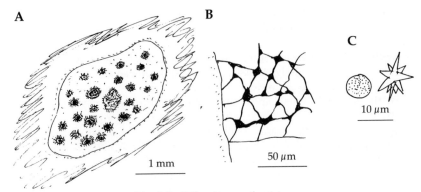

Fig. 343. *Didymium perforatum*:
A: plasmodiocarp; B: capillitium; C: spore and peridial crystal.

Didymium serpula Fr.
Syst. Mycol. **3**: 126. 1829. Sweden.
Syn. *Didymium complanatum* Rostaf.

Sporocarps flat plasmodiocarps, 0.1–0.15 mm thick, 2–8 mm long but may reach 40 mm, sometimes perforated, dark grey or greyish-white. **Hypothallus** inconspicuous. **Peridium** membranous, covered to a varied extent with white, stellate, or sometimes less regular, crystals. **Columella** absent. **Capillitium** of slender, yellow-brown threads attached to subglobose vesicles, 30–50 μm diam, filled with yellow granular material. **Spores** brown in mass, pale violet-brown in transmitted light, 8–11 μm diam, minutely warted. **Plasmodium** yellow. [Fig. 344]

Illustrations: DM 2: 128–9; E: pl. 117; L3: pl. 107; MA: fig. 353; NB: 277.
Habitat: leaf litter, especially of oak.
Distribution: scattered, frequent in the south, thinning northwards to Argyll [35, H3]. Widespread in Europe, North and central America, Africa, Asia and Australia.

Notes: the presence of the large vesicles in the capillitium is sufficient to identify this species.

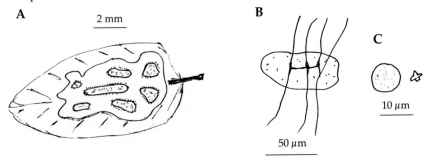

Fig. 344. *Didymium serpula*:
A: plasmodiocarp; B: capillitium; C: spore and peridial crystal.

Didymium squamulosum (Alb. & Schwein.) Fr.
Symb. Gast.: 119. 1818. Germany.

Sporocarps stalked or sessile sporangia or short plasmodiocarps, 0.3–1 mm diam, to 1.5 mm high, globose or depressed-globose in appearance but actually discoid and folded around a deep umbilicus, white or pale grey. **Hypothallus** white, discoid. **Stalk** usually less than the sporangial diam in height, stout, calcareous, usually white but may be tinged pink or ochraceous. **Peridium** membranous, slightly iridescent, thickly covered with white, stellate crystals. **Columella** white, discoid or hemispherical. **Capillitium** variable, the threads may branch or not, be thin or coarse, pale or dark, often with conspicuous swellings. **Spores** black in mass, dark violet-brown in transmitted light, 8–11 μm diam, minutely warted, with clusters of larger warts. **Plasmodium** colourless, white or yellow, often becoming pink as the sporangia form. [Fig. 345]

Illustrations: DM 2: 131; E: pl. 121; L3: pl. 109; MA: fig. 354; NB: 278–9.
Habitat: in leaf litter and herbaceous plant debris of all kinds, including herbivore dung.
Distribution: abundant throughout the British Isles, throughout the year, one of the commonest of all myxomycetes [111, H38, C]. Cosmopolitan.

Notes: the white stalk and the obvious white columella make the stalked form easy to identify. The plasmodiocarpous forms, and occasionally the sessile sporangia, are more difficult to characterise, but, fortunately, they are nearly always accompanied by typical sporangia from the same plasmodium. As is clear from the description, this is a very variable species; it is agamic and many of the variants, such as that with crinkly flakes of peridial lime associated with a stout form on holly leaves, may represent clones and could be regarded as microspecies.

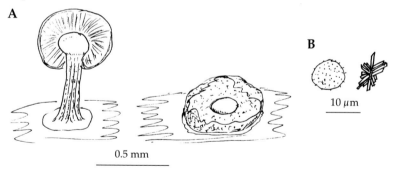

Fig. 345. *Didymium squamulosum*: A: sporangia; B: spore and peridial crystal.

Didymium sturgisii Hagelst.
Mycologia **19**: 397. 1927. Colorado.
Syn. *Didymium anomalum* Sturgis

Sporocarps thin plasmodiocarps, 0.1–0.2 mm thick, rounded or irregular in outline, 1–10 mm long, white or grey. **Hypothallus** inconspicuous. **Peridium**

membranous, white or yellow, lightly covered with white angular or stellate crystals. **Columella** absent but the base of the sporocarp is thickened, from which arise numerous erect pillars, 7–22 μm thick, filled with calcareous crystals, reaching the peridium, to which they are attached. **Capillitium** often lacking, but may consist of slender, dark, wavy, branching and anastomosing threads. **Spores** black in mass, bright violet-brown in transmitted light, 10–12 μm diam, minutely and irregularly warted. **Plasmodium** pale greyish-brown (in bark culture). [Fig. 346]

Illustrations: L3: pl. 213; MA: fig. 355.
Habitat: fallen bark.
Distribution: rare, known only from a collection made in Weybridge, Surrey, in 1922 [1]. Recorded from France, Spain, India and North America, generally rare.

Notes: the internal structures, whether they represent capillitium or just peridial invaginations is not certain, make this species easy to identify. It has recently been found quite widely on bark of living oaks in Spain; it is possible that it is a rare corticolous species and the occurrence on fallen bark supports this idea. With climatic change affecting distribution patterns of many micro-organisms it is worth looking out for this species in the south of England.

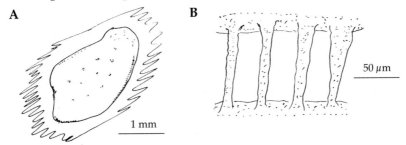

Fig. 346. *Didymium sturgisii*: A: plasmodiocarp; B: capillitium.

Didymium trachysporum G. Lister
Essex Nat. **20**: 113. 1923. Leytonstone, Essex.

Sporocarps sessile sporangia or plasmodiocarps, either hemispherical or pulvinate, 0.1–0.6 mm diam, or slender, curved branched or ring-shaped bodies, white or cream. **Hypothallus** inconspicuous. **Peridium** double, the outer layer resembles an egg-shell crust but also has a powdery covering of crystals, the inner layer membranous, colourless, shining. **Columella** absent, replaced by the pale yellow base of the sporocarp. **Capillitium** scanty, mostly a network of threads, which may have vesicle-like expansion containing lime crystals. **Spores** black in mass, dark purple-brown in transmitted light, 9–10 μm diam, heavily marked with large dark warts, which may be arranged in rows, producing an irregular reticulation. **Plasmodium** colourless. [Fig. 347]

Illustrations: L3: pl. 218; MA: fig. 356; NB: 270.
Habitat: straw, thatch, grass litter and, very occasionally, on bulbs in water culture.

Distribution: rare, scattered from Somerset to Aberdeen [11]. Widely recorded from Europe, especially in the Mediterranean region, and North America.

Notes: the appearance suggests *D. difforme* with a powdery coating but the spores are more strongly marked and the purple iridescent inner peridium of the common species is also lacking. In the Mediterranean and in the deserts of America, this species is found commonly on decaying cacti, especially *Opuntia* pads. It has also been reported from herbivore dung.

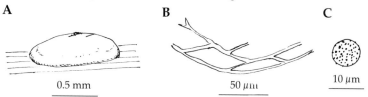

Fig. 347. *Didymium trachysporum*: A: plasmodiocarp; B: capillitium; C: spore.

Didymium tubulatum E. Jahn
Ber. Deutsch. Bot. Ges. **36**: 663. 1919. Germany.
Syn. *Didymium difforme* var. *repandum* G. Lister

Sporocarps plasmodiocarps, broad, to 0.2 mm tall and to 10 mm diam, white, the surface showing small, shallow pits. **Hypothallus** inconspicuous. **Peridium** double, the outer layer an egg-shell crust, the inner membranous, purple-brown, shining; the inner peridium forming invaginations between top and bottom in the form of hollow, pillar-like tubes, 10–15 μm diam, which correspond to the pits on the surface. **Columella** absent. **Capillitium** sparse, of a few dichotomously branched, colourless tubules. **Spores** black in mass, dark purple-brown in transmitted light, 14–16 μm diam, paler on one side, densely warted and with one or two fine lines at the sides of the pale area. **Plasmodium** colourless. [Fig. 348]

Illustrations: NB: 267.
Habitat: on grass and straw litter and, more rarely, on leafy shoots of shrubs in compost or in hedge bottoms.
Distribution: uncommon, scattered from Devon to Edinburgh [13]. Not widely recorded, perhaps simply not separated from *D. difforme*, but known from the Netherlands, Spain and Germany.

Notes: the characteristic pillars with the pits on the peridium are diagnostic and the differences in the spores should enable clear separation from the superficially similar *D. difforme*.

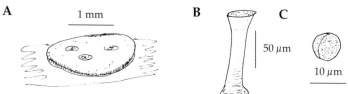

Fig. 348. *Didymium tubulatum*: A: plasmodiocarp; B: capillitium; C: spore.

Didymium vaccinum (Durieu. & Mont.) Buchet
Bull. Soc. mycol. Fr. **36**: 110. 1920. Algeria.

Sporocarps short-stalked sporangia, rarely sessile or forming short plasmodiocarps, hemispherical, looking like egg-cups, to 1 mm high and wide, the sessile forms half that and the plasmodiocarps to 4 mm long, white or pale ochraceous. **Hypothallus** merely a rim around the base of the sporocarp. **Stalk** thick, calcareous, grooved, ochraceous. **Peridium** double, domed, the outer layer an egg-shell crust of compacted crystals, the inner membranous, dehiscing by a circumscissile line at the base, allowing the peridium to fall off as a lid, leaving a cup-like base. **Columella** hemispherical, large, ochraceous to pale red. **Capillitium** radiating from the columella, of stiff, sparingly branched threads, colourless or lilac- or yellow-brown, with a few swellings containing calcareous deposits. **Spores** black in mass, dark purple-brown in transmitted light, with a pale area, 9–12 μm diam, with large, dark, widely spaced warts. **Plasmodium** yellow. [Fig. 349]

Illustrations: E: pl. 117; L3: pl. 106; MA: fig. 357; NB: 271.
Habitat: straw heaps and bales, grass litter and thatch.
Distribution: uncommon, scattered from Sussex to Perthshire [20]. Widespread in the Mediterranean region and in the warmer parts of Europe, North and South America, China and Japan.

Notes: this is another species which is common on cacti in the deserts of the Americas and Africa and is also found wherever *Opuntia* cacti become naturalised. The *Diderma*-like, domed peridium and the fat stalk are unmistakable.

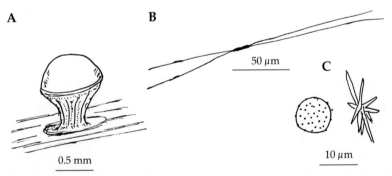

Fig. 349. *Didymium vaccinum*:
A: sporangium; B: capillitium; C: spore and peridial crystal.

LEPIDODERMA de Bary
in Rostafinski, *Vers. Syst. Mycet.*: 7. 1873.

Sporocarps stalked or sessile sporangia or plasmodiocarps. Differs from *Didymium* in that the peridial lime is in the form of thin plates rather than separate crystals. 10 species, mostly alpine, the type is *L. tigrinum* (Schrad.) Rostaf.

Notes: the genus is very close to *Didymium* but the species usually appear more robust because the lime is in a 'thicker' form. *D. nivicola* was cited as a synonym of *L. carestianum* and *L. granuliferum* (Phillips) R.E. Fr. is superficially like *D. dubium*. The situation is further complicated by the observation that the crystalline lime in *Didymium*, especially *nivicola*, may re-crystallise as plates after wetting by meltwater!

KEY TO SPECIES

1	Sporocarps stalked	2
–	Sporocarps sessile or plasmodiocarpous	3
2 (1)	Stalk long, peridial scales large, well spaced	*tigrinum*
–	Stalk short, peridial scales small, closely packed	*crassipes*
3 (1)	Sporocarps closely packed, short plasmodiocarps; alpine	4
–	Sporocarps of clustered, sessile, prolate, sporangia; lowland	*chailletii*
4 (3)	Peridium shining, pinkish or yellowish-grey, covered with small, smooth-edged calcareous scales, 30–50 µm diam, which form a more or less continuous, polished surface, capillitium threads not anastomosing, thin	*aggregatum*
–	Peridium dull, dark grey, covered with larger calcareous scales, 40–70 µm diam, which are well spaced, capillitium threads anastomosing, thick	*carestianum*

Lepidoderma aggregatum Kowalski
Mycologia **63**: 511. 1971. California.

Sporocarps short plasmodiocarps, clustered in lines, 1.5–3 mm long, grey-yellow-brown, shining. **Hypothallus** membranous, not conspicuous. **Peridium** single, membranous but firm, with a closely packed covering of smooth-edged calcareous scales, 30–50 µm diam, variously shaped but often rectangular. **Columella** hemispherical, light brown. **Capillitium** of thin, branching threads with few cross-connections, bearing occasional small swellings. **Spores** dark brown in mass, pale brown in transmitted light, 11–15 µm diam, densely covered with dark spines up to 1 µm long. **Plasmodium** white. [Fig. 350]

Illustrations: DM 2: 144.
Habitat: on vegetation at the edge of melting snow on mountains in the spring.
Distribution: known from a few sites in the Scottish Highlands [5]. Apart from

the mountains of northern California this species is now known from the Alps in Austria, France and Switzerland.

Notes: the smoother, more yellow appearance of the peridium, the smooth edges of the peridial scales and the thin, non-anastomosing capillitium separate this from the similar *L. carestianum*, with which it often grows.

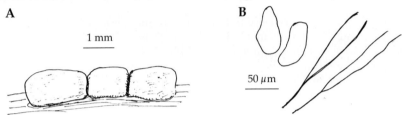

Fig. 350. *Lepidoderma aggregatum*:
A: plasmodiocarps; B: capillitium and peridial scale.

Lepidoderma carestianum (Rabenh.) Rostaf.
Mon.: 188. 1874. Italy.

Sporocarps short plasmodiocarps, closely clustered in lines, 0.8–1.5 mm long, dark grey to almost black, dull. **Hypothallus** membranous, shared by the whole development, yellow- to dark brown, sometimes impregnated with lime. **Peridium** tough, dark, covered with calcareous plates with obvious gaps, the plates 40–70 µm diam, nearly square or slightly rounded, the edges crinkly or scalloped. **Columella** hemispherical, yellow to milk-coffee-brown. **Capillitium** of thick threads, branching and anastomosing freely, with a few small swellings. **Spores** nearly black in mass, dark brown in transmitted light, 11–15 µm diam, densely covered with dark spines 0.5–1 µm long. **Plasmodium** black. [Fig. 351]

Illustrations: DM 2: 146; L3: pl. 115, *a,f*, not *b–d*; MA: fig. 359.
Habitat: on vegetation at the edge of melting snow on mountains in the spring.
Distribution: not uncommon in the Scottish Highlands [9]. Widespread on the mountains of Europe and North America.

Notes: separated from *L. aggregatum* by the greyer appearance, the thicker, anastomosing capillitium and the larger, crinkly-edged peridial scales; from *L. chailletii* by the plasmodiocarpous habit, the larger peridial scales, the larger, darker spores and the black plasmodium.

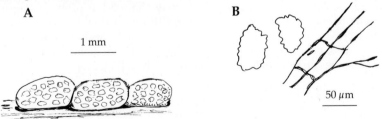

Fig. 351. *Lepidoderma carestianum*:
A: plasmodiocarps; B: capillitium and peridial scale.

Lepidoderma chailletii Rostaf.
Mon.: 189. 1874. Czech Republic
Syn. *Lepidoderma carestianum* var. *chailletii* (Rostaf.) G. Lister

Sporocarps sessile sporangia, clustered, prolate, 0.5–1 mm diam, sometimes constricted in a stalk-like base, dull grey. **Hypothallus** shared by the whole development, rough and impregnated with lime. **Peridium** subcartilaginous, covered densely with small, rounded scales, with smooth edges, 20–20 µm diam, which are white or very pale yellow. **Columella** pale to yellowish-brown, clavate to hemispherical. **Capillitium** of stiff, sparsely branching threads with few anastomoses. **Spores** dark brown in mass, pale lilac-brown in transmitted light, 10–13 µm diam, spinulose. **Plasmodium** white. [Fig. 352]

Illustrations: L3: pl. 116; MA: fig. 360.
Habitat: on heathy litter and leaf litter in acid woods.
Distribution: uncommon, scattered from Devon to Cheshire [11]. Often combined with *L. carestianum* and not always separately recorded, but known from France, Switzerland, Czech Republic, North America and Australia.

Notes: the sporangiate habit, smaller, paler, less spiny spores, smaller peridial plates and the white plasmodium separate this from *L. carestianum*, with which many authors combine it.

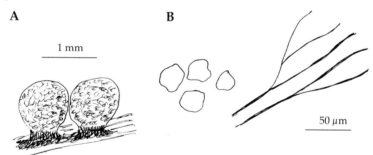

Fig. 352. *Lepidoderma chailletii*: A: sporangia; B: capillitium and peridial scale.

Lepidoderma crassipes Flatau, Massner & Schirmer
Z. Mykol. **53**: 146. 1987. Germany.

Sporocarps short-stalked sporangia, gregarious, hemispherical with a flattened base, 1–1.4 mm diam, height 1.3–1.8 mm, speckled grey and yellow. **Hypothallus** red-brown, shared by the whole group. **Stalk** yellow-red-brown, thick and very wide at the base. **Peridium** dark brown, cartilaginous, heavily sprinkled with a mixture of white and yellow scales, 10–25 µm diam, the crystalline scales producing a slight iridescence. **Columella** hemispherical, ochraceous. **Capillitium** radiating from the columella, of wavy, lilac-brown threads with pale tips. **Spores** dark brown in mass, violet-grey in transmitted light, 10–11.5 µm diam, finely warted. **Plasmodium** not seen. [Fig. 353]

Illustrations: DM 2: 148.
Habitat: on mossy wood.
Distribution: only known from a recent collection from Co. Wicklow [H1]. Recorded from France, Germany and Switzerland.

Notes: readily separated from *L. tigrinum* by the small, closely compacted peridial plates and the slightly iridescent sporangia, with much shorter, fatter stalks. It is probably commoner than the single record suggests but herbarium material of *L. tigrinum* has not yet been investigated.

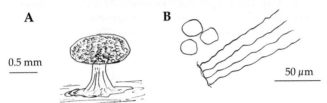

Fig. 353. *Lepidoderma crassipes*: A: sporangium; B: capillitium and peridial scale.

Lepidoderma tigrinum (Schrad.) Rostaf.
in Fuckel, *Jahrb. Nass. Ver. Nat.* **27–28**: 73. 1873. Germany.

Sporocarps stalked sporangia, subglobose, slightly flattened, umbilicate below, gregarious, 0.8–1.5 mm diam, to 2.8 mm in total height, bluish-grey with a pattern of white, rounded or angular scales. **Hypothallus** orange-brown, spongy, shared by the group. **Stalk** 1–2 mm high, stout, furrowed, bright orange-brown with orange lime crystals inside. **Peridium** cartilaginous, usually dark grey. **Columella** large, hemispherical, orange-brown, calcareous. **Capillitium** abundant, of dark, wavy threads radiating from the columella, little branched. **Spores** black in mass, greyish-brown in transmitted light, 10–13 μm diam, minutely spinulose. **Plasmodium** orange. [Fig. 354]

Illustrations: DM 2: 153; E: pl. 49; L3: pl. 114; MA: fig. 362.
Habitat: on mosses on wet rocks in ravines, near waterfalls and in Atlantic woods, and on cyanobacteria and mosses on rotten coniferous wood.
Distribution: frequent, northern and western [56, H11]. Not uncommon in temperate parts of Europe, North America, India and Japan.

Notes: one of the easiest species to identify, only *L. crassipes* being similar, but that has short stalks, and small, tightly packed speckle-like scales.

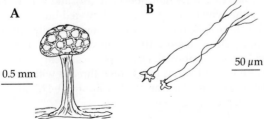

Fig. 354. *Lepidoderma tigrinum*: A: sporangium; B: capillitium.

LEPTODERMA G. Lister
J. Bot., Lond. **51**: 1. 1913.

Sporocarps sessile sporangia. **Peridium** membranous with dark inclusions, iridescent, thicker at the base where there are small scales of crystalline calcium carbonate embedded. **Columella** usually present. **Capillitium** dark, netted, with nodules. A single species, *L. iridescens* G. Lister

Notes: often placed in *Stemonitales* but the peridial lime and the nodular capillitium suggest a closer affinity with *Didymiaceae*. This is another case where cultural studies may help but the species is too uncommon for this to have been accomplished.

Leptoderma iridescens G. Lister
J. Bot., Lond. **51**: 1. 1913. Leighton Buzzard, Bedfordshire.

Sporocarps sessile sporangia, scattered, rarely in groups, pulvinate on a constricted base, 0.5–0.8 mm diam, grey-purple, iridescent. **Hypothallus** dark. **Peridium** membranous, wrinkled, including at the base crystalline scales 2–15 μm diam, dehiscing via vertical tears. **Columella** convex, dark. **Capillitium** a network of wavy, black threads, radiating from the columella, the tips and bases pale, the bases often expanded and containing granular matter, which may be calcareous, the threads with small nodules. **Spores** dark brown in mass, violet grey in transmitted light, 10–13 μm diam, coarsely warted. **Plasmodium** grey. [Fig. 355]

Illustrations: L3: pl. 131,218; MA: fig. 363.
Habitat: plant litter.
Distribution: rare, scattered from Somerset to Inverness [8]. Scattered across Europe and North America but never common.

Notes: when the lime scales are present this is usually easy to identify; when the lime is absent it could look like a sessile *Lamproderma* or a limeless phase of a *Physarum*, although the capillitium is quite wrong for these.

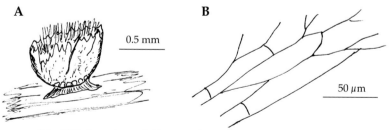

Fig. 355. *Leptoderma iridescens*: A: sporangium; B: capillitium.

MUCILAGO Battarra
Fungi Avimin.: 76. 1755.

Sporocarps aethalia, usually encrusting plant stems with a thick mass of anastomosing tubes filled with spores and capillitium, the whole covered by dense, crystalline cortex. **Capillitium** slender, limeless. **Pseudocapillitium** membranous, calcareous, consisting of the walls of the constituent sporangial units. A single species, *M. crustacea* F.H. Wigg.

Mucilago crustacea F.H. Wigg.
Prim. Fl. Holsat.: 112. 1780. Italy.
Syn. *Mucilago spongiosa* (Leyss.) Morgan
var. **crustacea**

Sporocarps aethalia, in large, white, finger-shaped masses, to 7 cm long, 5 cm broad and 2 cm thick, but usually smaller. **Hypothallus** spongy, membranous, heavily impregnated with white crystalline lime. **Cortex** dense, spongy or powdery, forming flakes, all composed of uniformly sized crystals. **Capillitium** abundant, of dark branching and anastomosing threads, with nodular swellings. **Pseudocapillitium** consisting of the walls of the constituent sporangia, thin, hyaline, iridescent. **Spores** black in mass, very dark brown in transmitted light, 11–13 µm diam, densely warted. **Plasmodium** creamy-white, becoming pale yellow prior to fruiting. [Fig. 356]

Illustrations: DM 2: 155–6; E: pl. 115; L3: pl. 117; MA: fig. 331; NB: 296.
Habitat: encrusting the stems of living plants, including young trees, but especially on grasses in limestone grassland.
Distribution: very common in limestone areas of the British Isles, much rarer in acid areas [100, H13, C]. Cosmopolitan.

Notes: the newly emerged plasmodia resemble dogs' vomit on the grass but within 24 hours the calcareous cortex has hardened and the black spore mass has matured. The only other species with which this could be confused is *Fuligo candida*. This is particularly true of var. *solida* Sturgis, of the present species (not British), which is compact and only told from the *Fuligo* by its crystalline lime. Normally this is an unmistakable species. The author has received numerous requests over the years concerning the eradication of this species as a 'pest' of pastures and lawns. It is, of course, harmless and disappears at the first heavy rain shower.

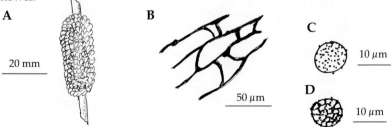

Fig. 356. *Mucilago crustacea*:
A: aethalium; B: capillitium; C: spore; D: var. *dictyospora*, spore.

var. **dictyospora** R.E. Fr.
Ark. Bot. **1**: 66. 1903. Bolivia.

Differs from the type simply in having reticulate spores.

Habitat: straw heaps.
Distribution: known only from a single, old record from Bedfordshire [1]. Not usually recorded and only reported from Bolivia.

Notes: few authors include this variety as distinct, hence the few records; it is probably more widespread in the British Isles but it is not usually necessary to examine the spores of this very common species!

TRABROOKSIA H.W. Keller
Mycologia **72**: 396. 1980.

Sporocarps sessile sporangia or plasmodiocarps, completely devoid of calcareous deposits. **Peridium** membranous, glossy or iridescent. **Capillitium** of membranous tubular simple or branched invaginations from the upper peridium, narrowing to short, slender threads attached to the base. A single species, *T. applanata* H.W. Keller.

Trabrooksia applanata H.W. Keller
Mycologia **72**: 396. 1980. Kentucky.

Sporocarps sessile sporangia or effuse plasmodiocarps, to 5 mm long and 2 mm wide, up 0.1 mm thick, the sporangia subglobose, 0.2–0.4 mm diam, silvery, glossy brown or iridescent. **Peridium** thin, membranous, pitted from the attachment of the capillitial tubes. **Columella** absent. **Capillitium** abundant, of parallel, thin-walled tubes dropping down from the peridium, 2.2–4.5 μm diam, simple or forked below, narrowing to short, slender, hyaline threads attached to the base. **Spores** brown in mass, violet-brown in transmitted light, 11–13 μm diam, minutely spinulose. **Protoplasmodium** watery white. [Fig. 357]

Illustrations: original description.
Habitat: on the bark of living trees, sometimes associated with mosses.
Distribution: rare, known from Wiltshire, Caernarfon, Denbigh and Co. Armagh [3. H1]. Elsewhere known only from North America and Japan.

Notes: the capillitium resembles that of *Badhamiopsis ainoae* and, indeed limeless forms of that species could easily be mistaken for this, except for the larger spores of the *Trabrooksia*.

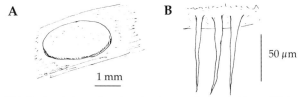

Fig. 357. *Trabrooksia applanata*: A: plasmodiocarp; B: capillitium.

POSTSCRIPT

The last forty years have seen a renewed interest in myxomycetes in Great Britain and Ireland and species new to our islands turn up regularly. I hope that this book will accelerate the process. In the near future a new edition of the *Census Catalogue* will be issued, bringing up to date the records on a vice-county basis. An atlas of distribution maps, showing the presence of all these species on a 10 km National Grid square basis, is also in preparation. Both of these projects will be updated at regular intervals.

In order to ensure that new records are incorporated, readers are invited to send information directly to me, including name of species, location, date, grid reference, some indication of substrate, collector and identifier. Specimens which cannot be confidently identified using the keys and descriptions may also be sent, preferably in matchboxes, with details as above, together with an indication of whether the specimen is to be returned. A stamped addressed envelope or label for the return of information and/or the specimen will be very much appreciated.

The address to use is:

Dr Bruce Ing
Clwyd Mycological Institute
24 Avon Court
Mold
Flintshire
CH7 1JP
Telephone/Fax: 01352 755168
email: bruce.ing@which.net

APPENDIX

DERIVATION OF THE NAMES OF BRITISH MYXOMYCETES

The majority of species have names which refer to a structural characteristic and come from Latin (Lat.) or Greek (Gr.) A few are derived from place names or regions and several commemorate scientists, including a number of distinguished mycologists.

Amaurochaete
from Gr. *amauros* (dark) and *chaite* (mane)
atra - from Lat. *ater* (black)
tubulina - from Lat. *tubulinus* (like organ pipes)

Arcyodes
from Gr. *arkys* (net) and *oides* (like)
incarnata - from Lat. *incarnatus* (flesh-coloured)

Arcyria
from Gr. *arkys* (net)
affinis - from Lat. *affinis* (related)
cinerea - from Lat. *cinereus* (ash-coloured)
denudata - from Lat. *denudatus* (naked)
ferruginea - from Lat. *ferrugineus* (rust-coloured)
incarnata - from Lat. *incarnatus* (flesh-coloured)
insignis - from Lat. *insignis* (conspicuous)
leiocarpa - from Gr. *leios* (smooth) and *karpon* (fruit)
major - from Lat. *major* (larger)
minuta - from Lat. *minutus* (very small)
obvelata - from Lat. *obvelatus* (veiled)
oerstedtii - in honour of A. Oerstedt (1816–1874)
pomiformis - from Lat. *pomiformis* (apple-shaped)
stipata - from Lat. *stipatus* (crowded)

Badhamia
in honour of C.D. Badham (1806 – 1857)
affinis - from Lat. *affinis* (related)

apiculospora - from Lat. *apiculus* (little point) and Gr. *spora* (seed)
capsulifera - from Lat. *capsula* (capsule) and *fero* (bear)
dubia - from Lat. *dubius* (doubtful)
foliicola - from Lat. *folia* (leaf) and *colo* (dwell)
gracilis - from Lat. *gracilis* (graceful)
lilacina - from Lat. *lilacinus* (lilac-coloured)
var. megaspora - from Gr. *megas* (large) and *spora* (seed)
macrocarpa - from Gr. *makros* (large) and *karpon* (fruit)
nitens - from Lat. *nitens* (shining)
panicea - from Lat. *paniceus* (bread-like)
populina - from Lat. *populinus* (of poplars)
rugulosa - from Lat. *rugulosus* (wrinkled)
utricularis - from Lat. *utriculus* (bladder)
versicolor - from Lat. *versicolor* (changing colour)
viridescens - from Lat. *viridescens* (becoming green)

Badhamiopsis
from *Badhamia* + Gr. *opsis* (like)
ainoae - from the Ainu people of Japan

Brefeldia
in honour of O. Brefeld (1839–1925)
maxima - from Lat. *maximus* (greatest)

Calomyxa
from Gr. *kalos* (beautiful) and *myxa* (slime)

metallica - from Lat. *metallicus* (metallic)

Ceratiomyxa

from Gr. *keras* (horn) and *myxa* (slime)

fruticulosa - from Lat. *fruticulosus* (shrubby)

var. arbuscula - from Lat. *arbusculus* (shrub)

Clastoderma

from Gr. *klastos* (broken) and *derma* (skin)

debaryanum - in honour of Anton de Bary (1831–1888)

pachypus - from Gr. *pachys* (thick) and *pous* (foot)

Collaria

derived from the collar at the base of the sporangium

arcyrionema - from Gr. *arkys* (net) and *nema* (thread)

elegans - from Lat. *elegans* (elegant)

lurida - from Lat. *luridus* (sallow)

rubens - from Lat. *rubens* (red)

Colloderma

from Gr. *kolla* (glue) and *derma* (skin)

oculatum - from Lat. *oculatus* (with eyes)

robustum - from Lat. *robustus* (stout)

Comatricha

from Lat. *coma* (hair) and Gr. *thrix* (hair)

alta - from Lat. *altus* (tall)

ellae - in honour of 'Elly' Nannenga-Bremekamp (1916–1996)

fragilis - from Lat. *fragilis* (fragile)

laxa - from Lat. *laxus* (loose)

longipila - from Lat. *longus* (long) and *pila* (pillar)

mirabilis - from Lat. *mirabilis* (wonderful)

nigra - from Lat. *niger* (black)

pulchella - from Lat. *pulchellus* (small beautiful)

var. fusca - from Lat. *fuscus* (dark brown)

reticulospora - from Lat. *reticulum* (net) and Gr. *spora* (seed)

rigidireta - from Lat. *rigidus* (stiff) and *retum* (net)

tenerrima - from Lat. *tenerrimus* (most slender)

Cornuvia

in honour of M. Cornu (1843–1901)

serpula - in reference to *Serpula* a genus of shelled, marine worms

Craterium

from Gr. *krater* (bowl)

aureonucleatum - from Lat. *aureus* (golden) and *nucleatus* (with a kernel)

aureum - from Lat. *aureus* (golden)

brunneum - from Lat. *brunneus* (brown)

dictyosporum - from Gr. *diktyon* (net) and *spora* (spore)

leucocephalum - from Gr. *leukos* (white) and *kephale* (head)

minutum - from Lat. *minutus* (very small)

muscorum - from Lat. *muscus* (moss)

Cribraria

from Lat. *cribrum* (sieve)

argillacea - from Lat. *argillaceus* (clay-coloured)

atrofusca - from Lat. *ater* (black) and *fuscus* (dark brown)

aurantiaca - from Lat. *aurantiacus* (orange-coloured)

cancellata - from Lat. *cancellatus* (latticed)

var. fusca - from Lat. *fuscus* (dark brown)

dictydioides - from *Dictydium* and Gr. *oides* (like)

intricata - from Lat. *intricatus* (complex)

macrocarpa - from Gr. *makros* (large) and *karpon* (fruit)

microcarpa - from Gr. *mikros* (small) and *karpon* (fruit)

minutissuma - from Lat. *minutissimus* (smallest)

mirabilis - from Lat. *mirabilis* (wonderful)

oregana - from the state of Oregan, USA

paucicostata - from Lat. *paucus* (few) and *costatus* (ribbed)

persoonii - in honour of C.H. Persoon (1761–1836)

piriformis - from Lat. *piriformis* (pear-shaped)

var. *notabilis* - from Lat. notabilis

(striking)

rufa - from Lat. *rufus* (red)

splendens - from Lat. *splendens* (shining)

tenella - from Lat. *tenellus* (slender)

violacea – from Lat. *violaceus* (violet-coloured)

vulgaris - from Lat. *vulgaris* (common)

Diachea

from Gr. *diacheo* (fall apart)

leucopodia - from Gr. *leukos* (white) and *pous* (foot)

subsessilis - from Lat. *sub* (under) and *sessilis* (sitting)

Diacheopsis

from *Diachea* and Gr. *opsis* (like)

insessa - from Lat. *insessus* (seated)

mitchelii - in honour of David Mitchell

Dianema

from Gr. *dianema* (spur)

corticatum - from Lat. *corticatus* (with bark)

depressum - from Lat. *depressus* (flattened)

harveyi - in honour of F.L. Harvey (1850–1900)

nivale - from Lat. *nivalis* (of snow)

repens - from Lat. *repens* (creeping)

Dictydiaethalium

from Gr. *diktydion* (net) + *aethalium*

plumbeum - from Lat. *plumbeus* (lead-coloured)

Diderma

from Gr. *dis* (double) and *derma* (skin)

alpinum - from Lat. *alpinus* (of the Alps)

asteroides - from Gr. *aster* (star) and *oides* (like)

chondrioderma - from Gr. *chondros* (cartilage) and *derma* (skin)

cinereum - from Lat. *cinereus* (ash-coloured)

cingulatum - from Lat. *cingulatus* (girdled)

deplanatum - from Lat. *deplanatus* (flattened)

donkii - in honour of M.A. Donk (1908-1972)

effusum - from Lat. *effusus* (spreading)

floriforme - from Lat. *floriformis* (flower-shaped)

globosum - from Lat. *globosus* (globose)

hemisphaericum - from Lat. *hemisphaericus* (hemispherical)

lucidum - from Lat. *lucidus* (shining)

lyallii - in honour of Dr Lyall (U.S.A.)

montanum - from Lat. *montanus* (of mountains)

niveum - from Lat. *niveus* (snow white)

ochraceum - from Gr. *ochros* (yellow earth)

platycarpum - from Gr. *platys* (broad) and *karpon* (fruit)

radiatum - from Lat. *radiatus* (spoked)

sauteri - in honour of A.E. Sauter (1800–1881)

simplex - from Lat. *simplex* (simple)

spumarioides - from *Spumaria* + Gr. (like)

testaceum - from Lat. *testaceus* (of reddish tiles)

trevelyanii - in honour of W.C. Trevelyan (1797–1879)

umbilicatum – from Lat. *umbilicatus* (with a navel)

var. macrosporum - from Gr. *makros* (large) and *spora* (seed)

Didymium

from Gr. *didymos* (double)

anellus - from Lat. *anellus* (little ring)

applanatum - from Lat. *applanatus* (flattened)

bahiense - from Bahia (Brazil)

clavus - from Lat. *clavus* (nail)

comatum - from Lat. *comatus* (maned)

crassicolle - from Lat. *crassus* (thick) and *collis* (neck)

crustaceum - from Lat. *crustaceus* (crusty)

difforme - from Lat. *dis* (away) and *forma* (shape)

dubium - from Lat. *dubius* (doubtful)

elegantissimum - from Lat. *elegantissimus* (most elegant)

eximium - from Lat. *eximius* (notable)

laxifila - from Lat. *laxus* (loose) and *filum* (thread)

listeri - in honour of Arthur Lister
(1830–1908)

macrospermum - from Gr. *makros*
(large) and *sperma* (seed)

megalosporum - from Gr. *megalos*
(giant) and *spora* (seed)

melanospermum - from Gr. *melanos*
(black) and *sperma* (seed)

minus - from Lat. *minus* (lesser)

nigripes - from Lat. *niger* (black)
and *pes* (foot)

nivicola - from Lat. *niva* (snow) and
colo (dwell)

ochroideum - from Gr. *ochros* (yellow
earth) and *oides* (like)

ovoideum - from Lat. *ovum* (egg) and
Gr. *oides* (like)

perforatum - from Lat. *perforatus*
(perforated)

pertusum - from Lat. *pertusus*
(perforated)

serpula - from *Serpula*, a genus of
coiled marine worms

squamulosum - from Lat. *squamulosus*
(scaly)

sturgisii - in honour of W.C. Sturgis
(1892–1942)

trachysporum - from Gr. *trachys*
(rough) and *spora* (seed)

tubulatum - from Lat. *tubulatum*
(tubular)

vaccinum - from Lat. *vacca* (cow)

verrucosporum - from Lat. *verruca*
(wart) and Gr. (seed)

Echinostelium

from Gr. *echinos* (hedgehog) and *stele*
(column)

apitectum - from Lat. *apex* (tip) and
tectus (covered)

arboreum - from Lat. *arboreus* (tree-
like)

brooksii - in honour of Travis Brooks
(1917-1976)

coelocephalum - from Gr. *koilos*
(hollow) and *kephale* (head)

colliculosum - from Lat. *colliculosus*
(with a little collar)

corynophorum - from Gr. *koryne*
(club) and *phoreo* (bear)

elachiston - from Gr. *elachistos*
(smallest)

fragile - from Lat. *fragilis* (fragile)

minutum - from Lat. *minutus* (very
small)

Elaeomyxa

from Gr. *elaios* (oil) and *myxa* (slime)

cerifera - from Lat. *cera* (wax) and *fero*
(bear)

Enerthenema

from Gr. *enerthe* (beneath) and *nema*
(thread)

papillatum - from Lat. *papillatus*
(pimpled)

Enteridium

from Gr. *enteron* (intestine)

intermedium - from Lat. *intermedius*
(intermediate)

liceoides - from *Licea* + Gr. *oides* (like)

lobatum - from Lat. *lobatus* (lobed)

lycoperdon - from *Lycoperdon*, a puff-
ball

minutum - from Lat. *minutus* (very
small)

olivaceum - from Lat. *olivaceus* (olive-
coloured)

simulans - from Lat. *simulans*
(imitating)

splendens - from Lat. *splendens*
(shining)

var. juranum - from the Jura
Mountains, Switzerland

Fuligo

from Lat. *fuligo* (soot)

candida - from Lat. *candidus* (white)

cinerea - from Lat. *cinereus* (ash-
coloured)

gyrosa - from Gr. *gyros* (circle)

intermedia - from Lat. *intermedius*
(intermediate)

megaspora - from Gr. *megas* (large)
and *spora* (seed)

muscorum - from Lat. *muscus* (moss)

rufa - from Lat. *rufus* (red)

septica - from Gr. *septikos* (decaying)

var. flava - from Lat. *flavus* (yellow)

Hemitrichia

from Gr. *hemi* (half) + *Trichia*

abietina - from Lat. *abietinus* (of fir
trees)

calyculata - from Gr. *kalyx* (cup)

chrysospora - from Gr. *chrysos* (golden) and *spora* (seed)

clavata - from Lat. *clavatus* (club-shaped)

intorta - from Lat. *intortus* (twisted)

leiotricha - from Gr. *leios* (smooth) and *thrix* (hair)

minor - from Lat. *minor* (smaller)

pardina - from Lat. *pardus* (leopard)

serpula - from *Serpula,* a genus of coiled marine worms

Lamproderma

from Gr. *lampros* (bronze) and *derma* (skin)

anglicum - from Lat. *anglicus* (English)

arcyrioides - from *Arcyria* + Gr. *oides* (like)

atrosporum - from Lat. *ater* (black) and Gr. *spora* (seed)

carestiae - in honour of A. Carestia (1825–1908)

columbinum - from Lat. *columbinus* (dove-coloured)

cribrarioides - from *Cribraria* + Gr. *oides* (like)

debile - from Lat. *debilis* (weak)

echinulatum - from Lat. *echinus* (sea urchin)

gulielmae - in honour of Gulielma Lister (1860–1949)

sauteri - in honour of A.E. Sauter (1800–1881)

scintillans - from Lat. *scintillans* (glistening)

Leocarpus

from Gr. *leios* (smooth) and *karpon* (fruit)

fragilis - from Lat. *fragilis* (fragile)

Lepidoderma

from Gr. *lepis* (scale) and *derma* (skin)

aggregatum - from Lat. *aggregatus* (clustered)

carestianum - in honour of A. Carestia (1825–1908)

crassipes - from Lat. *crassus* (thick) and *pes* (foot)

tigrinum - from Lat. *tigrinus* (tiger-patterned)

Leptoderma

from Gr. *leptos* (thin) and *derma* (skin)

iridescens - from Lat. iridescens (iridescent)

Licea

derivation unclear

belmontiana - from Belmonte Arboretum, Netherlands

biforis - from Lat. *biforis* (with two flaps)

bryophila - from Gr. *bryon* (moss) and *phileo* (love)

castanea - from Lat. *castaneus* (chestnut)

chelonoides - from Gr. *chelone* (turtle) and *oides* (like)

clarkii - in honour of Malcolm Clark (1911–1991)

crateriformis - from Lat. *crater* (bowl) and *forma* (shape)

denudescens - from Lat. *denudescens* (becoming naked)

deplanata - from Lat. *deplanatus* (flattened)

eleanorae - in honour of Eleanor B. Ing (b. 1941)

erddigensis - from Erddig Park (National Trust) near Wrexham, north Wales

gloeoderma - from Gr. *gloios* (sticky) and *derma* (skin)

inconspicua - from Lat. *inconspicuus* (inconspicuous)

iridis - from Lat. *iris* (rainbow)

kleistobolus - from Gr. *kleistos* (hidden) and *boleo* (throw)

marginata - from Lat. *marginatus* (margined)

microscopica - from Gr. *mikros* (small) and *skopeo* (see)

minima - from Lat. *minimus* (least)

operculata - from Lat. *operculatus* (with a lid)

parasitica - from Lat. *parasiticus* (parasitic)

pedicellata - from Lat. *pedicellatus*

(stalked)

perexigua - from Lat. *perexiguus* (very small)

pusilla - from Lat. *pusillus* (very small)

pygmaea – from Lat. *pygmaeus* (very small)

scyphoides - from Gr. *skypha* (cup) and *oides* (like)

synsporos - from Gr. *syn* (together) and *spora* (seed)

tenera - from Lat. *tener* (delicate)

testudinacea - from Lat. *testudo* (tortoise)

variabilis - from Lat. *variabilis* (variable)

Lindbladia
in honour of M.A. Lindblad (1821–1899)

tubulina - from Lat. *tubulinus* (like organ pipes)

Listerella
in honour of Arthur Lister (1830–1908)

paradoxa - from Gr. *paradoxos* (strange)

Lycogala
from Gr. *lykos* (wolf) and *gala* (milk)

confusum - from Lat. *confusus* (confused)

conicum - from Lat. *conicus* (conical)

epidendrum - from Gr. *epi* (on) and *dendron* (tree)

exiguum - from Lat. *exiguus* (very small)

flavofuscum - from Lat. *flavus* (yellow) and *fuscus* (dark brown)

terrestre - from Lat. *terrestris* (of the earth)

Macbrideola
in honour of T.H. Macbride (1848–1934)

cornea - from Lat. *corneus* (horny)

decapillata - from Lat. *decapillatus* (shaven)

macrospora - from Gr. *makros* (large) and *spora* (seed)

scintillans - from Lat. *scintillans* (glistening)

synsporos - from Gr. *syn* (together) and *spora* (seed)

Metatrichia
from Gr. *meta* (after) + *Trichia*

floriformis - from Lat. *floriformis* (flower-shaped)

vesparium - from Lat. *vesparium* (wasps' nest)

Minakatella
in honour of K. Minakata (Japan)

longifila - from Lat. *longus* (long) and *filum* (thread)

Mucilago
from Lat. *mucilago* (slime)

crustacea - from Lat. *crustaceus* (crusty)

Oligonema
from Gr. *oligos* (few) and *nema* (thread)

flavidum - from Lat. *flavidus* (yellow)

schweinitzii - in honour of L.D. Schweinitz (1780–1834)

Paradiachea
from Gr. *para* (beside) + *Diachea*

anglica - from Lat. *anglicus* (English)

howardii - in honour of H.J. Howard (1884–1957)

Paradiacheopsis
from Gr. *para* (beside) + *Diacheopsis*

acanthodes - from Gr. *akanthos* (spine) and *oides* (like)

cribrata - from Lat. *cribrum* (sieve)

fimbriata - from Lat. *fimbriatus* (fringed)

microcarpa - from Gr. *mikros* (small) and *karpon* (fruit)

rigida - from Lat. *rigidus* (stiff)

solitaria - from Lat. *solitarius* (solitary)

Perichaena
from Gr. *perichainos* (gaping)

chrysosperma - from Gr. *chrysos* (golden) and *sperma* (seed)

corticalis - from Lat. *corticalis* (of bark)

depressa - from Lat. *depressus* (flattened)

liceoides - from *Licea* + Gr. *oides* (like)

luteolum - from Lat. *luteolus* (yellow)

pedata - from Lat. *pedatus* (stalked)

vermicularis - from Lat. *vermicularis* (worm-like)

Physarum
from Gr. *physa* (bladder)
albescens - from Lat. *albescens* (becoming white)
auriscalpium - from Lat. *auriscalpium* (ear-pick)
bethelii - in honour of E. Bethel (1863–1925)
bitectum - from Lat. *bis* (twice) and *tectus* (covered)
bivalve - from Lat. *bivalvis* (two-valved)
brunneolum - from Lat. *brunneolus* (light brown)
carneum - from Lat. *carneus* (flesh-coloured)
cinereum - from Lat. *cinereus* (ash-coloured)
citrinum - from Lat. *citrinus* (lemon-coloured)
compressum - from Lat. *compressus* (compressed)
confertum - from Lat. *confertus* (crowded)
conglomeratum - from Lat. *conglomeratus* (gathered together)
contextus - from Lat. *contextus* (woven)
crateriforme - from Lat. *crater* (bowl) and *forma* (shape)
decipiens - from Lat. *decipiens* (deceiving)
didermoides - from *Diderma* + Gr. *oides* (like)
echinosporum - from Gr. *echinos* (hedgehog) and *spora* (seed)
flavicomum - from Lat. *flavus* (yellow) and *coma* (hair)
galbeum - from Lat. *galbeus* (yellow)
globuliferum - from Lat. *globulus* (little sphere) and *fero* (bear)
javanicum - from Java, Indonesia
lateritium - from Lat. *lateritius* (brick-red)
leucophaeum - from Gr. *leukos* (white) and *phaios* (brown)
leucopus - from Gr. *leukos* (white) and *pous* (foot)

limonium - from Lat. *limonius* (lemon-coloured)
listeri - in honour of Arthur Lister (1830–1908)
lividum - from Lat. *lividus* (lead-coloured)
mucosum - from Lat. *mucosus* (slimy)
murinum - from Lat. *murinus* (mouse-coloured)
mutabile - from Lat. *mutabilis* (changeable)
nitens - from Lat. *nitens* (shining)
notabile - from Lat. *notabilis* (striking)
nucleatum - from Lat. *nucleatus* (with a kernel)
nudum - from Lat. *nudus* (naked)
nutans - from Lat. *nutans* (nodding)
oblatum - from Lat. *offero* (show)
obscurum - from Lat. *obscurus* (dark)
ovisporum - from Lat. *ovum* (egg) and Gr. *spora* (seed)
penetrale - from Lat. *penetralis* (penetrating)
psittacinum - from Lat. *psittacinum* (parrot-coloured)
pulcherripes - from Lat. *pulcher* (beautiful) and *pes* (foot)
pusillopse - from *pusillum* + Gr. (like)
pusillum - from Lat. *pusillus* (very small)
robustum - from Lat. *robustus* (stout)
rubiginosum - from Lat. *rubiginosus* (reddish)
scoticum - from Lat. *scoticus* (Scottish)
sessile - from Lat. *sessilis* (seated)
straminipes - from Lat. *stramen* (straw) and *pes* (foot)
vernum - from Lat. *vernus* (of the Spring)
virescens - from Lat. *virescens* (becoming green)
viride - from Lat. *viridis* (green)
var. aurantium - from Lat. *aurantius* (orange)
var. incanum - from Lat. *incanus* (grey)
Pocheina
in honour of F. Poche (fl. 1913)
rosea - from Lat. *roseus* (rose-coloured)

Prototrichia
from Gr. *protos* (first) + *Trichia*
metallica - from Lat. *metallicus*
(metallic)

Stemonaria
derived from *Stemonitis*
longa - from Lat. *longus* (long)
Stemonitis
from Gr. *stemon* (thread)
axifera - from Lat. *axis* (axle) and *fero*
(bear)
flavogenita - from Lat. *flavus* (yellow)
and *genitus* (brought forth)
foliicola - from Lat. *folius* (leaf) and
colo (dwell)
fusca - from Lat. *fuscus* (dark brown)
herbatica - from Lat. *herbaticus* (of
grass)
inconspicua - from Lat. *inconspicuus*
(inconspicuous)
lignicola - from Lat. *lignum* (wood)
and *colo* (dwell)
nigrescens - from Lat. *nigrescens*
(becoming black)
smithii - in honour of C.L. Smith
(U.S.A.)
splendens - from Lat. *splendens*
(shining)
var. webberi - in honour of H.J.
Webber (U.S.A.)
virginiensis - from Virginia (U.S.A.)
Stemonitopsis
from *Stemonitis* + Gr. *opsis* (like)
aequalis - from Lat. *aequalis* (equal)
amoena - from Lat. *amoenus* (pleasing)
gracilis - from Lat. *gracilis* (graceful)
hyperopta - from Gr. *hyperoptos*
(overlooked)
microspora - from Gr. *mikros* (small)
and *spora* (seed)
reticulata - from Lat. *reticulatus*
(netted)
subcaespitosa - from Lat. *sub* (under)
and *caespitosus* (tufted)
typhina - from *Typha,* the reed-mace
Symphytocarpus
from Gr. *sym* (together), *phyton* (plant)
and *karpon* (fruit)

amaurochaetoides - from
Amaurochaete + Gr. *oides* (like)
flaccidus - from Lat. *flaccidus* (floppy)
herbaticus - from Lat. *herbaticus* (of
grass)
impexus - from Lat. *impexus*
(uncombed)
trechispora - from Gr. *trachys* (rough)
and *spora* (seed)

Trabrooksia
in honour of Travis Brooks (1917–
1976)
applanata - from Lat. *applanatus*
(flattened)
Trichia
from Gr. *thrix* (hair)
affinis - from Lat. *affinis* (related)
alpina - from Lat. *alpinus* (of the Alps)
botrytis - from Gr. *bortytis* (bunch of
grapes)
var. cerifera - from Lat. *cera* (wax) and
fero (bear)
contorta - from Lat. *contortus* (twisted)
var. attentuata - from Lat. *attenuatus*
(stretched)
var. inconspicua - from Lat.
inconspicuus (inconspicuous)
var. iowensis - from Iows, U.S.A.
var. karstenii - in honour of P.A.
Karsten (1834–1917)
decipiens - from Lat. *decipiens*
(deceiving)
var. hemitrichioides - from *Hemitrichia*
+ Gr. *oides* (like)
var. olivacea - from Lat. *olivaceus*
(olive-coloured)
favoginea - from Lat. *favus*
(honeycomb)
fimicola - from Lat. *fimes* (dung) and
colo (dwell)
flavicoma - from Lat. *flavus* (yellow)
and *coma* (hair)
lutescens - from Lat. *lutescens*
(becoming yellow)
munda - from Lat. *mundus* (neat)
persimilis - from Lat. *persimilis* (very
like)
scabra - from Lat. *scaber* (rough)

varia - from Lat. *varius* (variable)

verrucosa - from Lat. *verrucosus* (warted)

Tubifera

from Lat. *tuba* (tube) and *fero* (bear)

ferruginosa - from Lat. *ferruginosus* (rust-coloured)

Willkommlangea

in honour of H. Willkomm and J. Lange

reticulata - from Lat. *reticulatus* (netted)

GLOSSARY

Aculeate – furnished with long spines, like a hedgehog.

Aethalium – sporocarp derived for the whole of the plasmodium, without separation into sporangia.

Agamic – form of reproduction without fertilisation.

Anastomose, -sis, -ses – the formation of cross-connections resulting in a tangled, net-like structure.

Aphanoplasmodium – the delicate, semi-aquatic plasmodium of the *Stemonitidales*, without differentiation into a thickened centre and transparent margins.

Badhamioid – of the capillitium in some *Physaraceae*, where calcareous tubes are not connected by hyaline tubules.

Capillitium – the system of thread and other structures within the sporocarp which separate and help to disperse the spores.

Columella – a central structure within a sporangium, an extension of the stalk, from which the capillitium extends.

Cortex – a thick, common covering over an aethalium.

Depressed – flattened.

Dictydine granules – the small, spherical structures within the peridial net of *Cribrariaceae*, possibly containing calcium salts.

Discoid – disc-shaped.

Effuse – spreading like a thin sheet without definite margins, of a plasmodiocarp.

Elater – tubular, unbranched structures, spirally bound, typical of *Trichia*.

Fugacious – quickly disappearing on maturity, deciduous.

Fusiform – spindle-shaped.

Globose – spherical.

Gregarious – in groups.

Heterothallic – reproducing by the pairing of different mating-types, i.e. outbreeding.

Homothallic – reproducing by the pairing of similar mating-types, i.e. inbreeding.

Hyaline – transparent and colourless, even glassy.

Hypothallus – the thin structure, derived from the non-cellular parts of the plasmodium, on which the sporocarps sit.

Lenticular – lens-, or lentil- shaped.

Lime – calcium carbonate, not calcium oxide (which is chemically correct!)

Microcyst – an encysted myxomonad.
Myxamoeba – the amoeboid, feeding stage, before the formation of the plasmodium.
Myxoflagellate – the flagellated cell which merges from the spore on germination, before the formation of myxamoebae.
Myxomonad – a collective term for myxoflagellates and myxamoebae.

Node – (a) the thickened portion of the peridial net of *Cribraria*, (b) the rounded or angular structures containing calcium carbonate in the capillitium of *Physaraceae*.

Oblate – round with a flattened top, a squashed sphere.

Peridium, -ial – the outer covering or wall of a sporocarp.
Phaneroplasmodium – the plasmodium of, typically, the *Physarales*, massive and with a series of thickened veins and thinner margins.
Physaroid – of the capillitium in *Physaraceae*, with nodes and limeless tubules.
Plasmodiocarp, -ous – a sporocarp which is either elongate and one sporangial unit wide or wider and effuse, but still retaining the internal organisation appropriate to a sporangium.
Plasmodium – the final vegetative phase of the life-cycle, resulting, usually, from the fusion of myxamoebae and resulting nuclear division.
Prolate – taller than broad.
Protoplasmodium – the plasmodium of minute corticolous species, giving rise to a single sporocarp and not migrating.
Pseudoaethalium – sporocarp produced from the whole of the plasmodium but with partial separation into individual sporangia, which share a cortex and may have joined capillitia.
Pseudocapillitium – within an aethalium, the remains of the constituent sporangial walls.
Pseudocolumella – a structure derived from the calcareous elements in the capillitium aggregating near the centre or base of the sporangium, often resting on the basal plate of the peridium, but not an extension of the stalk, sometimes within a separate membrane.
Pulvinate – cushion-shaped, with a rounded outline and, usually, a broad base.
Pyriform – pear-shaped.

Reticulum, -ate – a net, of surface markings, or spore markings or a network in a capillitium.

Sclerotium – an encysted plasmodium, which may be reconstituted with water.
Sessile – without a stalk, sitting on the substrate.
Spine – a long, pointed out-growth from the surface of a spore, or from a capillitial thread.
Spinule, -ose – a small, fine spine.
Sporangium – a spore capsule, either stalked or sessile.

Spore – the resting and dispersal stage in the life-cycle, produced within the sporocarp.

Sporocarp – the spore-producing stage of the life-cycle.

Sporulation – the development of sporocarps from the plasmodium.

Stellate – star-shaped.

Stalk – the structure which lifts the sporangium above the substrate.

Subglobose – nearly spherical, but often slightly broader than tall.

Substrate – what the myxomycete is sitting on.

Turbinbate – top-shaped.

Umbilicus, -ate – with a navel-like depression, usually on the underside of the sporangium, around the stalk.

Wart – a short, not tapering, flat-topped projection from the surface of a spore.

BIBLIOGRAPHY

Carlile, M. J. 1971. Myxomycetes and other slime molds, *in* Booth, C., ed. *Methods in Microbiology*, Vol. 4, pp. 237–265. London, Academic Press.
[Detailed methodology for culturing slime moulds.]

Emoto, Y. 1977. *The Myxomycetes of Japan*. Tokyo, Sangyo Tosho Publ. Co.
[Beautifully illustrated account of the Japanese species known then, following the sequence of Lister, 1925; very expensive to buy!]

Farr, M.L. 1958. Taxonomic studies in the Myxomycetes. 1. *The Trichia favoginea* complex. *Mycologia* **50**: 357–369.
[A detailed analysis of material, mostly American, of this difficult species group; the conclusions are not widely accepted in Europe!]

Farr, M.L. 1981. *How to know the true slime molds*. Dubuque, Iowa, W.C. Brown
[A small book with good introduction and illustrated keys, suitable for use primarily in North America.]

Gilbert, H.C. & Martin, G.W. 1933. Myxomycetes found on the bark of living trees. *Studies in Natural History at Iowa University* **15**: 3–8.
[The original article which started moist chamber bark culture, although they did not actually invent the method.]

Hagiwara, H. & Izawa, M. 1983. *Myxomycetes*. Tokyo, National Science Museum.
[Beautiful, and useful, photographs of myxomycetes and habitats. In Japanese only, expensive.]

Hagiwara, H. & Izawa, M. 1997. *Magic of the Myxomycetes*. Tokyo, National Science Museum.
[Useful introduction to the biology, and artistic influence, of myxomycetes. Beautiful photographs. In English and Japanese.]

Hagiwara, H., Yamamoto, Y. & Izawa, M. 1995. Myxomycetes of Japan. Tokyo, Heibonsha Ltd.
[Another collection of beautiful photographs, including habitats, keys; in Japanese.]

Hawksworth, D.L., Kirk, P.M., Sutton, B.C. & Pegler, D.N. 1995. *Ainsworth & Bisby's Dictionary of the Fungi*. 8th edn. Wallingford, CAB International.
[The most complete thesaurus of mycological terms and names, references to the literature, glossaries and valuable mini-articles.]

Ing, B. 1968. *A Census Catalogue of British Myxomycetes*. Woking, British Mycological Society.
[A checklist of the British species with details of their occurrence in Watsonian vice-counties.]

Ing, B. 1980. A revised census catalogue of British myxomycetes – part 1.
Bulletin of the British Mycological Society **14**: 97–111.
[An update of the 1968 list.]

Ing, B. 1982. *A Provisional Atlas of British Myxomycetes*. Huntingdon, Biological
Records Centre, Institute of Terrestrial Ecology.
[Distribution maps using the 10 km squares of the National Grid, of 99 selected
species.]

Ing, B. 1982. A revised census catalogue of British myxomycetes – part 2. *Bulletin
of the British Mycological Society* **16**: 26–35.
[Contains some analysis of records as well as new British species.]

Ing, B. 1983. A ravine association of myxomycetes. *Journal of Biogeography* **10**,
299–306.
[A detailed account of the myxomycetes living on mosses in ravines and by
waterfalls.]

Ing, B. 1984. On the identity of *Echinostelium roseum* B. Ing (Myxomycetes).
Transactions of the British Mycological Society **82**: 173.
[The minute pink myxomycete is shown to be a mixture of organisms and a *nomen
confusum*.]

Ing, B. 1985. A revised census catalogue of British myxomycetes – addenda and
Corrigenda 1. *Bulletin of the British Mycological Society* **19**: 109–115.
[Additional and revised records from the 1980/82 catalogue.]

Ing, B. 1994. The phytosociology of myxomycetes. *New Phytologist* **126**: 175–201.
[A review of the biogeography and plant associations of myxomycetes, world-
wide.]

Ing, B. 1998. Alpine myxomycetes in Scotland.
Botanical Journal of Scotland **50**, 47–53.
[A detailed account of the ecology and distribution of snow-line myxomycetes in
Great Britain].

Katsaros, P. 1989. *Illustrated Guide to Common Slime Molds*. Eureka, Mad River
Press.
[Basically a collection of good photographs of common species, but as with all
selections, not primarily an identification book.]

Lado, C. & Pando, F. 1997. *Flora Mycologica Iberica* **2**. *Myxomycetes* 1.
Ceratiomyxales, Echinosteliales, Liceales, Trichiales. Madrid, J. Cramer.
[A definitive account, in Spanish and English, of the species from Portugal, Spain
and the Balearics, well illustrated with line drawings. Taxonomically accurate and
up-to-date.]

Lister, G. 1925. *Monograph of the Mycetozoa*, edn 3. London, British Museum.
[Inevitably much out-of-date but still valuable for taxonomic insights and the most beautiful drawings.]

Martin, G.W. & Alexopoulos, C.J. 1969. *The Myxomycetes*. University of Iowa.
[Still the latest world monograph but very out of date, with poor illustrations and some taxonomic confusions.]

McHugh, R. 1986. The Irish distribution of the myxomycete *Clastoderma pachypus* Nann.-Brem. *Bulletin of the Irish Biogeographical Society* **9**: 10–14.
[A detailed analysis of the distribution in Ireland of this interesting species].

Nannenga-Bremekamp, N.E. 1967. Notes on myxomycetes XII. A revision of Stemonitales. *Proceedings of the Koninklijke Nederlandse Akademie van Wetenschappen-Amsterdam*, series C, **70**: 201–216.
[A compete re-organisation of the genera into a more comfortable system, followed in the current work.]

Nannenga-Bremekamp, N.E. 1982. Notes on myxomycetes XXI. The use of polarised light as an aid in the taxonomy of the Trichiales. *Proceedings of the Koninklijke Nederlandse Akademie van Wetenschappen-Amsterdam*, series C, **85**: 541–562.
[The presence of birefringence is used to separate families, although it is not necessarily diagnostic at the species level. This method is not followed in the current work.]

Nannenga-Bremekamp, N.E. 1991. *A Guide to Temperate Myxomycetes*. An English Translation of *De Nederlandse Myxomyceten*, by A. Feest & Y. Burggraaf. Bristol, Biopress Ltd.
[The title is misleading as it is really only useful for Dutch species and cannot be used to identify many taxa found in the British Isles. The line drawings and descriptions are valuable but the ecological and geographical information is inadequate.]

Neubert, H., Nowotny, W. & Baumann, K. 1993. *Die Myxomyceten*. Bd. 1. Gomaringen, Baumann.
[A beautifully illustrated and thorough account of the *Ceratiomyxales*, *Echinosteliales*, *Liceales* and *Trichiales* of Germany and Austria. Some, quite small, taxonomic errors, but a valuable book, if expensive. In German.]

Neubert, H., Nowotny, W., Baumann, K. & Marx, H. 1995. *Die Myxomyceten* Bd. 2. Gomaringen, Baumann.
[The second of three parts of this excellent series, this time covering the *Physarales*.]

Rogerson, C.T. & Stephenson, S.L. 1993. Myxomyceticolous fungi. *Mycologia* **85**: 456–469.
[A detailed account of the ascomycetes and their imperfect states which are associated with myxomycete fruit-bodies, with keys and descriptions; most valuable.]

Stephenson, S.L. & Stempen, H. 1994. *Myxomycetes – a Handbook of Slime Molds.* Portland, Timber Press.
[An excellent general account, especially of the ecology of myxomycetes. The illustrations vary, some are excellent, others misleading. The choice of species is not favourable to British users and the 'partial' keys to large genera are distinctly unhelpful. With these provisos it is still a very useful account.]

Whitney, K.D. 1980. The myxomycete genus *Echinostelium. Mycologia* **72**: 950–987.
[Virtually a monograph of the species known then; very valuable and well illustrated.]

USEFUL ADDRESSES

Herbaria
A valuable reference resource is provided by herbarium collections of myxomycetes. The following institutions all have useful collections which may be consulted. Please write to make an appointment well in advance as these institutions are not necessarily staffed full-time.

Department of Botany, The Natural History Museum, Cromwell Road, London SW7 5BD.
[Half of the Lister collection, the Howard collection, numerous type specimens, including some of Berkeley; world coverage.]

Mycology Section, Herbarium, Royal Botanic Gardens, Kew, Richmond, Surrey TW9 3AE.
[Half of the Lister collection, the Massee collection, numerous types, world coverage.]

Herbarium, Royal Botanic Garden Edinburgh, Inverleith Row, Edinburgh EH1 2HJ.
[Useful collection, mainly Scottish, including Greville material.]

Herbarium, Ulster Museum, Botanic Gardens, Belfast BT9 5AB.
[Useful collection, mostly Irish, includes Stelfox collection.]

Herbarium, National Museum of Wales, Cathays Park, Cardiff CF1 3NP.
[Small collection, mostly Welsh, includes Brazier collection].

Biosystematic Reference Collection, CABI Biosciences, Bakeham Lane, Egham, Surrey TW20 9TY.
[Small collection, mostly tropical but some British; includes Imperial Mycological Institute material.]

Herbarium, National Botanic Garden, Glasnevin, Dublin 9, Republic of Ireland.
[Small collection, mostly Irish, includes Gunn collection.]

Herbarium, Manx Museum, Douglas, Isle of Man.
[Small collection, mostly Manx, includes Milne collection.]

Department of Plant Science, University of Oxford, Parks Road, Oxford OX1 3PF.
[Useful collection, mostly British, includes C. Champion collection.]

Leicestershire Museum, New Walks, Leicester LE1 6TD.
[Small collection, mostly local, includes F.A. Sowter collection.]

Norwich Castle Museum, The Castle, Norwich NR1 3JU
[Valuable collection, mostly local, includes the H.J. Howard and E.A. Ellis
collections and some Lister material.]

Luton Museum, Wardown Park, Luton LU2 3HA.
[Good local collection, including the J.A. Saunders material.]

St Albans Museum, Hatfield Road, St Albans AL1 3RR.
[Modest local collection, some J.A. Saunders material.]

Haslemere Educational Museum, 78 High Street, Haslemere GU27 1LD.
[Useful local collection, including some Lister material.]

South London Botanical Institute, 323 Norwood Road, London SE24 9AQ
[Useful range of material from south-east England, includes S. Carter material.]

Organisations

British Mycological Society, PO Box 30, Stourbridge DY9 9PZ.
[The premier mycological society – details of membership, library facilities, local
groups, publications, forays, workshops, scientific meetings and the records
database available.]

Booksellers

Richmond Publishing Co. Ltd, PO Box 963, Slough SL2 3RS.
[Publishes and distributes books on all aspects of mycology and lichenology,
offers a comprehensive range of books, including foreign titles, good catalogue;
will supply most of the titles in this bibliography!]

The Internet

The number of web sites is too numerous to list here. Suffice it to say that
searching for 'myxomycetes' will generate copious information, some of it useful!

INDEX

Names in **bold** are those accepted here, names in *italics* are synonyms, names in normal type are for non-British species referred to in the text. Page numbers in **bold** are for descriptions, all other references are in normal type.